1988

New Directions in the Philosophy of Mathematics

NEW DIRECTIONS IN THE PHILOSOPHY OF MATHEMATICS

An Anthology

Edited by Thomas Tymoczko

BIRKHÄUSER
Boston · Basel · Stuttgart

Library of Congress Cataloging in Publication Data

New directions in the philosophy of mathematics.

Bibliography: p.
1. Mathematics—Philosophy—Addresses, essays, lectures. I. Tymoczko, Thomas
QA8.6.N48 1985 510′.1 84-21520
ISBN 0-8176-3163-1

CIP-Kurztitelaufnahme der Deutschen Bibliothek

New directions in the philosophy of mathematics
: an anthology / ed. by Thomas Tymoczko. —
Boston ; Basel ; Stuttgart : Birkhäuser, 1985.
ISBN 3-7643-3163-1

NE: Tymoczko, Thomas [Hrsg.]

ISBN 0-8176-3163-1
ISBN 3-7643-3163-1

9 8 7 6 5 4 3 2 1
Printed in USA

For Alice Dickinson
Mathematician, Teacher, Ringer of Changes

There is a solitude of space
A solitude of sea
A solitude of death, but these
Society shall be
Compared with that profounder site
That polar privacy
A soul admitted to itself—
Finite Infinity.

Emily Dickinson

Contents

Preface

The origin of this book was a seminar in the philosophy of mathematics held at Smith College during the summer of 1979. An informal group of mathematicians, philosophers and logicians met regularly to discuss common concerns about the nature of mathematics. Our meetings were alternately frustrating and stimulating. We were frustrated by the inability of traditional philolsophical formulations to articulate the actual experience of mathematicians. We did not want yet another restatement of the merits and vicissitudes of the various foundational programs—platonism, logicism, formalism and intuitionism. However, we were also frustrated by the difficulty of articulating a viable alternative to foundationalism, a new approach that would speak to mathematicians and philosophers about their common concerns. Our meetings were most exciting when we managed to glimpse an alternative. Occasionally some reading would suggest a new perspective on mathematics or pose fresh problems with philosophical merit and mathematical relevance. Then the philosophy of mathematics would seem to come alive again.

Toward the end of the seminar, my colleague, Stan Stahl, mathematical logician turned computer scientist, suggested the idea of an anthology of readings suited to the modern reader. From the first, we conceived of the anthology as a bridge linking those disciplines concerned with the general character of mathematics. So we insisted that it include representatives from mathematics, philosophy, logic and related fields. In addition, we preferred accessible articles written in English or generally familiar notations. It seemed prudent to direct the essays to a sophisticated amateur since most of us are only amateurs in at least one of the fields relevant to the philosophy of mathematics!

Originally the anthology was to be divided into three major sections. The first was a group of essays that challenged the dogmas underlying foundationalist views of mathematics. The second focused on mathematics as actually practiced, thereby reexamining the data from which the philosophy of mathematics is to begin. The final section was to have reviewed some of the recent advances in mathematical logic which bear on general philosophical issues.

Alas, the exigencies of historical circumstances intervened. Stan Stahl dropped out as co-editor, and I realized that I could not do justice to each section in a single volume. So what was originally to be the third section has been omitted from the present anthology, although it is still projected as a separate volume. I took this step reluctantly, for there is much to be learned by using the tools that were originally developed by foundationalists. There are the recent and lively discussions of mathematical structures, the iterative concept of set and the new proposals for mathematical definitions of truth.[1] Moreover there is a resurgence of constructivism, including provocative reinterpretations of intuitionism by mathematicians and philosophers.[2] Nevertheless, to have included all points of view would have diluted each—and would have resulted in a very heavy book. Consequently I chose to develop a few approaches at length rather than attempt a survey of the field.

One result of this is that the present anthology has a more polemical cast to it than was originally intended. It seems to come out swinging against tradition, both by repudiating foundations of mathematics and by stressing the quasi-empirical concept of mathematical practice, a concept that many traditionalists regard as out-and-out heresy. Well, perhaps a little polemic is appropriate now and again to breathe new life into a discipline, and I have no objection to providing a stalking horse for future critics. I would only insist that any excess be attributed solely to me as editor and not to any of the individually well reasoned selections in the anthology.

This volume could not have been completed without the help of many individuals. First and foremost, of course, is Stan Stahl and the other participants of the seminar: James Callahan, David Cohen, Jim Henle, Joan Hutchinson and Stan Wagon. I've also benefitted from useful discussions with Murray Kiteley, Michael Albertson, Phyllis Cassidy and Andrew Boucher. Kathryn Pyne Addelson and Bert Mendelson provided valuable suggestions. I am grateful to Klaus Peters of Birkhäuser Boston, Inc. and to Philip Davis and Reuben Hersh for unflagging support. Last, but not least, I have benefitted enormously from the editorial assistance of Maria Fleming Tymoczko, a medievalist by training, a comparatist by profession and a philosopher by domestic necessity.

NOTES

1. Interest in mathematical structures was stimulated by P. Benacerraf's essay, "What Numbers Could Not Be," *Philosophical Review*, 74 (1965), 47–73. Among the replies to Benacerraf are M. Resnick's "Mathematical Knowledge and Pattern Cognition," *Canadian Journal of Philosophy*, V (1975), 23–39, and P. Kitcher's "The Plight of the Platonist," *Nous*, 12 (1978), 119–136.

For discussions of the iterative concept of set, see H. Wang, "The Concept of Set" in *From Mathematics to Philosophy*, Humanities Press, New York (1974), 181–223; G. Boolos, "The Iterative Conception of Set," *Journal of Philosophy*, 68 (1971), 215–231; and C. Parsons, "What is the Iterative Conception of Set?", *Logic, Foundations of Mathematics and Computability Theory*, D. Reidel, Dordrecht (1977), 335–367.

Recent investigations of truth were spurred by S. Kripke "Outline of a Theory of Truth," *Journal of Philosophy*, 72 (1975), 690–716, and considerably extended by A. Gupta, "Truth and Paradox", *Journal of Philosophical Logic*, 11 (1982), 1-60, and H. Herzenberger, "Notes on Naive Semantics," ibid., 61–102.

2. The foremost philosophical expositer of intuitionism is M. Dummett; see, for example, his essay "The Philosophical Basis of Intuitionistic Logic," *Logic Colloquium '73*, H.E. Rose and J.C. Sheperdson, editors, North-Holland, Amsterdam (1975), 5–40.

Among mathematicians, E. Bishop is perhaps the leading exponent of constructivism with *Foundations of Constructive Analysis*, McGraw-Hill, New York (1967). Special mention should also be made of the radical program of A.S. Yessenin-Volpin, "The Ultra-Intuitionistic Criticism and the Antitraditional Program for Foundations of Mathematics," *Intuitionism and Proof Theory*, A. Kino, J. Myhill, and R.E. Vesley, editors, North-Holland, Amsterdam (1980), 3–45. This program is most clearly explained by D. Isles, for example, in "On the Notion of Standard Non-Isomorphic Natural Numbers Series," *Constructive Mathematics: Proceedings, New Mexico, 1980,* Springer-Verlag, Berlin (1980), 274–313.

Introduction

The philosophy of mathematics is a formidable subject but a fascinating one, and the source of its appeal is the mystery of mathematics itself. Mathematics, Alfred North Whitehead once said, "may claim to be the most original creation of the human spirit." Its chief rival, Whitehead suggested, was music.[1] Pure mathematics stands at the pinnacle of rational thought. Mathematical results seem to be the paradigms of precision, rigor and certainty—from elementary theorems about numbers and geometric figures to the complex constructions of functional analysis and set theory. The results and methods of mathematics are often surprising and elegant, occasionally revealing an austere, abstract beauty more typically found in the arts. Mathematics permeates our intellectual life and has helped to shape modern society. Science is inconceivable apart from mathematics, and we often measure the rigor or 'hardness' of a science by the amount of mathematics it employs. We rely on mathematics when we build bridges, fly airplanes, use computers or get cash from automatic tellers. Whitehead's point is well taken: mathematics is a remarkable achievement.

The philosophy of mathematics begins when we ask for a general account of mathematics, a synoptic vision of the discipline that reveals its essential features and explains just how it is that human beings are able to do mathematics. The difficulty is that it is hard to arrange the various features for mathematics into a coherent whole. To account for the indubitability, objectivity and timelessness of mathematical results, we are tempted to regard them as true descriptions of a Platonic world outside of space-time. This leaves us with the problem of explaining how human beings can make contact with this reality. Alternatively, we could abandon the idea of a Platonic realm and view mathematics as simply a game played with formal symbols. This would explain how human beings can do mathematics, since we are game players *par excellence*, but it leaves us with the task of specifying the rules of the game and explaining why the mathematical game is so useful—we don't ask chess players for help in designing bridges. Still other approaches are possible which also clarify some aspects of mathematics at the cost of leaving other aspects totally mysterious. Nevertheless, tradition has viewed as primary the contrast between realist conceptions of mathematics and constructivist conceptions. Realism assumes the reality of a mathematical universe which is independent of mathematicians who *discover* truths about this reality. Constructivism insists that any mathematical reality is conditioned by the actual and potential constructions of mathematicians who *invent* mathematics. The dilemma as I have indicated, is that both views have considerable plausibility and both encounter serious difficulties.

Although quite interesting in itself, the philosophy of mathematics has far reaching ramifications for philosophy in general. Consider ontology and metaphysics, that part of philosophy dealing with the ultimate nature of reality. A typical metaphysical question is, are there abstract objects or are all objects concrete particulars existing in space-time? Obviously, if realism is the correct approach to mathematics then there *are* abstract objects, to wit, the objects of mathematics. Conversely, a defense of physicalism or the view that all objects are spatio-temporal objects, would most naturally involve a constructive interpretation of mathematics.

Or consider the philosophy of mind. If constructivism provided the correct account of mathematics, then a good theory of mind should account for mathematics as an internal mental activity. We would, as it were, be born with the possibility of doing mathematics. On the other hand, if realism is to be accommodated by a philosophy of mind, then it must endow the mind with a primitive faculty of mathematical intuition, or perception of the mathematical realm—a sort of extra-sensory perception. Thus, one's philosophy of mathematics colors one's conception of the mind, and vice-versa.

Finally, consider the philosophy of language. Realism as an account of mathematics disposes us to interpret mathematical languages model-theoretically, and in general, to develop our theory of semantics in terms of reference and truth. Constructivism in mathematics disposes us to prefer a more computational account of meaning and to develop our semantics in terms of meaning postulates and transformations. So we see how issues in the philosophy of mathematics can reverberate throughout philosophy and beyond it to such related fields as natural science, psychology, and linguistics. It is little wonder that the philosophy of mathematics has been traditionally regarded as an important testing ground for philosophical theories. Before accepting a general theory of mind or knowledge, a theory of what there is or of how language works, we are well advised to work out and evaluate its consequences for mathematics.

The philosophy of mathematics—or at least philosophical accounts of mathematics—has played an important role in philosophy going all the way back to Plato and Pythagoras. As a discipline, however, the philosophy of mathematics underwent an enormous change over a period centering on the turn of the century. If we analogize mathematics to science then, following Kuhn, we can characterize this change as revolutionary or the creation of a new paradigm.[2] The dominant question in the new philosophy of mathematics became: what is the foundation of mathematics? And the answer to this question, it was assumed, was to be found in the newly emerging discipline of mathematical logic. The new paradigms of the philosophy of mathematics included such achievements as Cantor's analysis of infinity, Frege's analysis of number and Russell and Whitehead's attempt at a grand unification. Early foundationalists were often quite explicit about their revolutionary aims. Russell and Whitehead called their masterprice *Principia Mathematica*, deliberately echoing Newton's *Philosophiae Naturalis Principia Mathematica. Principia Mathematica* was to do to the philosophy of mathematics, if not to mathematics proper, what Newton's work did to physics and its philosophy.

We will say more about the idea of foundations of mathematics later. For the moment, we can summarize it with the slogan that the business of the philosophy of mathematics is to provide the foundations of mathematics. Philosophy is kept in business by the fact that there are competing alternatives to the title of foundations. What philosophy does is to adjudicate among the competition, evaluating the conflicting claims. The instrument of adjudication is mathematical logic, the same instrument that was used to generate the competing foundations in the first place.

Nevertheless, the present anthology does not aim to tell the story of foundations. This is already well done elsewhere.[3] We come to bury Caesar, not to praise him. The last few decades have witnessed a growing dissatisfaction with the foundations approaches to mathematics. There are powerful limitations, often in the form of mathematical theorems, that each foundationalist approach has come up against. We are no nearer to the correct foundations today than we were a century ago. The same basic arguments and objections can be repeated at ever higher levels of abstraction. Moreover, close analysis has revealed certain key assumptions behind foundationalism that seemed obvious to its original proponents but seem much more implausible to us today. Finally, the controversy about foundations has lost its power to excite. It no longer has the revolutionary impact that it had in the early twentieth century, when each new move introduced an important new concept or distinction to mathematics and philosophy. Now the controversy leads us around in well worn circles that seem increasingly distant from the everyday concerns of mathematics and philosophy.

The first aim of the anthology, then, is to challenge the dogma of foundations. To this end, part one collects some of the more pointed and stimulating critiques of foundationalism. The authors include mathematicians, philosophers, and logicians. Individually each essay makes a strong case against foundationalism; collectively, their impact is overwhelming. There is an additional point served by bringing these essays together. To some extent, each conveys the impression of a lonely voice crying in the wilderness. It is worth emphasizing that the wilderness is becoming rather crowded and that the time is right for the post-foundationalists to move into the mainstream of the philosophy of mathematics.

In what new directions should the philosophy of mathematics set off once it abandons the search for foundations? The second part of this anthology explores one answer to this question. The essays collected there suggest that the philosophy of mathematics can be begun anew by reexamining the actual practices of mathematicians and those who use mathematics. If we look at mathematics without prejudice, many features will stand out as relevant that were ignored by the foundationalists: informal proofs, historical development, the possibility of mathematical error, mathematical explanations (in contrast to proofs), communication among mathematicians, the use of computers in modern mathematics, and many more. Foundationalists could ignore such issues because they interpreted actual practice in terms of foundations. To them, the activity of mathematics was essentially just the discovery of truths about sets, the verification of formal proofs, or some other foundational characterization. All the rest was irrelevant superstructure.

Apart from the foundational mythology, however, there is no justification for philosophy to continue to ignore the actual practice of mathematics. Indeed, it is this practice that should provide the philosophy of mathematics with its problems and the data for their solutions. Furthermore, as the early essays in the anthology show, the weakest links in foundationalism are precisely the assumptions it uses to discount mathematical practice. So the later essays are a natural extension of the earlier and take the opportunity to argue the positive cases for a recharacterization of mathematical experience. It is useful to have a label for this approach to the philosophy of mathematics. Following Lakatos and Putnam, I call it 'quasi-empiricism.'

This anthology delineates quasi-empiricism as a coherent and increasingly popular approach to the philosophy of mathematics. However it does not claim to be a complete representation of contemporary philosophy of mathematics. Foundationalists, for example, are not represented. More seriously, it does not address the basic dichotomy between realism and constructivism; is mathematics discovered or invented? This issue should be addressed, and I plan to do so in a later work.[4] Nevertheless there is a rationale for postponing that issue until we are more clear about the practice of mathematics.

Although realism and constructivism seem to be incompatible positions in the philosophy of mathematics, neither is incompatible with quasi-empiricism. In fact quasi-empiricism is continuous with contructivism; both take their start from mathematical practice. A difference between the approaches is that quasi-empiricism views the constructions of mathematicians more as social products, while constructivism views them in more strictly mathematical terms. The difference leads constructivists to impose stronger constraints on mathematical reasoning than does quasi-empiricism, which is more tolerant of diverse practices.

While quasi-empiricism opens a door for constructivism in the philosophy of mathematics, it hardly closes the door on realism. It might well turn out that the best characterization of mathematical practice is as an interaction between mathematicians and independently existing mathematical structures. To use an analogy, our philosophical understanding of astronomy might be advanced by emphasizing the *practice* of astronomy, the role of astronomers and telescopes and so forth, without ever denying that the practice is conditioned by a universe of astronomical objects. So too we can explore quasi-empiricism without denying realism in the philosophy of mathematics.

The rationale for presenting quasi-empiricism should now be clear. Although it might not settle the controversy between realism and constructivism, a deeper understanding of mathematical practice will better prepare us to settle the controversy.

Although this anthology does not completely represent the philosophy of mathematics, it does, I believe, gather together some of the more exciting essays published recently in the field. In this instance, the whole really is greater than the sum of all its parts; each essay reinforces the others. One purpose in bringing these essays together is to demonstrate their collective force. The collection will have succeeded if it stimulates the reader—mathematician or philosopher, professional, apprentice or amateur—to rethink his or her conception of mathematics.

NOTES

1. *Science and the Modern World*, New American Library, New York (1948), 25.

2. See his *The Structure of Scientific Revolutions*, University of Chicago Press, Chicago (1962).

3. For example, P. Benacerraf and H. Putnam, editors, *Philosophy of Mathematics,* Prentice Hall, Englewood Cliffs (1964). (Revised edition 1983.) There is also the more technical anthology edited by J. Hintikka, *The Philosophy of Mathematics*, Oxford University Press, Oxford (1963) and the source book edited by J. van Heijenoort, *From Frege to Gödel*, Harvard University Press, Cambridge (1967). For a simple introduction, the reader is directed to H. de Long's *A Profile of Mathematical Logic*, Addison-Wesley, Reading, Mass. (1970).

4. For an indication of my tastes in this direction, the reader is referred to footnotes 1 and 2 in the Preface, pp. x–xi.

PART I

Challenging Foundations

The authors of the essays in the first collection represent the major perspectives on the philosophy of mathematics; two are mathematicians, two are philosophers, and one a logician. Although their arguments are drawn from a variety of sources, they have a common target, namely, that view of the philosophy of mathematics known as 'foundationalism'. The essays argue that the search for foundations is misguided and that philosophy should abandon it. In this preliminary essay I will introduce the idea of foundations to readers who are not familiar with it. But first I would like a word with the more experienced readers who are familiar with the notion of foundations of mathematics and recognize its dominant position in modern philosophy of mathematics.

Many such readers, I suspect, will acknowledge dissatisfaction with the foundational approach to the philosophy of mathematics. More would do so if they felt they had a choice, but many people assume that 'the philosophy of mathematics' simply means 'foundational studies'. 'Foundational studies', in turn, is practically equivalent to 'mathematical logic'. We have to work to disentangle the major schools of foundationalism—platonism, logicism, formalism and intuitionism—from the major branches of mathematical logic—set theory, proof theory, model theory, and recursion theory. Such identifications are worth fighting against, for they consign the philosophy of mathematics to an extremely small group of experts. It is not enough to be an accomplished mathematician versed in general philosophy, nor to be an accomplished philosopher versed in general mathematics. In addition, one must buy into a certain research program and collect a Ph.D. in mathematical logic.

Reuben Hersh captures the present situation among mathematicians quite well.

> We are still in the aftermath of the great foundationist controversies of the early twentieth century. Formalism, intuitionism and logicism, each left its trace in the form of a certain mathematical research program that ultimately made its own contribution to the corpus of mathematics itself. As *philosophical* programs, as attempts to establish a secure foundation for mathematical knowledge, all have run their course and petered out or dried up. Yet there remains, as a residue, an unstated consensus that the philosophy of mathematics is research on the foundation of mathematics. If I find research in foundations uninteresting or irrelevant, I conclude that I'm simply not interested in philosophy (thereby depriving myself of any chance of confronting my own uncertainties about the meaning, nature, purpose or significance of mathematical research).[1]

The situation of philosophers is analogous to that of mathematicians. A typical intelligent philosopher, versed in general mathematics, will feel that he does not know enough mathematical logic to comprehend the philosophy of mathematics. When he finds research in foundations uninteresting, unimportant or incomprehensible, the typical philosopher concludes that he is not interested in mathematics, thereby depriving himself of any chance to use the ideas, problems and examples of mathematics in his philosophy.

The following essays should liberate both philosophers and mathematicians from foundational restrictions. They make in greater detail the point that is nicely summarized by Hilary Putnam.

> Philosophers and logicians have been so busy trying to provide mathematics with a 'foundation' in the past half-century that only rarely have a few timid voices dared to voice the suggestion that it does not need one. I wish here to urge with some seriousness the view of the timid voices. I don't think mathematics is unclear; I don't think mathematics has a crisis in its foundations; indeed, I do not believe mathematics either has or needs 'foundations'. The much touted problems in the philosophy of mathematics seem to me, without exception, to be problems internal to the thought of various system builders. The systems are doubtless interesting as intellectual exercises; debate between the systems and research within the systems doubtless will and should continue; but I would like to convince you (of course I won't, but one can always hope) that the various systems of mathematical philosophy, without exception, need not be taken seriously.[2]

Readers anxious to pursue this line of inquiry should turn immediately to the next essays. For those readers who are not too familiar with the foundational view, I offer a brief sketch of what it is and how it came to dominate the philosophy of mathematics.

Philosophers are prone to think in terms of foundations. Phrases like "the foundations of knowledge," "the foundation of morality," "foundations of physics" roll easily off our tongues. Ordinarily, philosophical speculation about foundations is ignored by a discipline that is making reasonable progress or else it is treated with a bemused tolerance. When a discipline is experiencing a crisis, however, philosophical speculation is positively reinforced.

If anyone ever experienced an intellectual crisis in a field, it was nineteenth-century mathematicians. They were trying to assimilate non-Euclidean geometries, to separate geometry from arithmetic and analysis, to ground the calculus, to assimilate infinity, discover the general nature of sets, avoid the paradoxes of set theory, and so on. At the same time they were experiencing an unparalleled increase in generality and abstraction in mathematics. Mathematicians were shifting from studying only 'the natural numbers given by God' to the consideration of arbitrary number systems, from solving equations to solving groups. In order to make sense of these changes, nineteenth- and early twentieth-century mathematicians needed a new set of criteria for assessing mathematics and mathematical proof. Symbolic logic promised a set of criteria and to nineteenth-century mathematicians and their immediate descendants, it more than delivered.

The greatest architect of foundationalism was Gottlob Frege. Unfortunately for Frege, his greatness was not publicly recognized during his lifetime and he died in relative obscurity. Fortunately for Frege, his students and correspondents included some of the greatest minds of the time who disseminated his ideas and established his position as the greatest logician since Aristotle.

When Frege began his work, 'logic' meant Aristotelian logic—subjects and predicates, the law of the excluded middle, syllogisms, and the like: fixed, immutable truths to be sure, but somewhat trivial or tautologous ones. Kant articulated the general conception of logic when he said

> since Aristotle [Logic] has not had to retrace a single step, unless we choose to consider as improvements the removal of some unnecessary subtleties, or the clearer definition of its matter, both of which refer to the elegance rather than to the solidity of the science. It is remarkable also, that to the present day, it has not been able to make one step in advance, so that, to all appearances, it may be considered as completed and perfect.
>
> Aristotle has omitted no essential point of the understanding; we have only to become more accurate, methodical and orderly.[3]

Against this backdrop, Frege's work made the revolutionary claim that Aristotle had mischaracterized logic! He offered an alternative characterization in terms of what we now call quantification theory with identity together with the rudiments of type theory and set theory. *Moreover*, and this is a crucial point, Frege argued that logic thus reconstrued was the foundation of mathematics in that all legitimate mathematical concepts could be defined in logical terms and all mathematical theorems could be deduced from the principles of logic. To be more precise, Frege argued that arithmetic and analysis were founded in logic. He distinguished these from geometry admitting that the truth of Euclidean-geometry was not founded in logic but rested instead on a primitive intuition of Euclidean space.[4] His main point was that arithmetic needed no such appeal to intuition—it could be derived solely from logical principles available in theory to any rational being. In other words, the laws of arithmetic followed from, and were but a special case of, the most general laws of thought. This solves the mystery of mathematical knowledge. Any rational being is capable of mathematics. At the same time, the laws of logic were the most general laws of being, 'the laws of the laws of nature', to use Frege's evocative phrase. When logic demonstrated the existence of something, for example numbers, these things had a real, objective existence—there was nothing more real. So Frege's theory provides for the objectivity of mathematics and justifies our picture of an independent mathematical reality whose nature mathematicians discover.

To make his argument, Frege needed to do two things:

(a) spell out his new version of logic, symbolic logic, and

(b) carry out in detail the derivation of classical mathematics from logic.

He proceeded to do this in three major works:

Begriffsschrift, a formula language, modeled upon that of arithmetic, for pure thought (1879).

Die Grundlagen der Arithmetik, the foundations of arithmetic, a logico-mathematical enquiry into the concept of number (1884).

Grundgesetze der Arithmetik, the basic laws of arithmetic (two volumes, 1893 and 1903).

Frege's achievement, in my opinion, is one of the greatest contributions to philosophy of all time. According to Montgomery Furth:

> Frege's investigations of the concepts of logical truth and of logical consequence . . . amounted to the creation single-handed of the subject of mathematical logic as later understood, issuing in a formal system of logic incorporating propositional calculus, first and second-order quantification theory, and a theory of sets developed within second-order quantification theory.[5]

Jean van Heijenoort says of the first book alone, a mere 88 pages:

> Its fundamental contributions, among lesser points, are the truth-functional propositional calculus, the analysis of the proposition into function and argument(s) instead of subject and predicate, the theory of quantification, a system of logic in which derivations are carried out exclusively according to the form of the expressions, and a logical definition of the notion of mathematical sequence. Any single one of these achievements would suffice to secure the book a permanent place in the logician's library.[6]

In other words, Frege was working out the rules governing the use of such concepts as

variable	many-place relation	formal expression
function	many-place function	definition
set	quantifier	proof

just when mathematics was in desperate need of those concepts! Mathematicians of his day were still treating variables as names of general nondescript numbers. They could summarize their knowledge of infinity with the lemniscate, ∞. They confused $\in$ with $\subseteq$. Philosophers still wondered about the reality of relations and whether every proposition might have the subject-predicate form, P(s).

Of course Frege's influence was not very direct; he was, by and large, ignored in his lifetime. However, Frege's work was just one of the paradigms of foundationalism. It was complemented by the works of Cantor, Dedekind, Zermelo, Peano, Russell and Hilbert among many others. Together these mathematicians, philosophers and logicians simultaneously forged the discipline of mathematical logic and many of the basic tools of modern mathematics. The foundation program, as a whole, directly influenced mathematical practice. Thus, leaving aside any theoretical or philosophical justification for foundations (and Frege had provided quite an elegant one), there remained a very crucial pragmatic justification for it. Foundationalism satisfied some very pressing needs of nineteenth- and early twentieth-century mathematicians.

Up to this point a reader might conclude that foundationalism is surely correct. What more could one ask of the philosophy of mathematics? Fair enough—I want here to emphasize the plausibility and attractiveness of the foundations picture, for the following essays are quite up to the task of refuting even the best versions of foundations. Nevertheless, I must admit that my account of foundationalism is so far misleading. I have presented it as if everyone *agreed* as to what the foundation of mathematics was—logic as described by Frege. But I've left something out of the account which, when filled in, explains why foundationalism breaks up into competing schools.

Very early on, Frege's system of logic was discovered to be inconsistent, as were many others of the paradigms mentioned above. They produced contradictions. The project of foundations became *to find* foundations which did the job that Frege's system was supposed to do but which were consistent, as Frege's system was not. The problem is that no one has ever been able to put the pieces together as simply and uniformly and completely as Frege had while still remaining consistent.

The discovery of Frege's inconsistency is itself a paradigm of mathematical logic and goes by the name of Russell's Paradox. The full story involves human drama as well as conceptual discovery and serves to explain the diaspora of foundationalism into conflicting schools. It's worthy of a summary.

As the final volume of the *Grungesetze* was going to press, when Frege was slipping the last brick into the foundations of mathematics as it were, he got a letter from the young British philosopher, Bertrand Russell. Russell tactfully pointed out that Frege's system was inconsistent and so it was certainly not a foundation of mathematics, or of anything else for that matter. The human tragedy is eloquently expressed by Russell in a letter to van Heijenoort.[7]

Dear Professor van Heijenoort,

I should be most pleased if you would publish the correspondence between Frege and myself, and I am grateful to you for suggesting this. As I think about acts of integrity and grace, I realise that there is nothing in my knowledge to compare with Frege's dedication to the truth. His entire life's work was on the verge of completion, much of his work had been ignored to the benefit of men infinitely less capable, his second volume was about to be published, and upon finding that his fundamental assumption was in error, he responded with intellectual pleasure clearly submerging any feelings of personal disappointment. It was almost superhuman and a telling indication of that of which men are capable if their dedication is to creative work and knowledge instead of cruder efforts to dominate and be known.

Yours sincerely,
BERTRAND RUSSELL

If anything, Russell understates the case.

The conceptual discovery was that the most natural connection between ontology and epistemology in mathematics, the principle that every natural property determines a set of things satisfying that property, is contradictory. This principle would permit the set of all sets not members of themselves, which is a logical impossibility. Russell's Paradox thus consists of two parts, Russell's rather elementary theorem (that $-\ (Ex)(y)\ (Rxy\ <=>\ -\ Ryy)\ )$ and Frege's rather profound mistake. Foundationalism, which does not recognize mistakes nor dignify elementary theorems, is forced to describe the situation as a paradox.

Russell's Paradox shook the logician's world and threatened the very concept of foundations of mathematics. To some, even arithmetic seemed to totter. But as we've seen, the foundations program was far too valuable and attractive to be abandoned without a fight. The goal was to reconstruct it while avoiding the paradoxes. However, there was no single way of doing this. Many techniques were available and choices among different techniques led to different schools of foundationalism.

Russell, in collaboration with Whitehead, attempted to salvage logicism, Frege's thesis that the foundation of mathematics was, literally, logic. In their influential work, *Principia Mathematica*, they replaced Frege's version of logic with an elaborate theory of types, but their system was cumbersome and was felt by many to paper over too many difficulties. Logicism has steadily lost ground as a plausible account of foundations, in part because of a proliferation of logical theories—beyond type theory and set theory there is infinitary logic, multi-valued logics, intuitionist logic, and so on.

One alternative was that set theory was the foundation of mathematics. Set theory has all the power of Russell's system, and a great deal more clarity and elegance. Set theoretic platonists hold that the universe of mathematics *is* the universe of sets and their foundational program was to characterize this universe and reconstruct classical mathematics in terms of sets. While maintaining the reality of mathematical objects, set theoretic platonism does little to advance our understanding of how mathematical truths are known. In addition, there is considerable uncertainty about the nature of this set theoretic universe (is it, for instance, one or many?)

and the axioms of set theory (is set theory identical with the formal system *ZF*?).

Another alternative to logicism was to replace Russell's characterization of logic with metamathematics, the logical manipulation of formal systems. According to such a formalism, mathematical theorems are merely the results of logical deductions from arbitrary axioms. The foundations of mathematics is metamathematics, the study of formal systems, which provides mathematicians with the tools they need—formal languages, theories and rules of inference. Formalism's hope of finding *the* consistent and complete formal theory adequate for mathematics was dashed by Gödel's discoveries and formalism has had difficulty reformulating its goal. Not just any formal theory can count as mathematics after all; for we can formalize parts of physics, and even parts of literature if the Russian literary formalists are correct. Moreover, the univocal sense of logic as a framework for formal systems has given way to a bewildering variety of formal logics with no clear front runner, as noted earlier.

Now it should be noted that while there is considerable disagreement among these schools, there is considerable overlap as well. They all shared in the development of a new conception of logic, now known as mathematical logic, and a new set of mathematical tools. In addition, we should note, at least in passing, the emergence of a renegade school in the philosophy of mathematics, intuitionism. Intuitionists denied that mathematics had foundations, and they returned to the Kantian idea of a primitive intuition of the natural numbers. They were no mere platonists, however, for they held a baroque theory of intuition which forced them to abandon classical logic all the way back to Aristotle's law of the excluded middle. When their theory of acceptable constructions is spelled out, it begins to look suspiciously like just another putative foundation for mathematics, and the least attractive foundation at that, to the general mathematician and philosopher.

Of course these basic foundations can be refined and crossbred to yield more sophisticated candidates such as modified platonism, second-order logicism, Turing Machine formalism and ultra-intuitionism. But we'll stop our account here. There, in a nutshell, is the story of the foundations of mathematics and its subsidiary schools. Those interested in learning more about foundations are referred to the excellent surveys and anthologies available.[8]

Those interested in learning why the foundations program fails as a philosophy of mathematics should continue on with the following essays.

NOTES

1. Hersh, "Introducing Imre Lakatos," *Mathematical Intelligencer*, 1 (1978), 148.

2. Putnam, "Mathematics Without Foundations," *Journal of Philosophy*, 64 (1967), 5.

3. The first quotation is from the *Critique of Pure Reason,* the second from *Introduction to Logic*. I borrow the references H. de Long's fine summary, *A Profile of Mathematical Logic*, Addison-Wesley, Reading, Mass. (1970), 36.

4. Frege makes this clear in *The Foundations of Arithmetic*, Basil Blackwell, Oxford (1968), 20–21.

5. M. Furth in the introduction to his translation of Frege's *The Basic Laws of Arithmetic*, University of California Press, Berkeley (1967), vi.

6. J. van Heijenoort, *From Frege to Gödel*, Harvard University Press, Cambridge (1967), 1.

7. Ibid., 127.

8. See the references noted on page xvii above.

REUBEN HERSH

Some Proposals for Reviving the Philosophy of Mathematics

Hersh's essay begins the challenge to foundationalism:

> The present impasse in mathematical philosophy is the aftermath of the great period of foundationist controversies from Frege and Russell through Brouwer, Hilbert and Gödel. What is needed now is a new beginning . . .
>
> Many of the difficulties and stumbling blocks in the philosophy of mathematics are created by inherited philosophical prejudices which we are free to discard if we choose to do so.

Hersh presents the case from the point of view of mathematicians. For him, philosophy of mathematics is primarily the working philosophy of the professional mathematician. In so far as that philosophy is restricted to the usual mix of foundational ideas, Hersh charges, it is generally inconsistent, always irrelevant and sometimes harmful in practice and teaching.

There are difficulties in each of the foundational theories and Hersh discusses several of these. However, his main concern is to understand how the preoccupation with foundations came about. At present, Hersh suggests, the best explanation of foundational concerns is in terms of the historical development of mathematics which he summarizes. Along the way, he isolates some of the basic presuppositions of foundation studies: "that mathematics must be provided with an absolutely reliable foundation" and "that mathematics must be a source of indubitable truth." Hersh's point is that it is one thing to accept the assumption when, like Frege, Russell or Hilbert, we feel that the foundation is nearly attained. But it is quite another to go on accepting it, to go on letting it shape our philosophy, *long after* we've abandoned any hope of attaining that goal.

Very well, if the concerns of foundations of mathematics are the wrong concerns, then how do we philosophize about mathematics ? Hersh's answer is clear: we begin with the ongoing *practice* of mathematicians. This is a deep

Reprinted, with permission, from Advances in Mathematics, Vol. 31, 1979, pp. 31–50.

and important point that will be returned to again and again throughout this anthology. The emphasis on mathematical practice is not just a mathematician's chauvinism. It is the practice of mathematics that provides philosophy with its data, its problems and its solutions. At the turn of the century it seemed as if foundationalism could capture the essence of mathematical practice and no wonder. As we've noted, foundations programs changed that practice. But in the last half century, foundational research and ordinary mathematical practice have evolved along quite different lines. To revive the philosophy of mathematics, we must return to its source for a fresh look.

If we view mathematical practice with an unjaundiced eye, Hersh suggests, we will observe prominent features that have been ignored by traditional philosophy. We might note, for example, that mathematical knowledge is inherently fallible and no foundation can make it infallible. When informed of Russell's Paradox, Frege is alleged to have said "Arithmetic totters." Hersh might agree but add that arithmetic doesn't totter too much and besides, everything totters. Mathematical knowledge is "fallible, corrigible, tentative and evolving as is every other kind of human knowledge."

In a similar vein, we might note that mathematical practice is essentially a public activity, not a private one. This obvious point is at odds with the standard foundational attitude that mathematics is essentially a private affair, taking place in a mind, and that public practice is only a symptom of it. The emphasis on mathematical practice, in our time, brings with it an emphasis on the mathematical *community* as the ultimate source of mathematical activity.

Hersh concludes his paper with a brief sketch of the new vista in philosophy of mathematics. It is not without flaws. Professional philosophers will be disturbed by the free and easy use of 'idea' as a basic explanatory notion. After two thousand years of philosophical reworking, the idea of 'idea' has become rather vague. Indeed in comparison the platonist's 'set' or the formalist's 'symbol' can look like a positive advance in clarity. In Hersh's framework idea takes on a more substantial meaning, however, very like 'cultural product of the mathematical subculture.' Of course this interpretation is likely to raise more questions than it answers from both mathematicians and philosophers. What accounts for the striking differences between mathematical products and other cultural products? Is mathematical creativity as unconstrained as artistic creativity? Hersh suggests some answers, but more importantly, he asks deep questions.

• • • • •

By "philosophy of mathematics" I mean the working philosophy of the professional mathematician, the philosophical attitude toward his work that is assumed by the researcher, teacher, or user of mathematics. What I propose needs reviving is the discussion of philosophical issues by working mathematicians, especially the central issue—the analysis of truth and meaning in mathematical discourse.

The purpose of this article is, first, to describe the philosophical plight of the working mathematician; second, to propose an explanation for how this plight has come about; and third, to suggest, though all too briefly, a direction in which escape may be possible. In summary, our argument will go as follows:

(1) The philosophical notions about mathematics commonly held by the working mathematician are incompatible with each other and with our actual experience and practice of mathematical work. Many practical problems and impasses confronting mathematics today have philosophical aspects. The dearth of well-founded philosophical discourse on mathematics has observable harmful consequences, in teaching, in research, and in the practical affairs of our organizations.

(2) The present impasse in mathematical philosophy is the aftermath of the great period of foundationist controversies from Frege and Russell through Brouwer, Hilbert, and Gödel. What is needed now is a new beginning, not a continuation of the various "schools" of logicism, formalism or intuitionism. To get beyond these schools, it is necessary to go back in history to their origin, to see what they had in common, and how they were rooted in the mathematics and philosophy of their day.

(3) Many of the difficulties and stumbling blocks in the philosophy of mathematics are created by inherited philosophical prejudices which we are free to discard if we choose to do so. Some of our philosophical difficulties will then simply evaporate; others will become tangible problems which can be investigated systematically, with reasonable hopes for progress.

Each statement will be amplified and argued at some length below.

1 THE PHILOSOPHICAL PLIGHT OF THE WORKING MATHEMATICIAN

Most writers on the subject seem to agree that the typical "working mathematician" is a Platonist on weekdays and a formalist on Sundays. That is, when he is doing mathematics, he is convinced that he is dealing with an objective reality whose properties he is attempting to determine. But then, when challenged to give a philosophical account of this reality, he finds it easiest to pretend that he does not believe in it after all.

We quote two well-known authors:

> On foundations we believe in the reality of mathematics, but of course when philosophers attack us with their paradoxes we rush to hide behind formalism and say, "Mathematics is just a combination of meaningless symbols," and then we bring out Chapters 1 and 2 on set theory. Finally we are left in peace to go back to our mathematics and do it as we have always done, with the feeling each mathematician has that he is working with something real. This sensation is probably an illusion, but is very convenient. That is Bourbaki's attitude toward foundations. (Dieudonné [8].)
>
> To the average mathematician who merely wants to know his work is securely based, the most appealing choice is to avoid difficulties by means of Hilbert's program. Here one regards mathematics as a formal game and one is only concerned with the question of consistency . . . . The Realist position is probably the one which most mathematicians would prefer to take. It is not

> until he becomes aware of some of the difficulties in set theory that he would even begin to question it. If these difficulties particularly upset him, he will rush to the shelter of Formalism, while his normal position will be somewhere between the two, trying to enjoy the best of two worlds. (Cohen [4].)

(Throughout the paper, the term "formalism" is used, as it is in these quotations from Dieudonné and Cohen, to mean the philosophical position that much or all of pure mathematics is a meaningless game. It should be obvious that to reject formalism as a philosophy of mathematics by no means implies any critique of mathematical logic. On the contrary, logicians, whose own mathematical activity *is* the study of formal systems, are in the best position to appreciate the enormous difference between mathematics as it is done and mathematics as it is schematized in the notion of a formal mathematical system.)

We will shortly offer an analysis of this supposed alternative of Platonism and formalism. At present we merely record this as a generally accepted fact about the mathematical world today: Most mathematicians live with two contradictory views on the nature and meaning of their work. Is it credible that this tension has no effect on the self-confidence and self-esteem of people who are supposed above all things to hate contradiction?

The question of what is interesting in mathematics is a practical question of the highest importance for anyone who is active in research or who is involved in hiring and promoting people who do research. Is it not astonishing that there is no public discussion on this question, no vehicle for public discussion of it, hardly even a language or viewpoint which could be used for such a discussion?

This is *not* to say that there can or should be explicit, agreed-upon standards of mathematical taste. On the contrary. Precisely because tastes differ, discussion on matters of taste is possible and necessary. Our very existence as a single profession, and our ability to agree in practice that certain deeds in mathematics are deserving the highest praise and reward, prove that there are common standards of excellence which we use as criteria for evaluating our work. To make these criteria explicit, to bring them into the open for discussion, challenge, and controversy, would be one important philosophical activity for mathematicians. Our inability to sustain such a public discussion on values in mathematics is an aspect of philosophical unawareness and incompetence.

The problems of truth and meaning are not technical issues in some recondite branch of logic or set theory. They confront anyone who uses or teaches mathematics. If we wish, we can ignore them. To do so, however, is to leave oneself the prisoner of one's unexamined philosophical preconceptions. It would be surprising if this had no practical consequences.

Let us pause to consider two possible examples of such practical consequences. The last half-century or so has seen the rise of formalism as the most frequently advocated point of view in mathematical philosophy.[1] In this same period, the dominant style of exposition in mathematical journals, and even in texts and treatises, has been to insist on precise details of definitions and proofs, but to exclude or minimize discussion of why a problem is interesting, or why a particular method of proof is used.

It would be difficult or impossible to document the connection between formalism in expository style and formalism in philosophical attitude. Still, ideas have consequences. One's conception of what mathematics *is* affects one's conception of how it should be presented. One's manner of presenting it is an indication of what one believes to be most essential in it.

Another example is the importation, during the '60's, of set-theoretic notation and axiomatics into the high-school curriculum. This was not an inexplicable aberration, as its critics sometimes seem to imagine. It was a predictable consequence of the philosophical doctrine that reduces all mathematics to axiomatic systems expressed in set-theoretic language.

The criticism of formalism in the high schools has been primarily on pedagogic grounds: "This is the wrong thing to teach, or the wrong way to teach." But all such arguments are inconclusive if they leave unquestioned the dogma that real mathematics *is* precisely formal derivations from formally stated axioms. If this philosophical dogma goes unchallenged, the critic of formalism in the schools appears to be advocating a compromise in quality: he is a sort of pedagogic opportunist, who wants to offer the student less than the "real thing." The issue, then, is not, What is the best way to teach? but, What is mathematics really all about? To discredit formalism in pedagogy, one must challenge its philosophical base: the formalist picture of the nature of mathematics. Controversies about high-school teaching cannot be resolved without confronting problems about the nature of mathematics. In the end, the critique of formalism can be successful only through the development of an alternative: a more convincing, more satisfactory philosophical account of the meaning and nature of mathematics.[2]

Mathematicians themselves seldom discuss the philosophical issues surrounding mathematics; they asume that someone else has taken care of this job. We leave it to the professionals.

But the professional philosopher, with hardly any exception, has little to say to the professional mathematician. Indeed, he has only a remote and inadequate notion of what the professional mathematician is doing. Certainly this fact is not discreditable; it is to be expected, in view of the formidable technical prerequisites for understanding what we do.

Still, it has to be said that if a mathematician, uncomfortable with his philosophical confusion, looks for help in the books and journals in his library, he will be badly disappointed. Some philosophers who write about mathematics seem unacquainted with any mathematics more advanced than arithmetic and elementary geometry. Others are specialists in logic or axiomatic set theory; their work seems as narrowly technical as that in any other mathematical specialty.

There are professional philosophers of science who seem to be reasonably conversant with quantum mechanics and general relativity. There do not seem to be many professional philosophers who know functional analysis or algebriac topology or stochastic processes. Perhaps there is not need to know such things, if mathematics can really be reduced to logic or arithmetic or set theory. But such a presumption is itself a philosophical stand which is (to put it mildly) subject to challenge.

There are a few penetrating comments on mathematics in Polanyi's "Personal Knowledge." But then, Polanyi was really a chemist. And there is the beautiful work "Proofs and Refutations" by I.M. Lakatos [17]. This dissertation, written under the influence of Karl Popper and George Pólya, is the most interesting and original contribution to the philosophy of mathematics in recent decades. The fact that Lakatos' work remains almost unknown to American mathematicians in a striking illustration of our intellectual blinders.

There are, indeed, occasional philosophical comments by leading mathematicians whose interests are not confined to set theory and logic. But the art of philosophical discourse is not well developed today among mathematicians, even among the most brilliant. Philosophical issues just as much as mathematical ones deserve careful argument, fully developed analysis, and due consideration of objections. A bald statement of one's own opinion is not an argument, even in philosophy.

In the usual university mathematics curriculum, the only philosophical questions considered are those raised by the various foundationist schools of 50 years ago. In regard to these, it is mentioned that none of them was able to carry out its program, and that there is no real prospect that any of them can resolve the problem of "foundations."

Thus, if we teach our students anything at all about the philosophical problems of mathematics, it is that there is only one problem of interest (the problem of the foundation of the real number system), and that problem seems totally intractable.

Nevertheless, of course, we do not give up mathematics. We simply stop thinking about it. Just *do* it. That, more or less, is the present situation in the philosophy of mathematics.

2 HOW DID WE GET HERE?

This dilemma of Platonism versus formalism, of a vacillation between two unacceptable philosophies, is a characteristic of our own historical epoch.

How did it come about?

I would like to suggest a historical schema—a conjecture, which perhaps could be investigated by a suitably qualified historian.

Even as an impressionistic conjecture, it may help give us an orientation on our present situation.

Until well into the nineteenth century, geometry was regarded by everybody, *including mathematicians,* as the firmest, most reliable branch of knowledge. Analysis derived its meaning and its legitimacy from its link with geometry.

I do not say "Euclidean geometry," because the use of the qualifier became necessary and meaningful only after the possibility of more than one geometry had been recognized. Before that, geometry was simply geometry—the study of the properties of space. These existed absolutely and independently, were objectively given, and were the supreme example of properties of the universe which were exact, eternal, and knowable with certainty by the human mind.

In the nineteenth century, several disasters took place.

One disaster was the discovery of non-Euclidean geometries, which showed that there was more than one thinkable geometry.

A greater disaster was the development of analysis so that it overtook geometrical intuition. The discovery of space-filling curves and continuous nowhere-differentiable curves were stunning surprises which showed the vulnerability of the one solid foundation—geometric intuition—on which mathematics had been thought to rest.

The situation was intolerable because geometry had served, from the time of Plato, as the supreme exemplar of the possibility of certainty in human knowledge. Spinoza and Descartes followed the "more geometrico" in establishing the existence of God, as Newton followed it in establishing his laws of motion and gravitation. The loss of certainty in geometry was philosophically intolerable, because it implied the loss of all certainty in human knowledge.

The mathematicians of the nineteenth century, of course, proved equal to the challenge. Led by Dedekind and Weierstrass, they turned from geometry to arithmetic as the foundation for mathematics.

Gradually it became clear that in reducing the continuum to arithmetic, one required a kind of mathematics which had hitherto gone unnoticed—set theory.

Set theory at first seemed to be almost the same thing as logic, and so the hope then appeared that instead of arithmetic, set theory-logic could serve as the foundation for all mathematics. It was not to be. As Frege put it in his famous postscript, "Just as the building was completed, the foundation collapsed." That is, Russell communicated to him the Russell paradox.

This was the "crisis in foundations," the central issue in the famous controversies of the first quarter of this century. Three principal remedies were proposed:

The program of "logicism," the school of Frege and Russell, was to find a reformulation of set theory, which could avoid the Russell paradox and thereby save the Frege-Russell-Whitehead program of establishing mathematics upon logic as a foundation.

The work on this program played a major role in the development of logic. But it was a failure in terms of its original intention. By the time set theory had been patched up to exclude the paradoxes, it was a complicated structure which one could hardly identify with "logic" in the philosophical sense of "the rules for correct reasoning." So it became untenable to argue that mathematics is nothing but logic—that mathematics is one vast tautology.

> I wanted certainty in the kind of way in which people want religious faith. I thought that certainty is more likely to be found in mathematics than elsewhere. But I discovered that many mathematical demonstrations, which my teachers expected me to accept, were full of fallacies, and that, if certainty were indeed discoverable in mathematics, it would be in a new field of mathematics, with more solid foundations than those that had hitherto been thought secure. But as the work proceeded, I was continually reminded of the fable about the elephant and the tortoise. Having constructed an elephant upon which the mathematical world could rest, I found the elephant tottering, and proceeded to construct a tortoise to keep the elephant from falling. But the tortoise was no more secure than the elephant, and after some twenty years

> of very arduous toil, I came to the conclusion that there was nothing more that I could do in the way of making mathematical knowledge indubitable. (Bertrand Russell, "Portraits from Memory.")

The response of Hilbert to this dilemma was the invention of "proof theory." The idea was to regard mathematical proofs as sequences of formal symbols, rearranged and transformed according to certain rules which correspond to the rules of mathematical reasoning. Then purely finite, combinatorial arguments would be found to show that the axioms of set theory would never lead to a contradiction. In this way, mathematics would be given a secure foundation—in the sense of a guarantee of consistency.

This kind of foundation is not at all the same as a foundation based on a theory known to be *true,* as geometry had been believed to be true, or at least impossible to doubt, as it is supposed to be impossible to doubt the law of contradiction in elementary logic.

The formalist foundation, like the logicist foundation, tried to buy certainty and reliability at a price. As the logicist interpretation tried to make mathematics safe by turning it into a tautology, the formalist interpretation tried to make it safe by turning it into a meaningless game. The "proof-theoretic program" comes into action only after mathematics has been coded in a formal language and its proofs written in a way checkable by machine. As to the *meaning* of the symbols, that becomes something extra-mathematical.

It is important to realize that Hilbert's writings and conversation display full conviction that mathematical problems are questions about real objects, and have meaningful answers which are true in the same sense that any statement about reality is true. If he nevertheless was prepared to advocate a formalist interpretation of mathematics, this was the price he considered necessary for the sake of obtaining certainty.

> The goal of my theory is to establish once and for all the certitude of mathematical methods. . . . The present state of affairs where we run up against the paradoxes is intolerable. Just think, the definitions and deductive methods which everyone learns, teaches and uses in mathematics, the paragon of truth and certitude, lead to absurdities! If mathematical thinking is defective, where are we to find truth and certitude? (Hilbert [12].)

As it happened, certainty was not to be had, even at this price. Gödel's incompleteness theorems showed that the Hilbert program was unattainable—that any formal system strong enough to contain elementary arithmetic would be unable to prove its own consistency.

Instead of providing foundations for mathematics, Russell's logic and Hilbert's proof theory became the starting points for new branches of mathematics. Model theory and other branches of mathematical logic have become an intrinsic part of the whole structure of contemporary mathematics—and as much or as little in need of foundations as the rest of the structure.

The third famous school that competed with the logicist and the formalist was the intuitionist. Brouwer's position was that the natural numbers were reliable and needed no deeper foundation; and that the only acceptable parts of mathematics were those that could be derived from the natural numbers "constructively." His notion of constructivity was strict enough to exclude the real number system as it is usually understood. As a consequence, even though his opinions were accepted at least in part by such men as Hermann Weyl and Henri Poincaré, the vast majority of mathematicians continued to work nonconstructively.

(Some aspects of the intuitionist viewpoint are still attractive to mathematicians who are seeking an alternative to Platonism and formalism; in particular, the insistence that mathematics be meaningful, and that mathematics be viewed as a certain kind of human mental activity. One can accept these ideas, while rejecting the dogma that any mathematics which cannot be obtained "constructively" from the natural numbers is deficient in meaning.)

This story is probably too long and familiar for many readers. But it makes the point: All three foundationist schools shared the same presupposition. For us today, in view of their common failure, the common presupposition is more important than the much-emphasized differences. By bringing out and challenging this presupposition, we can escape from the quagmire where mathematical philosophy has been trapped for fifty years.

The common presupposition was that mathematics must be provided with an absolutely reliable foundation. The disagreement was on strategy, on what had to be sacrificed for the sake of the agreed-on goal. But the goal was never attained, and there are few who still hope for its attainment.

At this point we can see the reason for the "working mathematician's" uneasy oscillation between formalism and Platonism. Our inherited *and unexamined* philosophical dogma is that mathematical truth should possess absolute certainty. Our actual experience in mathematical work offers uncertainty in plenty. Platonism and formalism, each in its own way, provide a nonhuman "reality" where one might imagine absolute certainty dwells.

Pick some familiar theorem: for example, the uncountability of the continuum; Cauchy's integral formula; the fundamental theorem of algebra.

Is it a true statement about the world? Does one *discover* such a theorem, and does such a discovery *increase* our knowledge?

If you answer yes to such questions, you may be called a *Platonist* (or a "realist"). You will then be faced with the next question: to what objects or features of the world do such statements refer? One does not meet roots of polynomials (or uncountable sets) or integrals of analytic functions while walking down the street, or even while traveling in outer space. Where, outside of our thoughts, can one encounter roots of polynomials, or uncountable sets?

Perhaps such things do not have any real existence after all, and the conviction that they exist and are objectively knowable is merely an illusion in which we indulge ourselves. Perhaps a theorem is nothing more than a formula that can be derived by the rules of logic from some given set of formulas (*axioms,* if you will).

If you prefer to retreat to this modest disclaimer, you may be called a formalist. Since you have now renounced any claim that mathematics is meaningful, you are no longer under the difficulty of analyzing its meaning. But this does not leave you free from philosophical difficulties. On the contrary. You now may be asked, how is it that all three of the examples we have given were known, understood and used long before the axioms on which they are "based" had been stated? If we say that a theorem has no meaning except as a conclusion from axioms, then do we say that Gauss did not know the fundamental theorem of algebra, Cauchy did not know Cauchy's integral formula, and Cantor did not know Cantor's theorem?

The basis for Platonism is the awareness we all have that the problems and concepts of mathematics exist independently of us as individuals. The zeroes of the zeta function are where they are, regardless of what I may think or know on the subject. It is then easy for me to imagine that this objectivity is given outside of human consciousness as a whole, outside of history and culture. This is the myth of Platonism. It remains alive because it corresponds to something real in the daily experience of the mathematician. Yet it remains alive only as a halfhearted, shamefaced Platonism, because it is incompatible with the general philosophy or world-view of most scientists—including mathematicians.[3] Platonism in the full sense—*belief in the existence of ideal entities, independent of or prior to human consciousness*—is of course tenable within a religious world-view (belief in a divine Mind.) For those whose general world view excludes mysticism, Platonism in the full sense is very difficult to maintain once the full force of scientific skepticism is focused on it.[4]

At this point the alternative becomes formalism. Instead of believing that our theorems are (or should be) truths about eternal extra-human ideals, we say instead that they are merely assertions about transformations of symbols (formal derivations). This viewpoint also involves an act of faith. How, indeed, do we *know* that our latest theorem about diffusion on manifolds is formally deducible from Zermelo–Fraenkel set theory? No such formal deduction is ever written down. If it were, and it were checked by a human reader, the likelihood of error would be greater than in checking an ordinary (not formalized) mathematical proof.

Platonism and formalism, each in its own way, falsify part of the reality of our daily experience. Thus we speak as formalists when we are compelled to face the mystical, antiscientific essence of Platonic idealism; we return to Platonism when we realize that formalism as a description of mathematics has only a distant resemblance to our actual knowledge of mathematics.

The claim I wish to advance in this paper is that we can abandon them both, if we abandon the search for absolute certainty in mathematical truth. What we can have instead is a philosophy that is true to the reality of mathematical experience, at the price of violating some ancient philosophical dogmas.

3 ANECDOTES AND GOSSIP

Let us clear our minds by turning away from the philosophical alternatives we are accustomed to, and turning instead to our actual experience.

Anyone who has ever been in the least interested in mathematics, or has even observed other people who were interested in it, is aware that mathematical work is work with ideas. Symbols are used as aids to thinking just as musical scores are used as aids to music. The music comes first, the score comes later. Moreover, the score can never be a full embodiment of the musical thoughts of the composer. Just so, we know that a set of axioms and definitions is an attempt to describe the main properties of a mathematical idea. But there may always remain an aspect of the idea which we use implicitly, which we have not formalized because we have not yet seen the counterexample that would make us aware of the possibility of doubting it.

The fact is that it is sometimes extraordinarily difficult to achieve understanding, certainty, or clarity in mathematics.

In every branch of contemporary mathematics, one hears a version of the following story (always by word of mouth, never in print).

"Many of the most important theorems of our subject were first discovered by the great Professor Nameless. His intuition was so powerful that he was able to come to his conclusions by methods that no one else was able to understand. Years later, others were able to find proofs of his results by arguments that could be followed by all the workers in the field. Of course, it turned out that (with perhaps one or two exceptions) all of Nameless' formulas and theorems were true. It was just that no one was quite able to follow his explanations of how he discovered them." I am certainly not going to violate tradition by filling in the missing name. The same story is told by probabilists, by partial differential equators, by algebraists and by topologists—only the name of the hero changes. This kind of knowledge *before* complete proof is inexplicable in terms of the formalist account of mathematics.

To give another instance—in an invited talk at an International Congress of Mathematicians, a famous professor describes some of his latest results. He adds that the correctness of these results is not quite certain, because there has not yet been time for other specialists in his area to check them, and of course, until you have checked with other people, you can never be quite sure you haven't overlooked something.

Even the greatest mathematicians make mistakes, sometimes important ones, and these may be found even in famous papers which have been well known for a long time.

In the *Proceedings of the American Mathematical Society,* September 1963, there appeared an article entitled "False Lemmas in Herbrand," by Dreben, Andrews, and Aanderaa. They showed that certain lemmas in a thesis published by Herbrand in 1929 are false. These lemmas are used in the proof of a theorem which has been well known and influential in logic for fifty years. The authors show how Herbrand's theorem may be proved by replacing the false lemmas with correct ones.[5]

In the *Bulletin of the American Mathematical Society,* March 1975, there appeared an article by S. Hellerstein and J. Williamson, entitled "Derivatives of Entire Functions and a Question of Pólya." They wrote: "In 1914, Pólya asked: If an entire function f and all its derivatives have only real zeroes, is f in U_0? (the Pólya-Laguerre class). In 1, 2] M. Alander proved that the answer to Pólya's question is affirmative for all f in U_{2p} with $p \leq 2$ and in [3] purported to have extended this result to arbitrary p. However, in a famous survey article on zeros of successive derivatives, Pólya refers to Alander's papers [1] and [2] but not to his more general result [3]. The first author of this announcement, while a graduate student under the direction of A. Edrei, brought this curious omission to the latter's attention. In response to Edrei's subsequent query, Pólya replied in a letter that he was aware of Alander's more general "proof" but was never convinced by it nor could he show that it was fallacious! Alander's proof involves a study of level curves of harmonic functions associated with functions in U_{2p}. Avoiding such geometric considerations, and using instead direct analytic arguments, we have succeeded in proving a stronger version of Alander's 'theorem.' "

Notice that both Alander's and Herbrand's theorems were true—even though their proofs were defective. This is the most typical case. Why is it so?

A very interesting article by Philip Davis [6] contains, among other things, a discussion of errors in mathematical publications, with some famous names and examples.

Davis suggests that the length and interdependence of mathematical proof mean that truth in mathematics is probabilistic. I think his argument shows something else: that mathematical *knowledge* is fallible, and in this respect similar to other kinds of knowledge.

Let us mean by "intuitive reasoning" or "informal reasoning" that reasoning in mathematics which depends on an implicit background of understanding, and which deal with concepts rather than symbols, as distinguished from calculation, which deals with symbols and can be mechanized. Then the checking of an analytic-algebraic proof, as actually done by a mathematician, is primarily a piece of intuitive reasoning. But there are many different kinds of intuitive reasoning. The proof that the angle sum of a Euclidean triangle equals two right angles can be written in a formal language and deduced using only modus ponens. To *understand* such a proof, the reader would have to supply a meaning to these statements—that is, he would have to reason intuitively. On the other hand, if the proof is given by drawing the familiar diagram, there is a different kind of intuition in which several steps of the symbolic proof are merged into a single insight. We have a choice, not between an intuitive fallible mode of reasoning and a formal, infallible mode, but between two modes of reasoning (verbal and diagrammatic) both of which are intuitive and fallible. (Parenthetical aside: The reasoning by words can be formalized, and this formalization itself can be studied for certain purposes. But it is entirely likely that the drawing of diagrams can also be formalized; see [7].)

All this is not to deny the existence of an interpersonally verifiable notion of "correct proof" at the intuitive level of the working mathematician. It is merely to point out that this notion is not very similar to the model of formal proof in which correctness can always be verified as a mechanical procedure.

We do not have absolute certainty in mathematics; we may have virtual certainty, just as in other areas of life. Mathematicians disagree, make mistakes and correct them, are uncertain whether a proof is correct or not.

Faced with these obvious facts, one has three choices. The commonest is hypocrisy. That is, pretend not to notice the gap between preaching and practice.

If we renounce hypocrisy, then we have to give up either the myth or the reality. Either say that mathematics as practiced every day by mathematicians is not what mathematics really ought to be, or else say that the theory, that mathematical proof is really (or approximately or in principle) a mechanical procedure, is not quite right.

A common response is to say, "True, we aren't always as careful or thorough as we should be, but that doesn't detract from the ideal."

In one sense this is unarguable. Certainly, we should try our best not to make mistakes. But if it is meant that we really ought to (if we only had the time and energy) write our proofs in a form that could be checked by a computing machine, then the point *is* certainly arguable. Especially by anyone with experience debugging programs!

It just is *not the case* that a doubtful proof would become certain by being formalized. On the contrary, the doubtfulness of the proof would then be replaced by the doubtfulness of the coding and programming.

What really happens every day is that the correctness of a formal proof (i.e., of code written for a computing machine) is checked by a human being who uses his understanding of the *meaning* of the steps of the computation to verify its formal correctness.

As it has become commonplace to use very large, complicated programs, it has become recognized that it is essential to write these programs in a manner to be readable by human beings—that is, to be understandable, not just formally correct. True, we cannot give a formal definition of "understandable." Nevertheless, it turns out in practice that it is *understanding that verifies the correctness of formal computation—not only the other way round.*

4 WHERE DO WE GO FROM HERE?

The discussion in Sections 2 and 3 was intended to make two points:

(1) The unspoken assumption in all foundationist viewpoints is that mathematics must be a source of indubitable truth.

(2) The actual experience of all schools—and the actual daily experience of mathematicians—shows that mathematical truth, like other kinds of truth, is fallible and corrigible.

Do we really have to choose between a formalism that is falsified by our everyday experience, and a Platonism that postulates a mythical fairyland where the uncountable and the inaccessible lie waiting to be observed by the mathematician whom God blesses with a good enough intuition? It is reasonable to propose a new task for mathematical philosophy: not to seek indubitable truth, but to give an account of mathematical knowledge as it really is—fallible, corrigible, tentative and evolving, as is every other kind of human knowledge. Instead of continuing to look in vain for foundations, or feeling disoriented and illegitimate for lack of foundations, we can try to look at what mathematics really is, and account for it as a part of human knowledge in general. That is, reflect honestly on what we do when we use, teach, invent, or discover mathematics—by studying history, by introspection, and by observing ourselves and each other with the unbiased eye of Martians or anthropologists.

Such a program requires a philosophical position which is radically different from the three classical points of view (formalist, Platonist, intuitionist). The position I will try to present differs from all three of them in the following sense. It denies the right of *any* a priori philosophical dogma to tell mathematicians what they should do, or what they really are doing in spite of themselves or without knowing it. Rather, it takes as its starting point the attitude that mathematics, as it is being done now and as it has evolved in history, is a reality which does not require justification or reinterpretation. What has to be done in the philosophy of mathematics is to explicate (from the outside, as part of general human culture, rather than from the inside, within mathematical terms) what mathematicians are doing. If this attempt is successful, the result will be a description of mathematics which mathematicians will recognize as true. It will be the kind of truth that is obvious once it is said, but up to then was perhaps too obvious for anyone to bother saying.

There is a comparison with the philosophy of science. At one time philosophers of science wrote elaborate rules of inductive discovery which scientists were supposed to follow. The fact that one could hardly find a scientist who had made a discovery in such a fashion seemed quite irrelevant to them. More recently, K. Popper and M. Polanyi have described science in a different manner, more closely related to a real knowledge of how science develops, and not so much based on the traditional philosophizing of Francis Bacon or John Stuart Mill. These writings of Popper and Polanyi are not completely ignored by practicing scientists. On the contrary, some scientists have testified that their work has benefited by the insights they received from these works on the philosophy of science.

We can try to describe mathematics, not as our inherited prejudices imagine it to be, but as our actual experience tells us it is. Certainly our experience does not tell us that it is a game with symbols (formalism) nor that it is a direct perception of ideal entities (Platonic idealism).

What would be the most straightforward, natural answer to the question, what is mathematics?

It would be that mathematics deals with ideas. Not pencil marks or chalk marks, not physical triangles or physical sets, but ideas (which may be represented or suggested by physical objects). What are the main properties of mathematical activity or mathematical knowledge, as known to all of us from daily experience?

(1) Mathematical objects are invented or created by humans.

(2) They are created, not arbitrarily, but arise from activity with already existing mathematical objects, and from the needs of science and daily life.

(3) Once created, mathematical objects have properties which are well-determined, which we may have great difficulty in discovering, but which are possessed independently of our knowledge of them. (For example, I define a function as the solution of a certain boundary-value problem. Then

the value of the function at some interior point is determined, although I may have no effective way of finding it out.)

These three points are not philosophical theses which have to be established. They are facts of experience which have to be understood. What has to be done is to analyze their paradoxes, and to examine their philosophical consequences.

To say that mathematicial objects are invented or created by humans is to distinguish them from natural objects such as rocks, X rays, or dinosaurs.

Recently, certain philosophers (Korner, Putnam) have argued that the subject matter of pure mathematics *is* the physical world—not its actualities but its possibilities. To exist in mathematics, they propose, means to exist *potentially* in the physical world. This view has the merit that it does permit us to say that mathematical statements have meaning, can be true or false. It has the defect, however, that it attempts to explain the clear by means of the obscure. Consider the theorem $2^c < 2^{(2^c)}$, or any theorem in homological algebra. No philosopher has yet explained in what sense such theorems should be regarded as referring to physical "possibilities."

The common sense standpoint of the working mathematician is that the objects of algebra, say, or of set theory, are just that—part of a theory. They are human ideas, of recent invention. They are not timelessly or tenselessly existing either as Platonic ideas or as latent potentialities in the physical world.

We may ask how these objects, which are our own creations, so often turn out to be useful in describing aspects of nature. To answer this specifically in detail is important and complicated. It is one of the major tasks for the history of mathematics, and for a psychology of mathematical cognition which may be coming into birth in the work of Piaget and his school. The answer in general, however, is easy and obvious. Human beings live in the world and all their ideas ultimately come from the world in which they live—refracted through their culture and history, which are in turn, of course, ultimately rooted in man's biological nature and his physical surroundings. Our mathematical ideas fit the world for the same reason that our lungs are suited to the atmosphere of this planet.[6]

Once created and communicated, mathematical objects are *there*. They become part of human culture, separate from their originator. As such, they are now objects, in the sense that they have well-determined properties of their own, which we may or may not be able to discover.

If this sounds paradoxical, it is because of a habit of thinking which sees in the world only two kinds of reality: the individual subject (the isolated ego) on the one hand, and the exterior world of nature on the other.

The existence of mathematics is enough to show the inadequacy of such a world view. The customs, traditions, and institutions of our society—all our nonmaterial culture—are aspects of the world which are neither in the private "inner" nor the nonhuman "outer" world.[7] Mathematics is also this third kind of reality—a reality that is "inner" from the viewpoint of society as a whole, yet "outer" from the viewpoint of each individual member of society.

That mathematical objects have properties which are well determined is as familiar as the fact that mathematical problems often have well-determined answers.

To explain more fully how this comes about is again a matter for actual investigation, not speculation. The rough outlines, however, are visible to anyone who has studied and taught mathematics.

To have the idea of counting, one needs the experience of handling coins or blocks or pebbles. To have the idea of an angle, one needs the experience of drawing straight lines that cross, on paper or in a sandbox. Later on, mental pictures or sample calculations prepare the ground for other new concepts.[8] A suitable shared experience of activity—first physical manipulation, later on, paper and pencil calculation—creates a common effect.

Of course, not everyone experiences the desired result. The student who never catches on to how we want him to handle the parentheses in our algebraic expression simply doesn't pass the course.

Why are we able to talk to each other about algebra? *We have been trained to do so, by a training that has been evolved for that purpose.* We can do this *without* being able to verbalize a formal definition of polynomials. Polynomials are objective, in the sense that they have certain properties, whether we know them or not. That is to say, our common notion has implicit properties. To unravel how this is so is a deep problem comparable to the problem of linguistics. No one understands clearly how it is that languages have mysterious, complicated properties unknown to the speakers of the language. Still, no one doubts that the locus of these properties is in the culture of the language speaker—not in the external world nor in an ideal other world. The properties of mathematical objects, too, are properties of shared ideas.

The observable reality of mathematics is this: we see an evolving network of shared ideas which have objective properties; these properties are ascertained by many kinds of reasoning and argument. These kinds of valid reasonings, which are called "proofs," are not universal; they differ from one branch of mathematics to another, and from one historical epoch to another.

Looking at this fact of human experience, there certainly is matter for explication.

How are mathematical objects invented?

What is the interplay of existing mathematics, ideas and needs from other branches of science, and direct mirroring of physical reality?

How does the notion of proof develop, becoming more refined and subtle as new dangers and sources of error are discovered?[9]

Does the network of mathematical ideas and reasoning, as part of our shared consciousness, have an integrity as a whole that is more than the strength of any one link in the reasoning, so that the collapse of any one part can affect only those parts closest to it?

These sorts of philosophical questions can be studied by the historian of mathematics—if we allow, as we should, his field of study to extend up to yesterday and today. The famous work of Thomas Kuhn is a paradigm of the kind of insight in the philosophy of science that is possible only on the basis of historical studies. Such work has yet to be done in the philosophy and history of mathematics.[10]

Such studies will never make mathematical truth indubitable. But then, why should mathematical truth be indubitable?

In daily life, we well know that our knowledge is subject to correction, is partial and incomplete. In the natural sciences, it is accepted that scientific progress consists of enlarging, correcting, and sometimes even rejecting and replacing the knowledge of the past. It is the possibility of correcting errors by confronting them with experience that characterizes scientific knowledge. This is precisely the reason why it is essential that we share our ideas and check each other's work.

This account of mathematics contains nothing new. It is merely an attempt to describe what mathematicians actually are doing and have been doing for centuries.

The novelty, if any, is the conscious attempt to avoid falsification or idealization.

SUMMARY AND CONCLUSION

The alternative of Platonism and formalism comes from the attempt to root mathematics in some nonhuman reality. If we give up the obligation to establish mathematics as a source of indubitable truths, we can accept its nature as a certain kind of human mental activity.

In doing this, we give up some age-old hopes; we may gain a clearer idea of what we are doing, and why.

> Could it be that in mathematics too we need a new Consciousness? . . . A new consciousness stressing the exchange, communication and experience of mathematical information, a Consciousness where mathematics is told in human words rather than in a mass of symbols, intelligible only to the initiated; a Consciousness where mathematics is experienced as an enlightening intellectual activity rather than an almost fully automated logical robot, ardently performing simultaneously a large number of seemingly unrelated tasks. (P. Henrici, *Quart. Appl. Math.* (April 1972), 38.)

A world of ideas exists, created by human beings, existing in their shared consciousness. These ideas have properties which are objectively theirs, in the same sense that material objects have their own properties. The construction of proof and counterexample is the method of discovering the properties of these ideas. This is the branch of knowledge which we call mathematics.

COMMENTS ON THE BIBLIOGRAPHY

The present article is strongly influenced by Lakatos' critique of formalism presented in the first few pages of [17] and accepts his aim [15] "to exhibit modern mathematical philosophy as deeply embedded in general epistemology and as only to be understood in this context."

No attempt is made here to discuss in detail the issues raised by intuitionism and constructivism. These were presented by Bishop, Stolzenberg, and

Kopell at a symposium published in *Historia Mathematica* 2 (November 1975). The spokesmen for the "classical" viewpoint at that symposium were remarkably unwilling to deal with the philosophical issues raised by Bishop. A conscientious evaluation of intuitionism from the classical point of view has been given by a physicist; see Bunge [3].

A "Platonist" viewpoint is espoused by Steiner [25], and a formalist one by Dieudonné [8]. Monk [18], Cohen [4], and Robinson [22] discuss the Platonist–formalist duality in the light of Cohen's results on independence of the continuum hypothesis and the axiom of choice. Putnam's "modal-logic" version of realism is presented in his recent book [21].

NOTES

1. See, e.g., [8].

2. These issues are developed by Thom [26, 27] and Dieudonné [10].

3. Two whole-hearted Platonists are R. Thom ("Everything considered, mathematicians should have the courage of their most profound convictions and thus affirm that mathematical forms indeed have an existence that is independent of the mind considering them. . . . Yet, at any given moment, mathematicians have only an incomplete and fragmentary view of this world of ideas" [26].) and K. Gödel ("Despite their remoteness from sense experience, we do have something like a perception also of the objects of set theory, as is seen from the fact that the axioms force themselves upon us as being true. I don't see any reason why we should have less confidence in this kind of perception, i.e., in mathematical intuition, than in sense perception. . . . They, too, may represent an aspect of objective reality" [11].). Thom's world of ideas is geometric, whereas Gödel's is the set-theoretic universe.

4. "I cannot imagine that I shall ever return to the creed of the true Platonist, who sees the world of the actual infinite spread out before him and believes that he can comprehend the incomprehensible" (Robinson [22]).

5. I am indebted to Rohit Parikh for the information that for many years Herbrand's thesis was not physically accessible to most logicians. Presumably his errors would have been corrected much sooner in normal circumstances.

6. "I have met people who found it astonishing that the cats have holes in their furs exactly at the places where the eyes are." (I am indebted to Wilhelm Magnus for this quotation from Lichtenberg, an 18th-century professor of physics at Göttingen.)

7. Related ideas are advocated by Popper [20] and especially by White [28]. They are implicit in the well-known writings of R.L. Wilder on mathematics as a cultural phenomenon. In a different sense, they are also implicit in the writings on "heuristic" of George Pólya and their philosophical elaboration by Imre Lakatos.

8. The work of Piaget [19] is little read by professional mathematicians, perhaps in part because some of his comments on groups and other abstract mathematical structures seem naive or misinformed. Nevertheless, one cannot overestimate the importance of his central insight: that mathematical intuitions are not absorbed from nature by passive observation, but rather are created by the experience of active manipulation of objects and symbols. The full import of this insight for mathematical epistemology has yet to be appreciated.

9. "Historically speaking, it is of course quite untrue that mathematics is free from contradiction; non-contradiction appears as a goal to be achieved, not as a God-given quality that has been granted us once for all. . . . There is no sharply drawn line between those contradictions which occur in the daily work of every mathematician, beginner or master of his craft, as the result of more or less easily detected mistakes, and the major paradoxes which provide food for logical thought for decades and sometimes centuries." (N. Bourbaki, "Foundations of Mathematics for the Working Mathematician," *J. Symbolic Logic 14* (1949), 1–8.)

10. "Under the present dominance of formalism, one is tempted to paraphrase Kant: the history of mathematics, lacking the guidance of philosophy, has become *blind*, while the philosophy of mathematics, turning its back on the most intriguing phenomena in the history of mathematics, has become empty" (Lakatos [17]). However, recent work in the history of mathematics shows an increasing interest in philosophical issues. See, for example, the articles on historiography in *Historia Mathematica 2* (November 1975).

ACKNOWLEDGMENTS

I am indebted to many friends for critical conversations and letters on the issues discussed here: Jose-Luis Abreu, Gus Blaisdell, Mario Bunge, Chandler Davis, Martin Davis, Philip Davis, Harold Edwards, Fritz John, Joe Keller, Morris Kline, Peter Lax, Wilhelm Magnus, Robert Osserman, George Pólya, Gian-Carlo Rota, Joel Smoller, Gabriel Stolzenberg, and Raymond Wilder. Some of the opinions here were first formulated in conversations with Phyllis Hersh, I also would like to acknowledge my indebtedness to an unpublished article by Joe Schatz, and to the published works of George Pólya, Imre Lakatos, and L.A. White.

A point of view similar to that expressed here was put forward recently in a very interesting paper by three computer scientists, R.A. DeMillo, R.J. Lipton, and A.J. Perlis, "Social Processes and Proofs of Theorems and Programs," presented at the SIGPLAN Conference, Principles of Programming Languages, May 1977, Los Angeles (Proceedings, pp. 206–214).

BIBLIOGRAPHY

[1] P. Benacerraf and H. Putnam (Eds.), "Philosophy of Mathematics, Selected Readings," Prentice-Hall, Englewood Cliffs, N.J., 1964.

[2] E. Bishop, "Aspects of Constructivism," New Mexico State University, Las Cruces, 1972.

[3] M. Bunge, "Intuition and Science," Prentice-Hall, Englewood Cliffs, N.J., 1962.

[4] P.J. Cohen, Comments on the foundations of set theory, *in* "Axiomatic Set Theory" (D. Scott, Ed.), pp. 9–15, Amer. Math. Soc., Providence, R.I., 1971.

[5] C. Davis, Materialist mathematics, *in* "Boston Studies in Philosophy of Science," Vol. XV, D. Reidel, Boston, 1974.

[6] P.J. Davis, Fidelity in mathematical discourse, *Amer. Math. Monthly* **79** (1972), 252–262.

[7] P.J. Davis, Visual geometry, computer graphics, and theorems of perceived type, *in* "Influence of Computing on Mathematical Research and Education," Proc. Symp. Appl. Math., Vol. 20, Amer. Math. Soc., Providence, R.I., 1974.

[8] J. Dieudonné, Modern axiomatic methods and the foundations of mathematics, *in* "Great Currents of Mathematical Thought," Vol. II, pp. 251–266, Dover, New York, 1971.

[9] J. Dieudonné, The work of Nicholas Bourbaki, *Amer. Math. Monthly* **77** (1970), 134–145.

[10] J.A. Dieudonné, Should we teach modern mathematics? *Amer. Sci.* **61** (1973), 16–19.

[11] K. Gödel, What is Cantor's continuum problem? *in* "Philosophy of Mathematics, Selected Readings" (P. Benacerraf and H. Putnam, Eds.), pp. 258–273, Prentice-Hall, Englewood Cliffs, N.J., 1964.

[12] D. Hilbert, On the infinite, *in* "Philosophy of Mathematics, Selected Readings," (P. Benacerraf and H. Putnam, Eds.), pp. 134–151, Prentice-Hall, Englewood Cliffs, N.J., 1964.

[13] *Historia Mathematica* **2** (1975), 425–624.

[14] S. Korner, On the relevance of post-Gödelian mathematics to philosophy, *in* "Problems in the Philosophy of Mathematics" (Lakatos, Ed.), pp. 118–133, North-Holland, Amsterdam, 1967.

[15] I. Lakatos, Infinite Regress and the Foundations of Mathematics, Aristotelian Society Supplementary Volume 36, pp. 155–184, 1962.

[16] I. Lakatos, A renaissance of empiricism in the recent philosophy of mathematics? *in* "Problems in the Philosophy of Mathematics" (I. Lakatos, Ed.), pp. 199–203, North-Holland, Amsterdam, 1967.

[17] I. Lakatos, "Proofs and Refutations," Cambridge Univ. Press, London/New York, 1976.

[18] J.D. Monk, On the foundations of set theory, *Amer. Math. Monthly* **77** (1970), 703–711.

[19] J. Piaget, "Genetic Epistemology," Columbia Univ. Press, New York, 1970.

[20] K.R. Popper, "Objective Knowledge," Oxford Univ. Press, London/New York, 1972.

[21] H. Putnam, "Mathematics, Matter and Method," Cambridge, Univ. Press, London/New York, 1975.

[22] A. Robinson, From a formalist's points of view, *Dialectica* **23** (1969), 45–49.

[23] A Robinson, Formalism 64, *in* "Proceedings, International Congress for Logic, Methodology and Philosophy of Science, 1964," pp. 228–246.

[24] J.A. Schatz, The nature of truth, unpublished manuscript.

[25] Mark Steiner, "Mathematical Knowledge," Cornell Univ. Press, Ithaca, N.Y., 1975.

[26] R. Thom, Modern mathematics: An educational and philosophical error? *Amer. Sci.* **59** (1971), 695–699.

[27] R. Thom, Modern mathematics: Does it exist? *in* "Developments in Mathematical Education" (A.G. Howson, Ed.), pp. 194–209, Cambridge Univ. Press, London/New York, 1973.

[28] L.A. White, The locus of mathematical reality, *Philos. Sci.* **14** (1947), 289–303. Reprinted in "The World of Mathematics," Vol. 4, pp. 2348–2364, Simon and Schuster, New York, 1956.

IMRE LAKATOS

A Renaissance of Empiricism in the Recent Philosophy of Mathematics?*

Lakatos begins his critique with a point already noted by Hersh: a basic assumption behind the foundation thesis is that mathematical knowledge is a priori and infallible. One can make this assumption without going on to insist that mathematical knowledge is innate or that mathematicians ideally never make mistakes, although these further steps are often taken. The real force of the assumption, as Lakatos suggests, is that mathematics is radically separate from the natural sciences where knowledge is so obviously a posteriori and fallible. It is just this conclusion that Lakatos attacks. His aim is to bridge the gap between philosophers' accounts of mathematics and their accounts of natural science. This is the point of empiricism in mathematics. However, Lakatos does not claim that mathematics is just like empirical science; at most it is quasi-empirical.

Drawing on Karl Popper's philosophy of science, Lakatos distinguishes between two kinds of theories, Euclidean theories and quasi-empirical theories. The distinction can be traced back to Aristotle but Lakatos' version is roughly this. The basic statements of a Euclidean theory are its axioms; its rules of inference are precisely determined. Truth (or acceptability for formalists) is injected into the system at the axioms and "flows downward" to their deductive consequences. An image of Euclidean theories is that they begin by stating the essential nature of their subjects and go on to describe its detailed variations. Knowledge, as given by proof, is infallible. The image of quasi-empirical theories, on the other hand, is that they begin while their subjects are still indeterminate. They can describe and manipulate many variations and their goal is to get to the underlying principles. Knowledge is fallible. The basic statements of a quasi-empirical theory are a special set of theorems, traditionally, observation sentences or experimental outcomes, and its rules of inference might be less precisely formulated. Truth and

Reprinted from Mathematics, Science and Epistemology by Imre Lakatos by permission of Cambridge University Press.

falsity are injected into the basic statements but logically, in quasi-empirical theories, it is not truth that flows downward but falsity that flows upward. Thus, the axioms or basic principles of quasi-empirical theories are usually the results of bold speculation that have survived the test of severe criticism. Lakatos' underlying argument is that mathematical theories, like those of science, are quasi-empirical.

It is crucial for his argument that Lakatos find 'potential falsifiers' for mathematical theories, beyond the obvious logical falsifiers (inconsistency). Otherwise, mathematics would not share in the fallibilism of science. Now the potential falsifiers of science are the 'hard facts' of experience and experiment. Lakatos suggests that the theorems of informal mathematics can be potential falsifiers for formal theories. This suggestion does secure a place for informal theories and proofs in the practice of mathematics. They no more can be superseded by formal theories than can experiments be superseded by theoretical science. Nevertheless, this leaves us with some questions about the nature of informal theories: eg., do they have potential falsifiers? Other essays in this volume address this interesting issue, especially those of Putnam, Kitcher, Tymoczko, and Lakatos himself.

Lakatos substantiates his assessments with numerous quotations from recognized experts, including many statements which question the claims for a priori and infallibility by the foundationalists. Lakatos uses these to defend his belief in the renaissance of empiricism. However, he had a very discerning eye. Often the statements were asides in papers developing some other aspect of the foundations position. The renaissance which Lakatos foresaw, and to which he contributed so much, is only now beginning to take hold.

This version of the paper was edited after Lakatos' death by John Worrall and Gregory Currie (see Acknowledgments).

• • • • •

INTRODUCTION

[According to logical empiricist orthodoxy, while science is *a posteriori*, contentful and (at least in principle) fallible, mathematics is *a priori*, tautologous and infallible.[1]] It may therefore come as a surprise for the historian of ideas to find statements by some of the best contemporary experts in foundational studies that seem to herald a renaissance of Mill's radical assimilation of mathematics to science. In the next section I present a rather long list of such statements. I then go on (in section 2) to explain the motivation and rationale of these statements. I then argue (in section 3) for what I call the 'quasi-empirical' nature of mathematics, as a whole. This presents a problem—namely what kind of statements may play the role of potential falsifiers in mathematics. I investigate this problem in section 4. Finally, in section 5, I examine briefly periods of stagnation in the growth of 'quasi-empirical' theories.

1 EMPIRICISM AND INDUCTION: THE NEW VOGUE IN MATHEMATICAL PHILOSOPHY?

Russell was probably the first modern logician to claim that the evidence for mathematics and logic may be 'inductive'. He, who in 1901 had claimed that the 'edifice of mathematical truths stands unshakable and inexpungnable to all the weapons of doubting cynicism,'[2] in 1924 thought that logic (and mathematics) is exactly like Maxwell's equations of electro-dynamics: both 'are believed because of the observed truth of certain of their logical consequences.'[3]

Fraenkel claimed in 1927 that 'the intuitive or logical self-evidence of the principles chosen as axioms [of set theory] naturally plays a certain but not decisive role; some axioms receive their full weight rather from the self-evidence of the consequences which could not be derived without them.[4] And he compared the situation of set theory in 1927 with the situation of the infinitesimal calculus in the eighteenth century, recalling d'Alembert's '*Allez en avant, et la foi vous viendra.*'[5]

Carnap, who at the 1930 conference in Königsberg still thought that 'any uncertainty in the foundations of the "most certain of all the sciences" is extremely disconcerting,'[6] [had decided by] 1958 that there is an analogy—if only a distant one—between physics and mathematics: 'the impossibility of absolute certainty.'[7]

Curry drew similar conclusions in 1963:

> The search for absolute certainty was evidently a principal motivation for both Brouwer and Hilbert. But does mathematics need absolute certainty for its justification? In particular, why do we need to be sure that a theory is consistent, or that it can be derived by an absolutely certain intuition of pure time, before we use it? In no other science do we make such demands. In physics all theorems are hypothetical; we adopt a theory so long as it makes useful predictions and modify or discard it as soon as it does not. This is what has happened to mathematical theories in the past, where the discovery of contradictions had led to modifications in the mathematical doctrines accepted up to the time of that discovery. Why should we not do the same in the future? Using formalistic conceptions to explain what a theory is, we accept a theory as long as it is useful, satisfies such conditions of naturalness and simplicity as are reasonable at that time, and is not known to lead us into error. We must keep our theories under surveillance to see that these conditions are fulfilled and to get all the presumptive evidence of adequacy that we can. The Gödel theorem suggests that this is all we can do; an empirical philosophy of science suggests it is all we should do.[8]

To quote Quine:

> We may more reasonably view set theory, and mathematics generally, in much the way in which we view theoretical portions of the natural sciences themselves; as comprising truths or hypotheses which are to be vindicated less by the pure light of reason than by the indirect systematic contribution which they make to the organizing of empirical data in the natural sciences.[9]

And later he said:

> To say that mathematics in general has been reduced to logic hints at some new firming up of mathematics at its foundations. This is misleading. Set theory is less settled and more conjectural than the classical mathematical superstructure than can be founded upon it.[10]

Rosser too belongs to the new fallibilist camp:

> According to a theorem of Gödel . . . if a system of logic is adequate for even a reasonable facsimile of present-day mathematics, then there can be no adequate assurance that it is free from contradiction. Failure to derive the known paradoxes is very negative assurance at best and may merely indicate lack of skill on our part.[11]

Church, in 1939 thought that: 'there is no convincing basis for a belief in the consistency either of Russell's or of Zermelo's system, even as probable.'[12]

Gödel in 1944 stressed that under the influence of modern criticism of its foundations, mathematics has already lost a good deal of its 'absolute certainty' and that in the future, by the appearance of further axioms of set theory, it will be increasingly fallible.[13]

In 1947, developing this idea, he explained that for some such new axiom,

> even in case it had no intrinsic necessity at all, a (probable) decision about its truth is possible also in another way, namely, inductively by studying its 'success', that is, its fruitfulness in consequences demonstrable without the new axiom , whose proofs by means of the new axiom, however, are considerably simpler and easier to discover, and make it possible to condense into one proof many different proofs. The axioms for the system of real numbers, rejected by the intuitionists, have in this sense been verified to some extent owing to the fact that analytical number theory frequently allows us to prove number theoretical theorems which can subsequently be verified by elementary methods. A much higher degree of verification than that, however, is conceivable. There might exist axioms so abundant in their verifiable consequences, shedding so much light upon a whole discipline, and furnishing such powerful methods for solving given problems (and even solving them, as far as that is possible, in a constructivistic way) that quite irrespective of their intrinsic necessity they would have to be assumed at least in the same sense as any well established physical theory.[14]

Also, he is reported to have said a few years later that:

> the role of the alleged 'foundations' is rather comparable to the function discharged, in physical theory, by explanatory hypotheses . . . The so-called logical or set-theoretical 'foundation' for number-theory or of any other well-established mathematical theory, is explanatory, rather than really foundational, exactly as in physics where the actual function of axioms is to *explain* the phenomena described by the theorems of this system rather than to provide a genuine 'foundation' for such theorems.[15]

Weyle says that non-intuitionistic mathematics can be tested, but not proved:

> No Hilbert will be able to assure us of consistency forever; we must be content if a simple axiomatic system of mathematics has met the test of our elaborate mathematical experiments so far . . . A truly realistic mathematics should be conceived, in line with physics, as a branch of the theoretical construction of the one real world, and should adopt the same sober and cautious attitude toward hypothetic extensions of its foundations as is exhibited by physics.[16]

Von Neumann, in 1947, concluded that

> After all, classical mathematics, even though one could never again be absolutely certain of its reliability . . . stood on at least as sound a foundation as, for example, the existence of the electron. Hence, if one was willing to accept the sciences, one might as well accept the classical system of mathematics.[17]

Bernays argues very similarly: It is of course surprising and puzzling that the more content and power mathematical methods have, the less is their self-evidence. But 'this will not be so surprising if we consider that there are similar conditions in theoretical physics.'[18]

According to Mostowski mathematics is just one of the natural sciences:

> [Gödel's] and other negative results confirm the assertion of materialistic philosophy that mathematics is in the last resort a natural science, that its notions and methods are rooted in experience and that attempts at establishing the foundations of mathematics without taking into account its originating in the natural sciences are bound to fail.[19]

[And Kalmár agrees:] 'the consistency of most of our formal systems is an empirical fact . . . Why do we not confess that mathematics, like other sciences, is ultimately based upon, and has to be tested in, practice?'[20]

These statements describe a genuine revolutionary turn in the philosophy of mathematics. Some describe their individual *volte-face* in dramatic terms. Russell in his autobiography, says: 'The splendid certainty which I had always hoped to find in mathematics was lost in a bewildering maze.'[21] Von Neumann writes: 'I know myself how humiliatingly easily my own views regarding the absolute mathematical truth changed . . . and how they changed three times in succession![22] Weyl, recognizing before Gödel that classical mathematics was *unrescuably* fallible, refers to [this state of affairs as] 'hard fact.'[23]

We could go on quoting; but surely this is enough to show that mathematical empiricism and inductivism (not only as regards the *origin* or *method,* but also as regards the *justification,* of mathematics) is more alive and widespread than many seem to think. But what is the background and what is the *rationale* of this new empiricist-inductivist mood? Can one give it a sharp, *criticizable* formulation?

2 QUASI-EMPIRICAL VERSUS EUCLIDEAN THEORIES

Classical epistemology has for two thousand years modelled its ideal of a theory, whether scientific or mathematical, on its conception of Euclidean geometry. The ideal theory is a deductive system with an indubitable truth-injection at the top (a finite conjunction of axioms)—so that truth, flowing down from the top through the safe truth-preserving channels of valid inferences, inundates the whole system.

It was a major shock for over-optimistic rationalism that science—in spite of immense efforts—could not be organized in such Euclidean theories. Scientific theories turned out to be organized in deductive systems where the *crucial* truth value injection was *at the bottom*—at a special set of theorems. But *truth* does not flow upwards. The important logical flow in such *quasi-empirical theories* is not the transmission of truth but rather the retransmission of *falsity*—from special theorems at the bottom ('basic statements') up towards the set of axioms.[24]

Perhaps the best way to characterize quasi-empirical, as opposed to Euclidean theories, is this. Let us call those sentences of a deductive system in which some truth values are initially injected, 'basic statements', and the subset of basic statements which receive the particular value true, 'true basic statements.' Then a system is Euclidean if it is the [*deductive*] *closure* of those of its basic statements which are assumed to be true. Otherwise it is quasi-empirical.

An important feature of both Euclidean and quasi-empirical systems is the set of particular (usually unwritten) conventions regulating truth value injections in the basic statements.

A Euclidean theory may be claimed to be true; a quasi-empirical theory—at best—to be well-corroborated, but always conjectural. Also, in a Euclidean theory the true basic statements at the 'top' of the deductive system (usually called 'axioms') *prove,* as it were, the rest of the system; in a quasi-empirical theory the (true) basic statements are *explained* by the rest of the system.

Whether a deductive system is Euclidean or quasi-empirical is decided by the pattern of truth value flow in the system. The system is Euclidean if the characteristic flow is the transmission of truth from the set of axioms 'downwards' to the rest of the system—logic here is an *organon of proof;* it is quasi-empirical if the characteristic flow is retransmission of falsity from the false basic statements 'upwards' towards the 'hypothesis'—logic here is an *organon of criticism.*[25] But this demarcation between patterns of truth value flow is independent of the particular conventions that regulate the original truth value injection into the basic statements. For instance *a theory which is quasi-empirical in my sense may be either empirical or non-empirical in the usual sense:* it is empirical only if its basic theorems are spatio-temporally singular basic statements whose truth values are decided by the time-honoured but unwritten code of the experimental scientist.[26] (We may speak, even more generally, of Euclidean versus quasi-empirical theories independently of *what* flows in the logical channels: certain or fallible truth and falsehood, probability and improbability, moral desirability or undesirability, etc. It is the *how* of the flow that is decisive.)

The methodology of a science is heavily dependent on whether it aims at a Euclidean or at a quasi-empirical ideal. The basic rule in a science which adopts the former aim is to search for self-evident axioms—Euclidean methodology is puritanical, antispeculative. The basic rule of the latter is to search for bold, imaginative hypotheses with high explanatory and 'heuristic' power,[27] indeed, it advocates a proliferation of alternative hypotheses to be weeded out by severe criticism—quasi-empirical methodology is uninhibitedly speculative.[28]

The development of Euclidean theory consists of three stages: first the naive prescientific stage of trial and error which constitutes the prehistory of the subject; this is followed by the foundational period which reorganizes the discipline, trims the obscure borders, establishes the deductive structure of the safe kernel; all that is then left is the solution of problems inside the system, mainly constructing proofs or disproofs of interesting conjectures. ([The discovery of] a decision method for theoremhood may abolish this stage altogether and put an end to the development.)

The development of a quasi-empirical theory is very different. It starts with problems followed by daring solutions, then by severe tests, refutations. The vehicle of progress is bold speculations, criticism, controversy between rival theories, problemshifts. Attention is always focussed on the obscure borders. The slogans are growth and permanent revolution, not foundations and accumulation of eternal truths.

The main pattern of Euclidean criticism is suspicion: Do the proofs really prove? Are the methods used too strong and therefore fallible? The main pattern of quasi-empirical criticism is proliferation of theories and refutation.

3 MATHEMATICS IS QUASI-EMPIRICAL

By the turn of this century mathematics, 'the paradigm of certainty and truth', seemed to be the last real stronghold of orthodox Euclideans. But there were certainly some flaws in the Euclidean organization even of mathematics, and these flaws caused considerable unrest. Thus the central problem of all foundational schools was: 'to establish once and for all the certitude of mathematical methods.'[29] However, foundational studies unexpectedly led to the conclusion that a Euclidean reorganization of mathematics as a whole may be impossible; that at least the richest mathematical theories were, like scientific theories, quasi-empirical. Euclideanism suffered a defeat in its very stronghold.

The two major attempts at a perfect Euclidean reorganization of classical mathematics—logicism and formalism[30]—are well known, but a brief account of them from this point of view may be helpful.

(a) *The Frege-Russell approach* aimed to deduce all mathematical truths—with the help of ingenious definitions—from indubitably true logical axioms. It turned out that some of the logical (or rather set-theoretical) axioms were not only not indubitably true but not even consistent. It turned out that the sophisticated second (and further) generations of logical (or set-theoretical) axioms—devised to avoid the known paradoxes—even if true, were not indubitably true (and not even indubitably consistent), and that the crucial evidence for them was that classical mathematics might be *explained*—but certainly not *proved* by them.

Most mathematicians working on comprehensive '*grandes logiques*' are well aware of this. We have already referred to Russell, Fraenkel, Quine and Rosser. Their 'empiricist' turn is in fact a quasi-empiricist one: they realized (independently even of Gödel's results) that the *Principia Mathematica* and the strong set-theories, like Quine's *New Foundations and Mathematical Logic,* are all quasi-empirical.

Workers in this field are conscious of the method they follow: daring conjectures, proliferation of hypotheses, severe tests, refutations. Church's account of an interesting theory based on a restricted form of the law of excluded middle (later shown to be inconsistent by Kleene and Rosser,[31]) outlines the quasi-empirical method:

> Whether the system of logic which results from our postulates is adequate for the development of mathematics, and whether it is wholly free from contradiction, are questions which we cannot now answer except by conjecture. Our proposal is to seek at least an empirical answer to these questions by carrying out in some detail a derivation of the consequences of our postulates, and it is

> hoped either that the system will turn out to satisfy the conditions of adequacy and freedom from contradiction or that it can be made to do so by modifications or additions.[32]

Quine characterized the crucial part of his *Mathematical Logic* as a 'daring structure . . . added at the constructor's peril'.[33] Soon it was shown by Rosser to be inconsistent and Quine then himself described his earlier characterization as one that had 'a prophetic ring'.[34]

One can never refute Euclideanism: even if forced to postulate highly sophisticated axioms, one can always stick to one's hopes of deriving them from some deeper layer of self-evident foundations.[35] There have been considerable and partly successful efforts to simplify Russell's *Principia* and similar logicistic systems. But while the results were mathematically interesting and important they could not retrieve the lost philosophical position. The *grandes logiques* cannot be proved true—nor even consistent; they can only be proved false—or even inconsistent.

(b) While the Frege-Russell approach aimed to turn mathematics into a unified classical Euclidean theory the *Hilbert approach* offered a radically new modification of the Euclidean programme, exciting both from the mathematical and the philosophical points of view.

Hilbertians claimed that classical analysis contains an absolutely true Euclidean kernel. [But alongside this there are 'ideal elements' and 'ideal statements' which, though indispensable for the deductive-heuristic machinery, are not absolutely true (in fact they are neither true nor false).] But if the whole theory, containing both the concrete-*inhaltlich* and the ideal statements can be proved consistent in a Euclidean meta-mathematics,[36] the entire classical analysis would be saved. That is, analysis *is* a quasi-empirical theory[37] but the Euclidean consistency proof will see to it that it should have no falsifiers. The sophistication of Cantorian speculation is to be safeguarded not by deeper-seated Euclidean axioms *in the theory itself*—Russell has already failed in this venture—but by an austere Euclidean *meta-theory*.[38]

Eventually, Hilbertians defined the set of statements whose truth values could be regarded as directly given (the set of finitistically true statements) so clearly that their programme could be refuted.[39] The refutation was provided by Gödel's theorem which implied the impossibility of a finitary consistency proof for formalized arithmetic. [The reaction of formalists is well summed up by Curry]:

> This circumstance has led to a difference of opinion among modern formalists, or rather, it strengthened a difference of opinion which already existed. Some think that the consistency of mathematics cannot be established on a priori grounds alone and that mathematics must be justified in some other way. Others maintain that there are forms of reasoning which are a priori and constructive in a wider sense and that in terms of these the Hilbert program can be carried out.[40]

That is, either meta-mathematics was to be recognized as a quasi-empirical theory or the concept of finitary or a priori had to be stretched. Hilbert chose the latter opinion. According to him the class of a priori methods was now to include, for example, transfinite induction up to ϵ_0, used in Gentzen's proof of the consistency of arithmetic.

But not everybody was happy about this extension. Kalmár, who applied Gentzen's proof to the Hilbert–Bernays system, never believed that his proof was Euclidean. According to Kleene: 'To what extent the Gentzen proof can be accepted as securing classical number theory . . . is . . . a matter for individual judgment, depending on how ready one is to accept induction up to ϵ_0 as a finitary method.[41] Or, to quote Tarski:

> there seems to be a tendency among mathematical logicians to overemphasize the importance of consistency problems, and the philosophical value of the results so far in this direction seems somewhat dubious. Gentzen's proof of the consistency of arithmetic is undoubtedly a very interesting metamathematical result which may prove very stimulating and fruitful. I cannot say, however, that the consistency of arithmetic is now much more evident to me (at any rate, perhaps to use the terminology of the differential calculus, more evident than by epsilon) than it was before the proof was given. To clarify a little my reactions: let G be a formalism just adequate for formalizing Gentzen's proof, and let A be the formalism of arithmetic. It is interesting that the consistency of A can be proved in G; it would perhaps be equally interesting if it should turn out that the consistency of G can be proved in A.[42]

However, even those who find transfinite induction up to ϵ_0 infallible would not be happy to go on stretching the concept of infallibility so as to accommodate consistency proofs of stronger theories. In this sense 'the real test of proof-theory will be the proof of the consistency of *analysis,*'[43] and this has still to be seen.

Gödel's and Tarski's incompleteness results however reduce the chances of the final success of Hilbert's programme still further. For if *extant* arithmetic cannot be proved by the original Hilbertian standards, the gradual, consistent (and indeed, ω-consistent) [augmentation] of theories containing arithmetic by further axioms can only be reached by still more fallible methods. That is, the future development of arithmetic will increase its fallibility. Gödel himself has pointed this out in his paper on Russell's mathematical logic:

> [Russell] compares the axioms of logic and mathematics with the laws of nature and logical evidence with sense perception, so that the axioms need not necessarily be evident in themselves, but rather their justification lies (exactly as in physics) in the fact that they make it possible for these 'sense perceptions' to be deduced; which of course would not exclude that they also have a kind of intrinsic plausibility similar to that in physics. I think that (provided 'evidence' is understood in a sufficiently strict sense) this view has been largely justified by subsequent developments, and it is to be expected that it will be still more so in the future. It has turned out that (under the assumption that modern mathematics is consistent) the solution of certain arithmetical problems requires the use of assumptions essentially transcending arithmetic, i.e., the domain of the kind of elementary indisputable evidence that may be most fittingly compared with sense perception. Furthermore it seems likely that for deciding certain questions of abstract set theory and even for certain related questions of the theory of real numbers new axioms based on some hitherto unknown idea will be necessary. Perhaps also the apparently unsurmountable difficulties

which some other mathematical problems have been presenting for many years are due to the fact that the necessary axioms have not yet been found. Of course, under these circumstances mathematics may lose a good deal of its 'absolute certainty'; but, under the influence of the modern criticism of the foundations, this has already happened to a large extent. There is some resemblance between this conception of Russell and Hilbert's 'supplementing the data of mathematical intution' by such axioms as, e.g., the law of excluded middle which are not given by intuition according to Hilbert's view; the borderline however between data and assumptions would seem to lie in different places according to whether we follow Hilbert or Russell.[44]

Quine says that in the field of *grande logique* construction 'at the latest, the truism idea received its deathblow from Gödel's incompleteness theorem. Gödel's incompleteness theorem can be made to show that we can never approach *completeness* of elementhood axioms without approaching contradiction'.[45]

There are many possible ways of [augmenting systems including] arithmetic. One is through adding strong, arithmetically testable, axioms of infinity to *grandes logiques.*[46] Another is through constructing strong ordinal logics.[47] A third one is to allow non-constructive rules of inference.[48] A fourth one is the model-theoretic approach.[49] But all of them are fallible, not less fallible—and not less quasi-empirical—than the ordinary classical mathematics which was so much in want of foundations. This recognition—that not only the *grandes logiques,* but also mathematics is quasi-empirical—is reflected in the 'empiricist' statements by Gödel, von Neumann, Kalmár, Weyl and others.

It should however be pointed out that some people believe that some of the principles used in these different methods are a priori and they were arrived at by 'reflection'. For instance, Gödel's empiricism is qualified by the hope that set-theoretical principles may be found which are a priori true. He claims that Mahlo's 'axioms show clearly, not only that the axiomatic system of set theory as used today is incomplete, but also that it can be supplemented without arbitrariness by new axioms which only unfold the content of the concept of set explained above'.[50] (Gödel, however, does not seem to be very sure of the a priori characterizability of the concept of set, as is evident from his already quoted quasi-empiricist remarks and also from his hesitation in his [1938], where he says that the axiom of constructibility 'seems to give a natural completion of the axioms of set theory, in so far as it determines the vague notion of an arbitrary infinite set in a definite way'.[51]) Weyl actually made fun of Gödel's over-optimistic stretching of the possibilities of a priori knowledge:

Gödel, with his basic trust in transcendental logic, likes to think that our logical optics is only slightly out of focus and hopes that after some minor correction of it we shall see *sharp,* and then everybody will agree that we see *right.* But he who does not share this trust will be disturbed by the high degree of arbitrariness involved in a system like *Z,* or even in Hilbert's system. How much more convincing and closer to facts are the heuristic arguments and the subsequent systematic constructions in Einstein's general relativity theory, or the

> Heisenberg–Schrödinger quantum mechanics. A truly realistic mathematics should be conceived, in line with physics, as a branch of the theoretical construction of the one real world, and should adopt the same sober and cautious attitude towards hypothetic extensions of its foundations as is exhibited by physics.[52]

Kreisel, however, extols this sort of aprioristic reflection by which, he claims, one gains set-theoretical axioms, and 'right' definitions, and calls anti-apriorism an 'antiphilosophic attitude' and the idea of progress by trial and error empirically false.[53] What is more, in his reply to Bar-Hillel, he wants to extend this method to science, thereby rediscovering Aristotelian essentialism. He adds: 'If I were really convinced that reflection is extraordinary or illusory I should certainly not choose philosophy as a profession; or, having chosen it, I'd get out fast.[54] In his comment on Mostowski's paper he tried to play down Gödel's hesitation as out of date.[55] But just as Gödel immediately refers to inductive evidence, Kreisel refers (in the Reply) to the 'limitations' of the heuristic of reflection. (So, after all, 'reflection', 'explication' *are* fallible.)

4 'POTENTIAL FALSIFIERS' IN MATHEMATICS

If mathematics and science are both quasi-empirical, the crucial difference between them, if any, must be in the nature of their 'basic statements', or 'potential falsifiers'. The 'nature' of a quasi-empirical theory is decided by the nature of the truth value injections into its potential falsifiers.[56] Now nobody will claim that mathematics is empirical in the sense that its potential falsifiers are singular spatio-temporal statements. But then what is the nature of mathematics? Or, what is the nature of the potential falsifiers of mathematical theories?[57] The very question would have been an insult in the years of intellectual honeymoon of Russell or Hilbert. After all, the *Principia* or the *Grundlagen der Mathematik* were meant to put an end—once and for all—to counterexamples and refutations in mathematics. Even now the question still raises some eyebrows.

[But comprehensive axiomatic set theories and systems of metamathematics, can be, and indeed have been, refuted.] Let us first take compehensive axiomatic set theories. Of course, they have *potential logical falsifiers*: statements of the form $p \,\&\neg p$. But are there other falsifiers? The potential falsifiers of science, roughly speaking, express the 'hard facts'. But is there anything analogous to 'hard facts' in mathematics? If we accept the view that a formal axiomatic theory implicitly defines its subject-matter, then there would be no mathematical falsifiers except the logical ones. But if we insist that a formal theory should be the formalization of some informal theory, then a formal theory may be said to be 'refuted' if one of its theorems is negated by the corresponding theorem of the informal theory. One could call such an informal theorem a *heuristic falsifier* of the formal theory.[58]

Not all formal mathematical theories are in equal danger of heuristic refutation in a given period. For instance, *elementary group theory* is scarcely in any danger: in this case the original informal theories have been so radically replaced by the axiomatic theory that heuristic refutations seem to be inconceivable.

Set theory is a subtler question. Some argue that after the total destruction of naive set theory by *logical* falsifiers one cannot speak any more of set-theoretical facts: one cannot speak of an *intended* interpretation of set theory any more. But even some of those who dismiss set-theoretical intuition may still agree that axiomatic set theories perform the task of being the dominant, unifying theory of mathematics in which all available mathematical facts (i.e. some specified subset of informal theorems) have to be explained. But then one can criticize a set theory in two ways: its axioms may be tested for consistency and its definitions may be tested for the 'correctness' of their translation of branches of mathematics like arithmetic. For instance, we may some day face a situation where some machine churns out a formal proof in a formal set theory of a formula whose intended meaning is that there exists a non-Goldbachian even number. At the same time a number theorist might prove informally that all even numbers are Goldbachian. If his proof can be formalized within our system of set theory, then our theory will be inconsistent. But if it cannot be thus formalized, the formal set theory will not [have been shown to] be inconsistent, but only to be a *false* theory of arithmetic (while still being possibly a true theory of some mathematical structure that is not isomorphic to arithmetic). Then we may call the informally proved Goldbach theorem a *heuristic falsifier*, or more specifically, an *arithmetical falsifier* of our formal set theory.[59] The formal theory is false in respect of the informal *explanandum* that it had set out to explain; we have to replace it by a better one. First we may try piecemeal improvements. It may have been only the definition of 'natural number' that went wrong and then the definition could be 'adjusted' to each heuristic falsifier. The axiomatic system itself (with its formation and transformation rules) would become useless as an explanation of arithmetic only if it was altogether 'numerically insegregative',[60] i.e. if it turned out that no finite sequence of adjustments of the definition eliminates *all* heuristic falsifiers.

Now the problem arises: *what class of informal theorems should be accepted as arithmetical falsifiers of a formal theory containing arithmetic?*

Hilbert would have accepted only finite numerical equations (without quantifiers) as falsifiers of formal arithmetic. But he could easily show that *all* true finite numerical equations are provable in his system. From this it followed that his system was complete with regard to true basic statements, therefore, if a theorem in it could be proved false by an arithmetical falsifier, the system was also inconsistent, for the formal version of the falsifier was already a theorem of the system. Hilbert's reduction of falsifiers to logical falsifiers (and thereby the reduction of truth to consistency) was achieved by a very narrow ('finitary') definition of arithmetical basic statements.

Gödel's informal proof of the truth of the Gödelian undecidable sentence posed the following problem: is the *Principia* or Hilbert's formalized arithmetic—on the assumption that each is consistent—true or false if we adjoin to it the negation of the Gödel sentence? According to Hilbert the question should have been meaningless, for Hilbert was an instrumentalist with regard to arithmetic outside the finitary kernel and would not have seen any difference between systems of arithmetic with the Gödel sentence or with its negation as long as they both equally implied the true basic statements (to which, by the way, his implicit meaning-and-truth-definition was restricted). Gödel proposed[61] to extend the range of (meaningful and true) basic statements from finitary numerical equations also to statements with quantifiers and the range of proofs to establish the truth of basic statements from 'finitary' proofs to a wider class of intuitionistic methods. It was this methodological proposal that divorced truth from consistency and introduced a new pattern of conjectures and refutations based on arithmetical falsifiability: it allowed for daring speculative theories with very strong, rich axioms while criticizing them from the outside by informal theories with weak, parsimonious axioms. *Intuitionism is here used not for providing foundations but for providing falsifiers, not for discouraging but for encouraging and criticizing speculation!*

It is surprising how far constructive and even finite falsifiers can go in testing comprehensive set theories. Strong axioms of infinity for instance are testable in the field of Diophantine equations.[62]

But comprehensive axiomatic set theories do not have only arithmetical falsifiers. They may be refuted by theorems—or axioms—of naive set theory. For instance Specker 'refuted' Quine's *New Foundations* by proving in it that the ordinals are not well-ordered by '$\leq$' and that the axiom of choice must be given up.[63] Now is this 'refutation' of the *New Foundations*, even a heuristic refutation? Should the well-ordering theorem of shattered naive set theory overrule Quine's system? Even if, with Gödel and Kreisel, we consider naive set theory as re-established by Zermelo's correction,[64] we could admit the well-ordering theorem and the axiom of choice as heuristic falsifiers only if we again extend the class of (intuitionistic) heuristic falsifiers to (almost?) *any* theorem in corrected naive set theory. (We may call the former the class of *strong heuristic falsifiers* and the latter the class of *weak heuristic falsifiers*). But this would surely be irrational: at best we have to consider them as two rival theories (*strictly* speaking *no* heuristic falsifier can be more than a rival hypothesis). After all nothing prevents us from forgetting about naive sets and focussing our attention on the new unintended model of *New Foundations.*[65]

Indeed, we can go even further. For instance, if it turned out that all strong set-theoretical systems are arithmetically false, we may modify our arithmetic—the new, non-standard arithmetic may possibly serve the empirical sciences just as well. Rosser and Wang, who—three years before Specker's result—showed that in no model of *New Foundations* does '$\leq$' well-order both finite cardinals and infinite ordinals as long as we stick to the intended interpretation of '$\leq$', discuss this possibility:

> One may question whether a formal logic which is known to have no standard model is a suitable framework for mathematical reasoning. The proof of the pudding is in the eating. For topics in the usual range of classical mathematical analysis, the reasoning procedures of Quine's *New Foundations* are as close to the accepted classical reasoning procedures as for any system known to us. However, in certain regions, notably when dealing with extremely large ordinals, the reasoning procedures of Quine's *New Foundations* reflect the absence of a standard model, and appear strange to the classically minded mathe-

matician. However, since the theory of ordinals is suspect when applied to very large ordinals, it is hardly a serious defect in a logic if it makes this fact apparent.

We suspect that the idea that a logic must have a standard model if it is to be acceptable as a framework for mathematical reasoning is merely a vestige of the old idea that there is such a thing as absolute mathematical truth. Certainly the requirements on a standard model are that it reflect certain classically conceived notions of the structure of equality, integers, ordinals, sets, *etc.* Perhaps these classically conceived notions are incompatible with the procedures of a strong mathematical system, in which case a formal logic for the strong mathematical system could not have a standard model.[66]

This of course [amounts to the claim] that the only real falsifiers are logical ones. [But other mathematicians,] Gödel for example, would surely reject the *New Foundations* on Specker's refutation: for him the axiom of choice and the well-ordering of ordinals are self-evident truths.[67]

No doubt the problem of basic statements in mathematics will attract increasing attention with the further development of comprehensive set theories. Recent work indicates that some very abstract axioms may soon be found testable in most unexpected branches of classical mathematics; e.g. Tarski's axiom of inaccessible ordinals in algebraic topology.[68] The continuum hypothesis also will provide a testing ground: the accumulation of further intuitive evidence against the continuum hypothesis may lead to the rejection of strong set theories which imply it. Gödel [1964] enumerates quite a few implausible consequences of the continuum hypothesis: a crucial task of his new Euclidean programme is to provide a self-evident set theory from which its negation is derivable.[69]

If one regards comprehensive set theories—and mathematical theories in general—as quasi-empirical theories, a host of new and interesting problems arise. Until now the main demarcation has been between the proved and the unproved (and the provable and unprovable); radical justificationists ('Positivists') equated this demarcation with the demarcation between meaningful and meaningless. [But now there will be a new demarcation problem]: *the problem of demarcation between testable and untestable (metaphysical) mathematical theories with regard to a given set of basic statements.* Certainly one of the surprises of set theory was the fact that theories about sets of very high cardinality are testable in respect to a relatively modest kernel of basic statements (and thus have arithmetical content).[70] Such a criterion will be interesting and informative—but it would be unfortunate if some people should want to use it again as a meaning criterion as happened in the philosophy of science.

[Another problem is that] testability in mathematics rests on the slippery concept of a heuristic falsifier. A heuristic falsifier after all is a falsifier only in a Pickwickian sense: it does not falsify the hypothesis, it only suggests a falsification—and suggestions can be ignored. It is only a rival hypothesis. But this does not separate mathematics as sharply from physics as one may think. Popperian basic statements too are only hypotheses after all. *The crucial role of heuristic refutations is to shift problems to more imporant ones,* to stimulate the development of theoretical frameworks with more content. One can show of most classical refutations in the history of science and mathematics that they are heuristic falsifications. The battle between rival mathematical theories is most frequently decided also by their relative explanatory power.[71]

Let us finally turn to the question: *what is the 'nature' of mathematics,* that is, on what basis are truth values injected into its potential falsifiers? This question can be in part reduced to the question: What is the nature of *informal* theories, that is, what is the nature of the potential falsifiers of *informal* theories? Are we going to arrive, tracing back problemshifts through informal mathematical theories to empirical theories, so that mathematics will turn out in the end to be *indirectly empirical,* thus justifying Weyl's, von Neumann's and—in a certain sense—Mostowski's and Kalmár's position? Or is *construction* the only source of truth to be injected into a mathematical basic statement? Or *platonistic intuition*? Or *convention*? The answer will scarcely be a monolithic one. Careful historico-critical case-studies will probably lead to a sophisticated and composite solution. But whatever the solution may be, the naive school concepts of static rationality like *a priori–aposteriori, analytic–synthetic* will only hinder its emergence. These notions were devised by classical epistemology to classify Euclidean certain knowledge—for the problemshifts in the growth of quasi-empirical knowledge they offer no guidance.[72]

5 PERIODS OF STAGNATION IN THE GROWTH OF QUASI-EMPIRICAL THEORIES

The history of quasi-empirical theories is a history of daring speculations and dramatic refutations. But new theories and spectacular refutations (whether logical or heuristic) do not happen every day in the life of quasi-empirical theories, whether scientific or mathematical. There are occasional long *stagnating periods* when a single theory dominates the scene without having rivals or acknowledged refutations. Such periods make many forget about the criticizability of the basic assumptions. Theories, which looked counterintuitive or even perverted when first proposed, assume authority. Strange methodological delusions spread: some imagine that the axioms themselves start glittering in the light of Euclidean certainty, others imagine that the deductive channels of elementary logic have the power to retransmit truth (or probability) 'inductively' from the basic statements to the extant axioms.

The classical example of an abnormal period in the life of a quasi-empirical theory is the long domination of Newton's mechanics and theory of gravitation. The theory's paradoxical and implausible character put Newton himself into despair: but after a century of corroboration Kant thought it was self-evident. Whewell made the more sophisticated claim that it had been solidified by 'progressive intuition'[73] while Mill thought it was inductively proved.

Thus we may name these two delusions 'the Kant–Whewell delusion', and the 'inductivist delusions'. The first reverts to a form of Euclideanism; the second establishes a new—inductivist—ideal of deductive theory where the channels of deduction can also carry truth (or some quasi-truth like probability) upwards, from the basic statements to the axioms.

The main danger of both delusions lies in their methodological effect: both trade the challenge and adventure of working in the atmosphere of permanent criticism of quasi-empirical theories for the torpor and sloth of a Euclidean or inductivist theory, where axioms are more or less established, where criticism and rival theories are discouraged.[74]

The gravest danger then in modern philosophy of mathematics is that those who recognize the fallibility and therefore the science-likeness of mathematics, turn for analogies to a wrong image of science. The twin delusions of 'progressive intuition' and of induction can be discovered anew in the works of contemporary philosophers of mathematics.[75] These philosophers pay careful attention to the degrees of fallibility, to methods which are a priori to some degree, and even to degrees of rational belief. But scarcely anybody has studied the possibilities of refutations [in mathematics].[76] In particular, nobody has studied the problem of how much of the Popperian conceptual framework of the logic of discovery in the empirical sciences is applicable to the logic of discovery in the quasi-empirical sciences in general and in mathematics in particular. *How can one take fallibilism seriously without taking the possibility of refutations seriously?* One should not pay lip-service to fallibilism: 'To a philosopher there can be nothing which is absolutely self-evident' and then go on to state: 'But in practice there are, of course, many things which can be called self-evident . . . each method of research presupposes certain results as self-evident.[77] Such *soft fallibilism* divorces fallibilism from criticism and shows how deeply ingrained the Euclidean tradition is in mathematical philosophy. It will take more than the paradoxes and Gödel's results to prompt philosophers to take the empirical aspects of mathematics seriously, and to elaborate a philosophy of critical fallibilism, which takes inspiration not from the so-called foundations but from the *growth* of mathematical knowledge.

NOTES

References can be found in the bibliography of this volume.

1. This empiricist position (and one of its central difficulties) is very clearly described by Ayer in his [1936]: 'whereas a scientific generalisation is readily admitted to be fallible, the truths of mathematics and logic appear to everyone to be necessary and certain. But if empiricism is correct no proposition which has a factual content can be necessary or certain. Accordingly the empiricist must deal with the truths of logic and mathematics in one of the two following ways: he must say either that they are not necessary truths, in which case he must account for the universal conviction that they are; or he must say that they have no factual content, and then he must explain how a proposition which is empty of all factual content can be true and useful and surprising' (pp. 72–3.).

2. Russell [1901*a*], p. 57.

3. Russell [1924], pp. 325–6. He obviously hesitated between the view that one can put up with this state of affairs (and work out some sort of inductive logic for the *Principia*), [and the view that] one has to go on with the search for self-evident axioms. In the Introduction to the second edition of the *Principia,* he says that one *cannot* rest content with an axiom that has mere inductive evidence (p. xiv), while on p. 59 he

devotes a little chapter to the (inductive) 'Reasons for Accepting the Axiom of Reducibility' (although still not giving up the hope of deducing it from some self-evident truth).

4. Fraenkel [1927], p. 61.

5. Ibid.

6. Carnap [1931], p. 31. English translation in Benacerraf and Putnam (*eds.*) [1964].

7. Carnap [1958], p. 240.

8. Curry [1963], p. 16. See also his [1951], p. 61.

9. Quine [1958], p. 4.

10. Quine [1965], p. 125.

11. Rosser [1953], p. 207.

12. Church [1939].

13. Gödel [1944], p. 213.

14. Gödel [1947], p. 521. The word 'probable' was inserted in the reprinted version, Gödel [1964], p. 265.

15. Mehlberg [1962], p. 86.

16. Weyl [1949], p. 235.

17. Neumann [1947], pp. 189–90.

18. Bernays [1939], p. 83.

19. Mostowski [1955], p. 42.

20. Kalmár [1967], pp. 192–3.

21. Russell [1959], p. 212. For further details about Russell's turn, cf. my [1962].

22. Neumann [1947], p. 190.

23. Weyl [1928], p. 87.

24. For an exposition of the story see Lakatos [1978b], chapter I. The concept and term 'basic statement' is due to Karl Popper; see his [1934], chapter V.

25. Cf. Popper [1963*a*]p., 64.

26. For a discussion cf. Lakatos [1978a], chapter 3.

27. For the latter concept of Lakatos [1978a], chapter 1.

28. The elaboration of empirical methodology—which of course is the paradigm of quasi-empirical methodology—is due to Karl Popper.

29. Hilbert [1925], p. 35.

30. Intuitionism is omitted: it never aimed at a reorganization but at a truncation of classical mathematics. *Not all the theorems of intuitionist mathematics are theorems of classical mathematics. In this sense, Lakatos is wrong to describe intuitionism as simply a 'truncation' of classical mathematics. Nevertheless, an important point remains. While Russell's logicism and Hilbert's formalism each regarded its task as the justification of the whole of classical mathematics, Brouwer's intuitionism was willing to jettison large parts of classical mathematics which do not meet its standards of justification. (*Eds.*)

31. Kleene and Rosser [1935].

32. Church [1932], p. 348.

33. Quine [1941*a*], p. 122. Some critics of Quine may say that it is only he who has made a 'daring' structure out of the natural simplicity of mathematics. But surely the

Cantorian paradise is a 'bold theoretical construction, and as such the very opposite of analytical self-evidence' (Weyl [1947], p. 64). Also cf. the Weyl quotation in section 2.

34. Quine [1941*b*], p. 163. By the way, the most interesting feature of Rosser's paper is the search for ways of testing the consistency of *ML*. Rosser shows that 'if one can prove *201 from the remaining axioms then the remaining axioms are inconsistent' (Rosser [1941], p. 97).

35. Also, one can choose to cut down a quasi-empirical theory to its Euclidean kernel (that is the essential aspect of the intuitionist programme).

36. Originally the meta-theory was not to be axiomatized but was to consist of simple, protofinitary thought-experiments. In Bologna (1928) von Neumann even criticized Tarski for axiomatizing it. (The generalization of the concept of 'Euclidean theory' to informal, unaxiomatized theories does not constitute any difficulty.)

37. To quote Weyl again: 'Whatever the ultimate value of Hilbert's program, his bold enterprise can claim one merit: it has disclosed to us the highly complicated and ticklish logical structure of mathematics, its maze of back-connections, which result in circles of which it cannot be gathered at a first glance whether they might not lead to blatant contradictions' (op. cit., p. 61).

38. Hilbert's philosophy, at least as here presented, cannot be subsumed so easily under Euclideanism. Meta-mathematics is an informal unaxiomatized theory and such theories do not have the required deductive structure to be candidates for Euclidean status. Informal theories can obviously be axiomatized, but one of Hilbert's central claims was that there was no need for this in the case of meta-mathematics (cf. n. 36). Each principle assumed in a meta-mathematical proof was to be so obviously true as not to be in need of justification (or, rather, to be immediately justified by the so-called 'global intuition'). (*Eds.*)

39. Herbrand [1930], p. 248. It took three decades to arrive at this definition.

40. Curry [1963], p. 11.

41. Kleene [1952], p. 479.

42. Tarski [1954], p. 19.

43. Bernays and Hilbert [1939], p. vii.

44. Gödel [1944], p. 213.

45. Quine [1941*a*], p. 127.

46. Such strong axioms were formulated by Mahlo, Tarski and Levy. As to the arithmetical testability of these axioms: 'It can be proved that these axioms also have consequences far outside the domain of very great transfinite numbers, which is their immediate subject matter: each of them, under the assumption of its consistency, can be shown to increase the number of decidable propositions even in the field of Diophantine equations' (Gödel [1947], p. 520).

47. This line of research was initiated by Turing ([1939]) and developed by Feferman ([1963]).

48. Cf. e.g. Rosser [1937]; Tarski [1939]; Kleene [1943].

49. Cf. Kemeny [1958], p. 164.

50. Gödel [1964], p. 264 (cf. Gödel [1947], p. 520).

51. Gödel [1938], p. 557.

52. Weyl, op. cit., p. 235.

53. Kreisel [1967*a*], p. 140.

54. Kreisel [1976*b*], p. 178.

55. Kreisel [1967*c*], pp. 97–8.

56. See *above,* p. 34.

57. It is hoped that this Popperian formulation of the age-old question will shed new light on some questions in the philosophy of mathematics.

58. It would be interesting to investigate how far the demarcation between logical and heuristic falsifiers corresponds to Curry's demarcation between mathematical truth and 'quasi-truth' (or 'acceptability'). Cf. his [1951], especially chapter XI. Curry calls his philosophy 'formalist' as opposed to '*inhaltlich*' or 'contensive' philosophies, like Platonism or intuitionism (Curry [1965], p. 80). However, besides his philosophy of formal structure, he has a philosophy of acceptability–but surely one cannot explain the growth of formal mathematics without acceptabilty considerations, so Curry offers an '*inhaltlich*' philosophy after all.

59. The expression 'ω-consistency', is as Quine pointed out (Quine [1953*a*], p. 117), misleading. A demonstration of the 'ω-inconsistency' of a system of arithmetic would in fact be a *heuristic* falsification of it. Ironically, the historical origin of the misnomer was that the phenomenon was used by Gödel and Tarski precisely to divorce truth ('ω-consistency') from consistency.

60. See Quine, loc. cit., p. 118.

61. See his intervention in 1930 in Königsberg; recorded in Gödel [1931].

62. See n. 46. (*Eds.*)

63. Specker [1953]: also cf. Quine [1963], p. 294ff.

64. Cf. Gödel [1947], p. 518 and Kreisel [1967].

65. For philosophers of science after Popper it should anyway be a commonplace that *explanans* and *explanardum* may be rival hypotheses.

66. Rosser and Wang [1950], p. 115.

67. In his original paper [1947], Gödel says that the axiom of choice is exactly as evident as the other axioms 'in the present state of our knowledge' (p. 516). In the 1964 reprint (Gödel [1964]) this has been replaced by 'from almost every possible point of view' (p. 259, n. 2). He proposed, after some hesitation, a further extension of the range of set-theoretical basic statements that in fact amounted to a new Euclidean programme—but immediately proposed a quasi-empirical alternative in the case of failure. (See especially the supplement to his [1964].)

68. Cf. Myhill [1960], p. 464.

69. Kreisel criticizes Gödel (Kreisel [1967*a*]) for not discussing his turn from proposing the constructibility axiom as a completion of set theory in 1938 to surreptitiously withdrawing it in 1947. One would think the reason for the turn is obvious: in the meantime he must have studied the work done on the consequences of the continuum hypothesis (mainly by Lusin and Sierpinski) and must have come to the conclusion that a set theory in which the hypothesis is deducible (like the one he suggested in 1938) is false. It may be interesting to note that according to Lusin a simple proposition in the theory of analytic sets which Sierpinski showed to be incompatible with the continuum hypothesis is 'indubitably true'—indeed he puts forward an impressive argument (Lusin [1935] and Sierpinski [1935]).

70. The term 'content' is here used in a Popperian sense: the 'arithmetical content is the set of arithmetical potential falsifiers.

71. Cf. Lakatos [1978b], chapter. 3.

72. Since this paper was written a good deal of further work has been done on testing proposed set-theoretical axioms, like the continuum hypothesis and strong axioms of finity. (A good survey is to be found in Fraenkel, Bar Hillel and Levy [1973]. See also Shoenfield [1971] for the axiom of measurable cardinals.) Levy and Solovay's work ([1967]) indicates that large cardinal axioms will not decide the continuum problem. As another line of attack, alternatives to the continuum hypothesis have been formulated and tested. An example is 'Martin's axiom', which is a consequence of the continuum hypothesis, but consistent with its negation (see Martin and Solovay [1970] and Solovay and Tennenbaum [1971]). Of the six consequences of the Continuum Hypothesis which Gödel regarded as highly implausible, three follow also from Martin's Axiom. But Martin and Solovay take a different attitude to that taken by Gödel. They have, they say, 'virtually no intuitions' about the truth or falsity of these three consequences. *(Eds.)*

73. E.G. Whewell [1860], especially chapter XXIX.

74. Cf. Kuhn, especially his [1963].

75. The main proponents of Whewellian progressive intuition in mathematics are Bernays, Gödel, and Kreisel (see *above,* pp. 34–5). Gödel also provides an inductivist criterion of truth, should progressive (or as Carnap would call it 'guided') intuition fail: an axiomatic set theory is true if it is richly verified in informal mathematics or physics. 'The simplest case of an application of the criterion under discussion arises when some set-theoretical axiom has number-theoretical consequences verifiable by computation up to any given integer' (supplement to Gödel [1964], p. 272).

76. Kalmár—with his criticism of Church's thesis—is a notable exception (see Kalmár [1959]).

77. Bernays [1965], p. 127.

*ACKNOWLEDGMENTS

This paper developed out of some remarks made by Lakatos at a Colloquium in the Philosophy of Science in London, 1965. These remarks were in the form of a reply to Professor Kalmár [1967]) and were published in Lakatos (*ed.*) [1967*a*], under the same title as the present paper.

Lakatos expanded these remarks into a longer paper which he completed in 1967. However, he withheld it from publication, intending to improve it further. Other interests prevented him from returning to the paper, and it appears here essentially as he left it in 1967. We have made a few minor presentational changes, and deleted some introductory sentences which relate only to the discussion of Kalmár's paper. (*Eds.*)

HILARY PUTNAM

What Is Mathematical Truth?

The themes of Putnam's essay are by now familiar: mathematical knowledge is not a priori, absolute and certain, rather it is quasi-empirical, fallible and probable, much like natural science. Putnam's arguments, however, are both original and forceful.

The claim to be argued is that ordinary mathematics, even number theory, is quasi-empirical. For Putnam, as for Lakatos, quasi-empirical methods "are analogous to methods of the physical sciences except that the singular statements which are 'generalized by induction', used to test 'theories', etc., are themselves the product of proof or calculation rather than being 'observation reports' in the usual sense."

Putnam first argues that quasi-empirical mathematics is logically possible. He constructs a hypothetical example of mathematicians who explicitly use quasi-empirical methods and he shows how well they can defend the cogency of their position. Indeed, on Putnam's account, they can even quote Gödel's Theorems against their critics, arguing that Gödel's results establish the need for synthetic (quasi-empirical) methods in mathematics.

Next Putnam argues that ordinary mathematics has been quasi-empirical all along. Established general principles such as the correspondence between the real numbers and the points on a line or the axiom of choice have been established by quasi-empirical methods. An especially interesting argument is based on Polya's example of Euler's theorem that $\Sigma\ 1/n^2 = \pi^2/6$. It is possible to prove this identity by traditional means and so claim to know it a priori. But it is also possible to know it by induction on 'observations'. We can calculate the values of the terms for finitely many places and compare the results. Once we have noted the agreement to thirty places, it is a quasi-empirical certainty that the identity holds. Knowledge is here based on probabilistic induction, heuristic and intuition, rather than on rigorous proof.

Reprinted from Mathematics, Matter and Method by Hilary Putnam by permission of Cambridge University Press.

The last half of Putnam's essay takes up the issue of realism. Is this backsliding into foundationalism? No, Putnam has clearly renounced the thesis that set theoretic platonism provides foundations for mathematics. The issue of realism that concerns Putnam can be developed along the following lines. The emphasis on quasi-empirical methods leads us to rely on social processes for establishing knowledge in addition to rigorous proofs. A similar situation arises in the philosophy of science. The claims of realism in both cases are that the sentences of the underlying theories are either true or false and, further, that what makes them true is to some extent external to the social processes themselves. Realism, thus construed, stands opposed to various reductionist philosophies which attempt to explain the theories only in terms internal to the social processes, such as sense data, measurements, symbol manipulation or social ritual. Realism insists that an adequate account of the theories in question must interpret them as being about some external reality.

Putnam suggests that the case for realism in the philosophy of mathematics is much like the case for realism in the philosophy of science. In the first place, there are the negative arguments that criticize particular reductions. In the second place, the positive argument is the same in both cases: Realism is the only philosophy that does not make the success of science or mathematics into a miracle.

• • • • •

In this paper I argue that mathematics should be interpreted realistically—that is, that mathematics makes assertions that are objectively true or false, independently of the human mind, and that *something* answers to such mathematical notions as 'set' and 'function'. This is not to say that reality is somehow bifurcated—that there is one reality of material things, and then, over and above it, a second reality of 'mathematical things'. A set of objects, for example, depends for its existence on those objects: if they are destroyed, then there is no longer such a set.[1] (Of course, we may say that the set exists 'tenselessly', but we may also say the objects exist 'tenselessly': this is just to say that in pure mathematics we can sometimes ignore the important difference between 'exists now' and 'did exist, exists now, or will exist'.) Not only are the 'objects' of pure mathematics conditional upon material objects; they are, in a sense, merely abstract possibilities. Studying how mathematical objects behave might better be described as studying what structures are abstractly possible and what structures are not abstractly possible.

The important thing is that the mathematician is studying something objective, even if he is not studying an unconditional 'reality' of nonmaterial things, and that the physicist who states a law of nature with the aid of a mathematical formula is abstracting a real feature of a real material world, even if he has to speak of numbers, vectors, tensors, state-functions, or whatever to make the abstraction.

Unfortunately, belief in the objectivity of mathematics has generally gone along with belief in 'mathematical objects' as an unconditional and nonphysical reality, and with the idea that the kind of knowledge that we have in mathematics is strictly a priori—in fact, mathematical knowledge has always been the paradigm of a priori knowledge. The present paper will argue that, on the contrary, mathematical knowledge resembles *empirical* knowledge—that is, that the criterion of truth in mathematics just as much as in physics is success of our ideas in practice, and that mathematical knowledge is corrigible and not absolute.

THE METHOD OF MATHEMATICAL PROOF

The first apparent stumbling block that confronts us if we wish to argue against the a priori character of mathematical knowledge is the method of mathematical proof. It does seem *at first blush* as if the sole method that mathematicians do use or *can* use is the method of mathematical proof, and as if that method consists simply in deriving conclusions from axioms which have been fixed once and for all by rules of derivation which been fixed once and for all. In order to start our investigation, let us, therefore, first ask whether this is really the only conceivable method in mathematics. And, since the axioms are most clear and most 'immutable' in elementary number theory,[2] let us restrict our attention to elementary number theory: if we can make the case that even the elementary theory of non-negative integers is not a priori, then we shall not have much trouble with, say, set theory.

MARTIAN MATHEMATICS

Let us now imagine that we have come in contact with an advanced civilization on the planet Mars. We succeed in learning the language of the Martians without too much difficulty, and we begin to read their newspapers, magazines, works of literature, scientific books and journals, etc. When we come to their mathematical literature, we are in for some surprises.

What first surprises us is the profundity of the results they claim to have obtained. Many statements that *our* best mathematicians have tried without success to prove—e.g. that every map can be colored with four colors, that the zeroes of the Riemann zeta functions in the strip above the unit interval all lie on the line 1/2—appear as assertions in their mathematical textbooks. Eagerly we start reading these textbooks in order to learn the proofs of these marvelous results. Then comes our biggest surprise: the Martians rely on quasi-empirical methods in mathematics!

By 'quasi-empirical' methods I mean methods that are analogous to the methods of the physical sciences except that the singular statements which are 'generalized by induction', used to test 'theories', etc., are themselves the product of proof or calculation rather than being 'observation reports' in the usual sense. For example, if we decided to accept the Riemann Hypothesis (the statement about the zeroes of the Riemann zeta function mentioned a moment ago) because extensive searches with electronic computers have failed to find a counterexample—many 'theorems' have been proved with its aid, and none of these has been disproved, the consequences of the hypothesis (it has, in fact, important consequences in the theory of prime numbers and in other branches of ordinary number theory and algebraic number theory) are plausible and of far-reaching significance, etc.—then we could say, not that we had *proved* the Riemann Hypothesis, but that we had 'verified' it by a quasi-empirical method. Like empirical verification, quasi-empirical verification is relative and not absolute: what has been 'verified' at a given time may later turn out to be false. But is there any reason, other than a sociological one, why quasi-empirical methods should not be used in mathematics? If it turned out the Martians do use quasi-empirical methods, and their mathematical practice is highly successful, could we say that they are irrational?

One standard response ('standard' for a philosopher of recent vintage, anyway) might be to argue that the Martians would be conceptually confused because they 'don't know what a proof is'. And one might go on to argue that if one doesn't know what a proof is, then one doesn't know what *mathematics* is, and (more dubiously) that if one doesn't know what mathematical proof is, then one doesn't understand the assertions in question (the Riemann Hypothesis, or whatever) *as* mathematical assertions.

But before we allow this line of argument to spin itself out too far, we may as well ask: What makes you say that they don't know what a proof is? Suppose the Martians say something like this when queried on this point:

> Mathematics is much like any other science in this respect: some assertions appear self-evident (e.g. $F = ma$ in physics, or, perhaps, some of the conservation principles) and others don't (the Law of Gravitation). Moreover, again as in other sciences, some assertions that don't *look* self-evident turn out to be consequences of evident principles (e.g. in Newtonian physics the Third Law—action equals reaction—is a consequence of the other laws)—and others are not. What you call 'proof' is simply deduction from principles that are (more or less) self evident. We recognize proof, and we value proof as highly as you do—when we can get it. What we don't understand is why you restrict yourself to *proof*—why you refuse to accept *confirmation*. After all, there are true mathematical statements that are neither immediately nor demonstratively necessary—epistemologically contingent mathematical truths. Not recognizing confirmation as well as proof debars you from ever discovering these truths.

If the Martians make *this* reply, then we cannot say they don't have the concept of proof. If anything, it's *we* who lack a concept—the concept of *mathematical confirmation.* The Martians know what a proof is; they use both methods—mathematical proof and confirmation; they are highly successful (so might we be if we developed the knack of making quasi-empirical mathematical inferences).

Finally, it might be objected that such methods are not necessary in principle; that mathematical statements just have the property that if they are true then they can be proved. But Gödel's theorem shows the contrary. Even if all statements that can be proved are epistemologically a priori and conversely[3] the statements that can be proved from axioms which are evident to us can only be a recursively enumerable set (unless an infinite number of irreducibly different principles are at least potentially evident to the human mind, a supposition I find quite incredible). And Gödel's theorem can (in a version due, fundamentally, to Tarski) be expressed by the statement that the class of truths of just elementary number theory is not recursively enumerable.

In particular, then, even if it were the case that all the axioms we use in mathematics are 'analytic', as some philosophers have claimed, and that deduction preserves 'analyticity' (which is never shown), it would not follow that all truths of mathematics are analytic. Indeed, if the analytic sentences are all consequences of some finite list of Meaning Postulates (in the first order logic sense of 'consequences'), then it is a consequence of the theorem just cited that there must be synthetic truths in mathematics. Worse, it is a consequence of this view that all the statements we can prove are analytic; that, although there are synthetic truths in mathematics, our refusal to use quasi-empirical methods debars us from ever discovering a single one of them. Since philosophers who favor this jargon generally hold that analytic truths have 'no content' and that synthetic truths have 'factual content', one wonders why these philosophers do not insist that we *must* use quasi-empirical methods!

WHY HAVE WE NOT USED QUASI-EMPIRICAL METHODS?

We are, then, faced with the following puzzle: if the use of quasi-empirical methods (not to say, *empirical* methods) is, in principle, justified in mathematics, then why have we not used them? Our answer to this puzzle is that the foregoing science fiction story about the Martians was a deliberate hoax: the fact is that *we* have been using quasi-empirical and even empirical methods in mathematics all along—we, us humans, right here on earth!

Thus, consider the basic postulate upon which the subject of analytical geometry is founded (and with it the whole study of space in modern mathematics, including the topological theory of manifolds). This is the postulate that there is a one-to-one order preserving correspondence between the points on the line and the real numbers. Consider the real numbers themselves. Were the real numbers and the correspondence postulate introduced in a rigorous mathematical fashion with a rigorous mathematical justification? They certainly were not. The fact is that the ancient Greeks lacked the mathematical experience, and hence lacked also the mathematical sophistication, to generalize the notion of 'number' to the extent required for the correspondence to exist. Thus, when they ran into the existence of incommensurables, they could only abandon the correspondence postulate, and with it the possibility of an algebraic treatment of geometry. Descartes, on the other hand, was willing to simply *postulate* the existence of a number—a 'real' number, as we now would say—corresponding to each distance.[4] He did not identify these numbers with sets of rationals or with sequences of rationals. But once he had shown how great the 'pay off' of the correspondence postulate was, not only in pure mathematics but also in mechanics, there was not the slightest question of abandoning either the correspondence postulate or these generalized numbers, the 'real' numbers. In particular it would be a mistake to argue that Descartes was only 'justified' *because* it was possible (even if he did not know it) to 'identify' real numbers with sets or sequences of rationals. Suppose it were *not* possible to identify real numbers with sets or sequences (i.e. to 'construct' them out of rationals—i.e. suppose these constructions had not been discovered). Would we have *given up* analytical geometry and mechanics? Or would we not rather have come simply to regard real numbers as *primitive* entities, much as most mathematicians regard the natural numbers (*pace* Frege, *pace* Russell!) or as Frege regarded *concepts*, or Zermelo regarded *sets*, or some mathematicians today regard *categories* and *functors*? And suppose we had a consistent axiomatizable mathematics of this kind, mathematics taking real numbers as primitive. Would it be unjustified? It doubtless increases the security of the system to find a way to introduce real numbers by definition (although the degree of security is hard to measure, since part of the price one has to pay is to take *sets* as primitive, and it seems weird today to regard sets as 'safer' than real numbers). But it is not, contrary to the logicists, *essential* to identify real numbers with logical constructions out of rationals.

The fact is that once the assumption of real numbers and of the correspondence between points and reals had shown their fertility in both physics and mathematics, there was no question, barring the discovery of mathematical contradiction (and possibly not even then—we would certainly have tried to circumvent any contradiction by means less drastic than abandoning the real number system, and doubtless we would have succeeded), there was, repeat, no question of abandoning the real number system. The existence of real numbers and the correspondence between real numbers and points on the line were discovered in part quasi-empirically, in part empirically. This is as much an example of the use of hypothetico-deductive methods as anything in physics is.

The same story repeats itself with the introduction of the methods of the differential and integral calculus by Newton and Leibnitz. If the epsilon-delta methods had not been discovered, then infinitesimals would have been postulated entities (just as 'imaginary' numbers were for a long time). Indeed, this approach to the calculus—enlarging the real number system—is just as consistent as the standard approach, as we know today from the work of Abraham Robinson.

The remarks we made about the introduction of the methods of analytical geometry apply with full force to this case too. If the calculus had not been 'justified' Weierstrass style, it would have been 'justified' anyway.[5] The point is that the real justification of the calculus is its *success*—its success in mathematics, and its success in physical science.

A very recent example of the fully conscious and explicit use of quasi-empirical argument to justify enlarging the axiomatic foundations of mathematics is the introduction of the axiom of choice by Zermelo. In his 1908 paper,[6] Zermelo defends his axiom against the critics of his 1904 paper. Peano, in particular, had pointed out that the axiom appeared to be independent of the axioms in Peano's *Formulaire,* and had gone on to suggest that Zermelo's proof of the proposition that every set can be well ordered was, therefore, no proof at all, since it rests on the 'unproved' assertion of the axiom of choice. Here is Zermelo's reply:[7]

> First, how does Peano arrive at his own fundamental principles and how does he justify their inclusion in the *Formulaire*, since, after all, he cannot prove them either? Evidently by analyzing the modes of inference that in the course of history have come to be recognized as valid and by pointing out that the

principles are intuitively evident and necessary for science—considerations that can all be urged equally well in favor of the disputed principle. That this axiom, even though it was never formulated in textbook system, has frequently been used, and successfully at that, in the most diverse fields of mathematics, especially in set theory, by Dedekind, Cantor, F. Bernstein, Schoenflies, J. König, and others is an indisputable fact, which is only corroborated by the opposition that, at one time or another, some logical purists directed against it. Such an extensive use of a principle can be explained only by its self-evidence, which, of course, must not be confused with its provability. No matter if this self-evidence is to a certain degree subjective—it is surely a necessary source of mathematical principles, even if it is not a tool of mathematical proofs, and Peano's assertion[8] that it has nothing to do with mathematics fails to do justice to manifest facts. But the question that can be objectively decided, whether the principle is *necessary for science,* I should now like to submit to judgment by presenting a number of elementary and fundamental theorems and problems that, in my opinion, could not be dealt with at all without the principle of choice. [Here follows a list of theorems that need the axiom of choice.]

In my opinion, Zermelo is right on two counts. First of all, he is right that 'self evidence' is somewhat subjective, but nonetheless counts for *something.* In empirical science too, it is wrong to think that intuition plays no role at all. Intuition is a *fallible* guide—that is what Francis Bacon taught us —but a fallible guide is still better than no guide at all. If our intuition were totally untrustworthy, we would never think of a correct or approximately correct theory to test in the first place. In mathematics, the desire that our axioms should be intuitively necessary is a legitimate one, especially when combined with the desideratum that Zermelo mentions—that they should formalize the actual practice of mathematicians. But it is noteworthy that what Zermelo characterizes as 'objective' is not the 'self-evidence' of the axiom of choice but its *necessity for science.* Today it is not just the axiom of choice but the whole edifice of modern set theory whose entrenchment rests on great success in mathematical application—in other words, on 'necessity for science'. What argument, other than a quasi-empirical one, can we offer for the axiom of Replacement? And the current rumblings in Category theory are evidence that the hypothetico-deductive evolution and testing of new mathematical existence statements (new 'objects') and axioms and methods is still going on.

The use of quasi-empirical methods in mathematics is not by any means confined to the testing of new axioms or new 'ontological commitments'. Although it is rare that either mathematicians or philosophers discuss it in public, quasi-empirical methods are constantly used to discover truths or putative truths that one then tries to prove rigorously. Moreover, some of the quasi-empirical arguments by which one discovers a mathematical proposition to be true in the first place are totally convincing to mathematicians. Consider, for example, how Euler discovered that the sum of the series $1/n^2$ *is* $\pi^2/6$. Euler proceeded in analogy with the factorization

$$P(x) = c_0\left(1 - \frac{x}{\epsilon_1}\right)\left(1 - \frac{x}{\epsilon_2}\right)\left(1 - \frac{x}{\epsilon_3}\right)\ldots\left(1 - \frac{x}{\epsilon_n}\right)$$

where $P(x)$ is a polynomial with roots ($\neq 0$) $\epsilon_1, \ldots, \epsilon_n$. He 'factored'

$\sin \pi x$ by considering the 'roots' to be the values for which $\sin \pi x = 0$, i.e. $x = 0, x = \pm 1, x = 2, \ldots$. Thus

$$\sin \pi x = c_0 x \left(1 - \frac{x}{1}\right)\left(1 + \frac{x}{1}\right)\left(1 - \frac{x}{2}\right)\left(1 + \frac{x}{2}\right)\ldots$$

(The factor 'x' is present because 0 is one of the 'roots'.) To evaluate the 'constant term' c_0 he used

$$\lim_{x \to 0} \frac{\sin \pi x}{x} = \pi = c_0$$

Thus:

$$\sin \pi x =_{(?!)} \pi x \left(1 - \frac{x^2}{1}\right)\left(1 - \frac{x^2}{4}\right)\left(1 - \frac{x^2}{9}\right)\ldots \tag{1}$$

But by Taylor's theorem:

$$\sin \pi x = \frac{\pi x}{1!} - \frac{1}{3!}\pi^3 x^3 + \frac{1}{5!}\pi^5 x^5 \ldots \tag{2}$$

Equating the coefficients of x^3 in (1) and (2) gives:

$$-\frac{\pi^3}{3!} = \pi\left(-\frac{1}{1} - \frac{1}{4} - \frac{1}{9} \ldots\right) \tag{3}$$

or

$$-\frac{\pi^2}{6} = -\sum \frac{1}{n^2} \tag{4}$$

so

$$\sum \frac{1}{n^2} = \frac{\pi^2}{6}$$

Euler, of course, was perfectly well aware that this was not a proof. But by the time one had calculated the sum of $1/n^2$ to thirty or so decimal places and it agreed with $\pi^2/6$, no mathematician doubted that the sum of $1/n^2$ was $\pi^2/6$, even though it was another twenty years before Euler had a proof. The similarity of this kind of argument to a hypothetico-deductive argument in empirical science should be apparent: intuitively plausible though not certain analogies lead to results which are then checked 'empirically'. Successful outcomes of these checks then reinforce one's confidence in the analogy in question.[9]

Let me give another example of this kind, this time from present-day mathematics. Many mathematicians are quite convinced that there are infinitely many 'twin primes' (i.e. infinitely many pairs n, $n + 2$, both prime, such as 5, 7, or 11, 13) even though there is no mathematical proof of this assertion. The argument they find convincing goes as follows: it seems plausible (and agrees with 'empirical' data) that the 'events' *n is a prime* and *$n + 2$ is a prime* are *independent* events in the statistical sense. But the frequency of primes less than n is approximately $1/\log n$. Hence the frequency of twin primes less than n must be (asymptotically) like $1/(\log n)^2$, which implies that the number of twin primes is infinite.

Bas van Frassen has asserted that it is a consequence of my view that the following is a good quasi-empirical inference in mathematics: computers have failed to turn up a counterexample of the Goldbach conjecture, *therefore* the Goldbach conjection is true. Of course, this is not a good quasi-empirical inference. And I do not pretend to be able to give rules by means of which we can tell which are and which are not good quasi-empirical inferences. After all, the analogous problem in philosophy of empirical science—the problem of inductive logic—has resisted solution for centuries, but people have not abandoned empirical science on that account. But I can say what is wrong with this simple 'induction' that the Goldbach conjecture is true. The fact is that neither in mathematics nor in empirical science do we trust the conclusion of a simple 'Baconian' induction to be exactly and-precisely correct. A universal generalization—a statement that can be overthrown by a single 'for instance'—cannot be verified by mere Baconian induction in any science. But just contrast the 'inductive' argument we gave for the existence of infinitely many twin primes with the bad argument for the Goldbach conjecture. Even if the events *n is a prime* and *n + 2 is a prime* are not strictly statistically independent, the conclusion will still be correct. In other words, the deduction that there are infinitely many twin primes is 'stable under small perturbations of the assumptions'. One confirms inductively a statistical statement,[10] not an exceptionless generalization, and then deduces from even the approximate truth of the statistical statement that there will be infinitely many twin primes. My impression is that there are very few mathematicians who are *not* convinced by this argument, even though it is not a proof.

Since we do use quasi-empirical methods a great deal in mathematics (and we aren't even Martians!) I believe that it would be of great value to attempt to systematize and study these methods. Perhaps such an enterprise is premature in the present state of our knowledge. However, a mathematical friend has suggested that model theoretic methods might be used, for example, to try to convert 'probability' arguments like the one for the existence of infinitely many twin primes, into proofs.

REALISM IN THE PHILOSOPHY OF MATHEMATICS

I am indebted to Michael Dummett for the following very simple and elegant formulation of realism: A realist (with respect to a given theory or discourse) holds that (1) the sentences of that theory or discourse are true or false; and (2) that what makes them true or false is something *external*—that is to say, it is not (in general) our sense data, actual or potential, or the structure of our minds, or our language, etc. Notice that, on this formulation, it is possible to be a realist with respect to mathematical discourse without committing oneself to the existence of 'mathematical objects'. The question of realism, as Kreisel long ago put it, is the question of the objectivity of mathematics and not the question of the existence of mathematical objects.

One way to spell this out is the following. Mathematics has, since Frege and Russell and Zermelo and Bourbaki been thought of as describing a realm of mathematical objects. In principle, all these objects can be identified with *sets*, in fact. The language in which these objects are described is highly asceptic—no modal notions, no intensional notions (e.g. 'proof'), indeed, in the by now standard case, no notions except those of the first order theory of 'epsilon' (set-membership). Mathematics has, roughly speaking, got rid of *possibility* by simply assuming that, up to isomorphism anyway, all possibilities are simultaneously *actual*—actual, that is, in the universe of 'sets'.

There is another possible way of doing mathematics, however, or at any rate, of viewing it. This way, which is probably much older than the modern way, has suffered from never being explicitly described and defended. It is to take the standpoint that mathematics has *no* objects of its own at all. You can prove theorems about anything you want—rainy days, or marks on paper, or graphs, or lines, or spheres—but the mathematician, on this view, makes no existence assertions at all. What he asserts is that certain things are *possible* and certain things are *impossible*—in a strong and uniquely mathematical sense of 'possible' and 'impossible'. In short, mathematics is essentially *modal* rather than existential, on this view, which I have elsewhere termed 'mathematics as modal logic'.[11]

Let me say a few things about this standpoint here.

(1) This standpoint is not intended to satisfy the nominalist. The nominalist, good man that he is, cannot accept modal notions any more than he can accept the existence of sets. We leave the nominalist to satisfy himself.

(2) We do have to say something about Hume's problem. It was Hume more than any other philosopher who drove the notions of possibility and necessity into disrepute. What bothered Hume was the following argument: *we only observe what is actual*. Since the only generalizations we can make on the basis of the observation of actual things are to the effect that all *A*s are *B*s—not that all *possible A*s are *B*s, or that all *A*s are *necessarily B*s, Hume concluded that necessity must necessarily be a subjective matter.

It seems to us that this argument rests on much too simple a view of the structure of scientific knowledge. Physical theory, for example, has not for a long time been a mere collection of statements of the form $(x)(Fx \rightarrow Gx)$. From classical mechanics through quantum mechanics and general relativity theory, what the physicist does is to provide mathematical devices for representing all the *possible*—not just the physically possible, but the mathematically possible—configurations of a system. Many of the physicist's methods (variational methods, Lagrangian formulations of physics) depend on describing the actual path of a system as that path of all the *possible* ones for which a certain quantity is a minimum or maximum. Equilibrium methods in economics use the same approach. It seems to us that 'possible' has long been a theoretical notion of full legitimacy in the most successful branches of science. To mimic Zermelo's argument for the axiom of choice, we may argue that the notion of possibility is intuitively evident and necessary for science. And we may go on to argue, as he did, that the intuitive evidence is somewhat subjective, but the necessity for science is objective. It seems to us that those philosophers who object to the notion of possibility may, in some cases at least, simply be ill-acquainted with physical theory, and not appreciate the extent to which an apparatus has been developed for *describing* 'possible worlds'. That we cannot directly *observe* the possible (unless it happens to be actual) should not count as an argument against the notion of possibility in this day and age.

(3) The notion of possibility does not have to be taken as a *primitive* notion in science. We can, of course, define a structure to be *possible* (mathematically speaking) just in case a model exists for a certain theory, where the notion of a model is the standard set theoretic one. That is to say, we *can* take the existence of sets as basic and treat possibility as a derived notion. What is often overlooked is that we can perfectly well go in the reverse direction: we can treat the notion of possibility as basic and the notion of set existence as the derived one. Sets, to parody John Stuart Mill, are permanent possibilities of selection.

It is clear that number theoretic statements, with however many quantifiers, can be translated into possibility statements. Thus a statement to the effect that for every number x there exists a number y such that $F(x, y)$, where $F(x, y)$ is a recursive binary relation, can be paraphrased as saying that it is not *possible* to produce a tape with a numeral written on it which is such that if one *were* to produce a Turing machine of a certain description and start it scanning that tape, the machine would never halt. In a previous paper, I showed that an arbitrary statement[12] of set theory—even one that quantifies over sets of unbounded rank—can be paraphrased by a possibility statement.

(4) The main question we must speak to is simply, *what is the point?* Given that one can either take modal notions as primitive and regard talk of mathematical existence as derived, or the other way around, what is the advantage to taking the modal notions as the basic ones? It seems to us that there are two advantages to starting with the modal concepts. One advantage is purely mathematical. Construing set talk, etc., as talk about possible or impossible structures puts problems in a different focus. In particular, different axioms are evident. It is not my intention to discuss these purely mathematical advantages here. The other advantage is philosophical. Traditionally, realism in the philosophy of mathematics has gone along with Platonism, as we remarked at the outset, where 'Platonism' connotes simultaneously an epistemological theory and an ontology. The main burden of this paper is that one does not have to 'buy' Platonist epistemology to be a realist in the philosophy of mathematics. The modal logical picture shows that one doesn't have to 'buy' Platonist ontology either. The theory of mathematics as the study of special *objects* has a certain implausibility which, in my view, the theory of mathematics as the study of ordinary objects with the aid of a special concept does not. While the two views of mathematics—as set theory and as 'modal logic'—are intertranslatable, so that there is not here any question of one being true and the other being false, the modal logical view has advantages that seem to me to go beyond mere provision of psychological comfort to those distressed by Platonism. There are real puzzles, especially if one holds a causal theory of reference in some form, as to how one can refer to mathematical objects at all. I think that these puzzles can be clarified with the aid of modal notions. But again, this goes beyond the burden of this paper.

Let us return now to the topic of realism. Realism with respect to empirical science rests on two main kinds of arguments, which we may classify loosely as negative arguments and positive arguments. Negative arguments are to the effect that various reductive or operationalist philosophies are just unsuccessful. One tries to show that various attempts to reinterpret scientific statements as highly derived statements about sense data or measurement operations or whatever are unsuccessful, or hopelessly vague, or require the redescription of much ordinary scientific discovery as 'meaning stipulation' in an implausible way, or something of that kind, with the aim of rendering it plausible that most scientific statements are best not philosophically reinterpreted at all. The positive argument for realism is that it is the only philosophy that doesn't make the success of science a miracle. That terms in mature scientific theories typically refer (this formulation is due to Richard Boyd), that the theories accepted in a mature science are typically approximately true, that the same term can refer to the same thing even when it occurs in different theories—these statements are viewed by the scientific realist not as necessary truths but as part of the only scientific explanation of the success of science, and hence as part of any adequate scientific description of science and its relations to its objects.

I believe that the positive argument for realism has an analogue in the case of mathematical realism. Here too, I believe, realism is the only philosophy that doesn't make the success of the science a *miracle*.

In my view,, there are *two* supports for realism in the philosophy of mathematics: *mathematical experience* and *physical experience*. The construction of a highly articulated body of mathematical knowledge with a long tradition of successful problem solving is a truly remarkable *social* achievement. Of course, one might say: 'well, in the middle ages they would have said "the construction of a highly articulated body of theological knowledge with a long tradition of successful problem solving is . . . " ' But 'Theological knowledge' was in fact highly *inconsistent*. Moreover, if one 'fixed it up' so as to restore consistency, the consistency would be a trivial result—doubtless it would follow from the existence of some kind of finite model. In mathematics we have (we think) a *consistent* structure—consistent notwithstanding the fact that no science other than mathematics deals with such *long* and rigorous deductive chains as mathematics does (so that the risk of *discovering* an inconsistency, if one is present is immeasurably higher in mathematics than in any other science) and notwithstanding the fact that mathematics deals with such complex infinite structures that, as we know form Gödel's work, no hope of a finitistic consistency proof exists. If there is *no* interpretation under which most of mathematics is *true*, if we are really just writing down strings of symbols at random, or even by trial and error, what are the chances that our theory would be consistent, let alone mathematically fertile?

Let us be careful, however. If this argument has force and I believe it does, it is not quite an argument for mathematical realism. The argument says that the consistency and fertility of classical mathematics is evidence that it—or most of it—*is true under some interpretation*. But the interpretation might not be a *realist* interpretation. Thus Bishop might say, 'indeed, most of classical mathematics is true under some interpretation; it is true under an intuitionist *re*interpretation!' Thus our argument has to stand on two legs: the other leg is *physical experience*. The interpretation under which mathematics is true has to square with the application of mathematics *outside* of mathematics.

In a little book I published not long ago (Putnam, 1971), I argued in detail that mathematics and physics are integrated in such a way that it is not possible to be a realist with respect to physical theory and a nominalist with respect to mathematical theory. In a sense, this means that our intuitions are inconsistent. For I believe that the position most people find intuitive—the one that I certainly found intuitive—*is* realism with respect to the physical world and some kind of nominalism or if-thenism with respect to mathematics. But consider a physical law, e.g. Newton's Law of Universal Gravitation. To say that this Law is true—to even say that it is approximately true at nonrelativistic distances and velocities—one has to quantify over such non-nominalistic entities as forces, masses, distances. Moreover, as I tried to show in my book, to account for what is usually called 'measurement'—that is, for the numericalization of forces, masses and distances—one has to quantify not just over forces, masses, and distances construed as physical properties (think of a particular mass as a property that any given thing may or may not have, where the notion of a property is such that the property does not have any intrinsic connection with one particular *number* rather than another), but also over *functions from* masses, distances, etc. *to* real numbers, or at any rate to rational numbers. In short—and this is an insight that, in essence, Frege and Russell already had—a reasonable interpretation of the *application* of mathematics to the physical world *requires* a realistic interpretation of mathematics. Mathematical experience says that mathematics is true under some interpretation; physical experience says that that interpretation is a realistic one.

To sketch the argument in a nutshell: if one is a realist about the physical world, then one wants to say that the Law of Universal Gravitation makes an objective statement about bodies—not just about sense data or meter readings. What is the statement? It is just that bodies behave in such a way that the quotient of two numbers *associated* with the bodies is equal to a third number *associated* with the bodies. But how can such a statement have any objective content at all if numbers and 'associations' (i.e. functions) are alike mere fictions? It is like trying to maintain that God does not exist and angels do not exist while maintaining at the very same time that it is an objective fact that God has put an angel in charge of each star and the angels in charge of each of a pair of binary stars were always created at the same time! If talk of numbers and 'associations' between masses, etc. and numbers is 'theology' (in the pejorative sense), then the Law of Universal Gravitation is likewise theology.

A Digression on intuitionism

It seems to me that the argument against nominalism just sketched also goes through against intuitionism. Let me be more precise. Intuitionism has two parts: intuitionism gives us a set of *notions* to use in doing mathematics (an *ideology*, in Quine's sense of the term) and it gives us a set of objects to quantify over (an ontology). The two questions: is intuitionist *ideology* adequate for mathematics/physics? and is intuitionist *ontology* adequate for mathematics/physics? are almost never separated when people discuss these questions (the work of Georg Kreisel is a happy exception to this sad state of affairs), but it is essential that they should be. It is my claim that even if the ideology and ontology of intuitionism prove adequate to derive *all* of classical mathematics, the *ideology* of intuitionism is wholly inadequate for physics. The Law of Universal Gravitation, for example, has the form

$$(x)[\theta(x) = \psi(x)] \tag{1}$$

where θ and ψ are empirically given sequences—'lawless' sequences. On the intuitionist interpretation of the logical connectives, what (1) *means* is that there is an integer n such that given the first n decimal places of both θ and ψ one can *prove* that (1) is true. Since this is absurd for lawless sequences, and since a proof of the absurdity of a proof of (1) counts as a proof of the intuitionist negation of (1), it is actually a theorem of intuitionist mathematics that

$$\sim (x)[\theta(x) = \psi(x)]$$

—i.e. the Law of Universal Gravitation is intuitionistically false! The reason Brouwer does not notice this is that he treats the empirical world as a 'decidable case' that is, as a finite system. But this requires him to be a thorough-going fictionalist. Indeed, in his Dissertation he not only takes the point of view that physical objects are fictions, but also asserts that other selves and even future states of his own mind are 'fictions'!

PHYSICAL APPLICATION AND NONDENUMERABILITY

I have argued that the hypothesis that classical mathematics is largely *true* accounts for the success of the physical applications of classical mathematics (given that the empirical premises are largely approximately true and that the rules of logic preserve *truth*). It is worthwhile pausing to remark just how much of classical mathematics has been developed *for* physical application (the calculus, variational methods, the current intensive work on nonlinear differential equations, just for a start), and what a surprising amount has *found* physical application. Descartes' assumption of a correspondence between the points on a line and the reals was a daring application of what we now recognize to be nondenumerable mathematics to physical space. Since space is connected with physical experience, it is perhaps not surprising that *this* found physical application. Likewise, the calculus was explicitly developed to study *motion*, so perhaps it is not surprising that this too found physical application; but who would have expected *spectral measure*, of all things, to have physical significance? Yet quantum mechanical probabilities are all computed from spectral measures. (In a sense, nothing has *more* physical significance than spectral measure!)

This raises a question which is extremely interesting in its own right, if somewhat tangential to our main concern: do we have evidence for the nondenumerability of physical space, or is this merely a physically meaningless, albeit useful 'idealization', as is so often asserted by philosophers of science?

The reason that I regard this question as tangential to the main question of this paper is that even if physical space turns out to be discrete, even if it only behaves as a nondenumerable space *would* behave (up to a certain approximation), still the explanation of the behavior of space presupposes a correct understanding of how a nondenumerable space *would* behave, and the claim we are making for classical mathematics is that it provides *this*.

THE IMPORTANCE OF PROOF

In this paper, I have stressed the importance of quasi-empirical and even downright empirical methods in mathematics. These methods are the source of new axioms, of new 'objects', and of new theorems, that we often know to be true *before* we succeed in finding a proof. Quasi-empirical/empirical inferences support the claim that mathematics is (largely) true, and place constraints on the interpretation under which it can be *called* 'true', but a word of caution is in order. None of this is meant to downgrade the notion of proof. Rather, Proof and Quasi-empirical inference are to be viewed as complementary. Proof has the great advantage of not increasing the risk of contradiction, where the introduction of new axioms or new objects does increase the risk of contradiction, at least until a relative interpretation of the new theory in some already accepted theory is found. For this reason, proof will continue to be the primary method of mathematical verification. But given that formal deductive proof is likely to remain the primary method of mathematical verification, and that it is developed to an astounding extent in the science of mathematics, it is surprising how little we really know about it. In part this is because proof theory developed as an ideological rather than a scientific weapon. Proof theory was burdened with the constraint that only finitist methods must be used—a constraint with no mathematical justification whatsoever. Only recently have workers like Georg Kreisel, Takeuti, Prawitz, and others begun to view proof theory as a non 'ideological' branch of mathematics which simply seeks to give us information about what proof really does.

I should like to conjecture that the modal logical interpretation (or, rather, family of interpretations) of classical mathematics may help in this enterprise. Modal logical interpretations sometimes bear a formal similarity to intuitionist reinterpretations while being fully realistic. Thus they may play a role in the study of proofs similar to the role that has been played by intuitionist and allied interpretations, while giving more or less different 'information'.

PHYSICS AND THE FUTURE OF MATHEMATICS

In this paper, I have not argued that mathematics is, in the full sense, an *empirical* science, although I have argued that it relies on empirical as well as quasi-empirical inference. The reader will not be surprised to learn that my expectation is that as physical science develops, the impact on mathematical axioms is going to be greater rather than less, and that we will have to face the fact that 'empirical' versus 'mathematical' is only a relative distinction; in a looser and more indirect way than the ordinary 'empirical' statement, much of mathematics too is 'empirical'.

In a sense, this final collapse of the notion of the a priori has already begun. After all, geometry was a part of mathematics—not just uninterpreted geometry, but the theory of physical space. And if space were Euclidean, doubtless the distinction between 'mathematical' and 'physical' geometry would be regarded as silly. When Euclidean geometry was dethroned, the argument was advanced that 'straight line' only means 'light ray' and 'any fool can plainly see' that interpreted geometry is empirical. It was kind of an oversight, in this view, that the theory of physical space was ever regarded as a priori. In the last few years the standard interpretation of quantum mechanics—viz that it no longer makes sense to separate epistemology and physics, that henceforth we can only talk about physical magnitudes as they are measured by particular experimental arrangements—has begun to be challenged by the upstart view that quantum mechanics is a complete realistic theory, that there is nothing special about measurement, and that we just happen to live in a world that does not obey the laws of Boolean logic.[13] Just as those who defended non-Euclidean geometry sought to minimize the impact of their proposals (or, rather, to make them more palatable) by adopting an extreme operationist style of presentation, so the main advocates of quantum logic—Finkelstein, Jauch, Mackey, Kochen—also adopt an extreme operationist style of presentation. They only claim that quantum logic is true given the precisely specified operational meaning of the logical connectives. Mackey and Jauch go so far as to suggest that there is some other study, called 'logic' (with, of course, no operational meaning at all) which they are not challenging. In my opinion, whatever their intentions, they *are* challenging logic. And just as the almost unimaginable fact that Euclidean geometry is false—false of *paths in space*, not just false of 'light rays'—has an epistemological significance that philosophy must some day come to terms with, however long it continues to postpone the reckoning, so the fact that Boolean logic is false—false of *the logical relations between states of affairs*—has a significance that philosophy and physics and mathematics must come to terms with.

The fact is that, if quantum logic is right, then not only the propositional calculus used in physics is affected, but also set theory itself. Just what the effects are is just beginning to be investigated. But it may well be that the answer to fundamental questions about, say, the continuum will come in the future not from new 'intuitions' alone, but from physical/mathematical discovery.

NOTES

1. The null set is an exception to this statement, of course; but set theory is relatively interpretable in the theory of *non-empty* sets, provided we are willing to assume that at least one object (other than a set) exists. Thus, 'unconditional' sets are not in any way necessary in mathematics (either in pure mathematics, or in mathematics as part of total science), except as constructions out of 'conditional' sets. One might, nonetheless, insist on the a priori existence of the null set *an sich*; but this seems a little strained, even for a metaphysician.

2. Actually, they are not 'immutable' at all; only the *consequences* (the set of theorems) is—more-or-less—immutable. Elementary number theory was not axiomatized until the end of the nineteenth century ('Peano's axioms'). And how 'immutable' is the set of theorems? Was mathematical induction in its seventeenth century form completely grasped by the ancients? Did even the great seventeenth century number theorists go beyond *recursive* induction?

3. I will argue later in this paper that some of the axioms of mathematics—in particular, the assumption of a one-to-one correspondence between points in space and triples of reals (or points on a line and reals), and the axiom of choice—are quasi-empirical; thus I do not myself accept the claim that *proved* statements (e.g. consequences of these assumptions) are epistemologically a priori. (In fact, I don't think there *is* any such thing as an a priori statement, unless 'a priori' just means unrevisable within a particular theoretical frame, characterized both by positive assumptions and a 'space' of theoretical alternatives.)

4. It may be argued that this postulate—due to Fermat as well as Descartes—is *no longer* assumed in mathematics. For, one can argue, we now distinguish between *physical* space and abstract Euclidean space. Mathematics is concerned with the latter (and with other abstract spaces) not the former. But the latter can simply be identified with the set of triples of reals; thus the Correspondence Postulate is true by *definition*.

Against this we would argue that geometry as the theory of physical space (the space in which *objects* are located and moved about) *was* part of *mathematics* from Euclid until (approximately) the time of Riemann's Inaugural Dissertation. Without the Correspondence Postulate there would have been no *motivation* for calling the set of triples of reals an abstract 'space', or for identifying anything as a *metric* or a *line* or a *curve*. Indeed, talk of acts and functions itself became accepted only after talk of 'curves' had paved the way.

5. I *don't* mean to deny the importance of removing contradictions from our theories. I mean that there is no unique way of removing contradictions from a somewhat useful theory, and in particular reductive definition is not the unique way, ever.

6. 'A New Proof of the Possibility of a Well Ordering,' reprinted in Heijenoort (1967), pp. 183–98.

7. Ibid. p. 187.

8. 'Additions,' *Revista de mathematica* 8, pp. 143–57; reprinted in Peano (1957) Vol. 1. The assertion Zermelo refers to is on p. 147.

9. The foregoing example comes from Polya, a great exponent of the importance of plausible reasoning in mathematics.

10. In fact more careful reasoning shows that the events in question cannot be *strictly* independent, and therefore 'the only reasonable conjecture'—the words are those of a world famous number theorist—is that the number of twin primes less than x 'must' be $1.23 \ldots 1/(\log x)^2$. Another world famous mathematician described this argument as 'totally convincing'—that is, the argument that there must be infinitely many twin primes.

11. In 'Mathematics without foundations,' chapter 3 Putnam (1975a).

12. Ibid.

13. See my 'The logic of quantum mechanics,' chapter 10 Putnam (1975a).

RENÉ THOM

"Modern" Mathematics: An Educational and Philosophic Error?

Although Thom's paper has engendered considerable discussion among mathematicians, its inclusion here might appear surprising. His topic, mathematics education in secondary schools, is not usually regarded as part of serious philosophy. And Thom, himself, defends a classical realist position, almost Platonism. So why is the paper in this anthology?

In regard to the first point, you recall that Hersh already argued that if we took our foundations seriously, it would shape our teaching of mathematics. Thom suggests that this has happened and that the outcome is very unsatisfactory. His direct attack on current pedagogical practices is thus an implicit critique of the foundation ideas supporting them.

In regard to Thom's realism let us note that in philosophical terms he is what is known as a 'naive realist.' His realism applies across the board to all areas of mathematics, to geometry as directly as to set theory. As his article makes clear, he opposes the set theoretic platonist's reductionism as vigorously as he opposes that of the formalist. So Thom clearly takes an anti-foundational position. Moreover, he suggests that an adequate philosophy of mathematics will have to deal with methods such as analogy, which are ignored by foundation studies. In addition he offers a penetrating challenge to the concept of rigor that foundations supposedly provides. What foundations promises, but never delivers, Thom observes, is a global rigor given once for all of mathematics (it is to be given by the correct theory of foundations). However all that our experience actually reveals is local rigor—rigor as a local property of mathematical reasoning.

Finally, in his article Thom considers three philosophies of mathematics: formalism, realism and his characterization of quasi-empiricism. "The empirical or sociological view. A proof P is accepted as rigorous if it obtains the endorsement of the leading specialists of the time." No one concerned to defend quasi-empiricism in mathematics would accept this characterization without qualification. However, the relevant point is that while Thom is quite insistent

Reprinted, with permission, from AMERICAN SCIENTIST, Vol. 59, No. 6, November-December 1971, pp. 695–99.

that formalism is wrong and that realism is correct, he appears willing to tolerate quasi-empiricism as a complement to realism. Indeed he argues in a manner reminiscent of Putnam that a realist view is necessary to account for the success of the social practice of mathematics.

• • • • •

In the minds of most of our contemporaries, so-called modern mathematics holds a place of high prestige lying somewhere between cybernetics and information theory in the bag of tricks promoted by deceptive publicity as the essentials of modern technology, the indispensable tools for the future development of all scientific knowledge. And, on another level, since the modernization of school curricula, many parents, no longer capable of helping their offspring, have become concerned. They no longer hear the old familiar notions in the vocabularly of their children and thus feel lost when confronted with the new terminology. Some, perplexed, see this as one more symptom of the generation gap and have adopted an obstructionist stance toward the new ideas. Others, on the contrary, particularly those in the teaching profession, have accepted the new curriculum, ideas, and symbols with enthusiasm. What should we make of all this?

Curriculum revisions

Let us list briefly the changes made in the curriculum:

1. *Added material:*

(a) "Elementary" set theory, the use of symbols ($\in$, $\subset$, $\cup$, $\cap$), the mappings of one set into another, and quantifiers. Most striking of all, sets now appear ubiquitously in the curriculum from kindergarten through the final year of secondary education. We will return to this point later.

(b) Development of algebraic notions; laws of composition on a set; concepts of group, ring, and field.

(c) Introduction earlier of fundamentals of differential and integral calculus, derivatives, indefinite integrals, elementary functions such as logarithm and exponential.

2. *Eliminated material:* Traditional Euclidean geometry, in particular the intricacies of plane geometry.

In sum, the reader will note that the curriculum has been modified by a substantial addition of material introduced in the secondary school years. The tendency to emphasize algebra at the expense of geometry is even greater in university teaching.

ALGEBRA AND GEOMETRY

The elimination of traditional Euclidean geometry is based on two arguments. The first is theoretical: the axiomatic work resulting from Hilbert's

Grundlagen der Geometrie has shown that the alleged rigor of the *Elements* of Euclid is in large part illusory; it is compromised by frequent appeals to intuition. As a consequence, the argument runs, it is better to avoid Euclidean geometry by developing the ideas of algebra, in which a rigorous presentation is possible. The second argument is a practical one: classical plane geometry, with its elaborate study of the triangle's properties, is useless and pedantic. Who in his lifetime ever needs to use the "Simpson's line" or the "nine-point circle"?

Let us first discuss the argument about utility. It is said that algebra is more useful and necessary than geometry. There is no question of denying the general scientific utility of linear algebra or of certain notions of multilinear algebra. As for general commutative algebra—polynomials, etc.—caution is in order. In ordinary life, who has ever needed to solve a second-degree equation or to use explicitly the notion of a module over a ring? The argument for the utility of algebra is not as compelling as it appears. As for differential and integral calculus—point (c) above—they are indispensable for any presentation of classical physics.

At an elementary level, certainly, the use of algebra leads to massive simplifications. Solving "through reasoning" the "word" problems one used to have as a twelve-year-old required an extraordinary dexterity of mind, whereas the algebraic solution was purely mechanical. Here the economy of thought introduced by algebra is undeniable. With more complex situations, however, the advantage of algebra tends to disappear. Descartes devised analytic geometry in order to reduce geometry to algebra. But it is a fact well known to all university applicants who have crammed for advanced standing in mathematics that the advantage of analytic methods over geometric ones for a qualitative theoretical problem is far from being decisive.

"Modernism"

For professional mathematicians, the use of algebra as an instrument of proof is highly important and perhaps essential. Contemporary mathematicians, steeped in the ideas of Bourbaki,[1] have had the natural tendency to introduce into secondary and university courses the algebraic theories and structures that have been so useful in their own work and that are uppermost in the mathematical thought of today. Yet one can ask with reason if the needs of specialists and their latest findings should be introduced into the school curriculum.

Mathematicians are not alone in succumbing to this temptation. I have read biology texts—both for beginners and advanced students—in which the double helix of DNA of Watson and Crick and the precise enzymatic mechanism of its replication are presented as definitive scientific truth. Innovations should not be introduced into the curriculum without a certain waiting period. In France, we should have been able to rely on the school inspection corps to assure the necessary curricular stability. However, for fear of having genuine skepticism interpreted as sclerosis due to old age, this institution has not functioned with all its desired efficacy. After all, texts must change and editors must live.

The problem of geometry

In the last analysis, the argument about the utility of material presented in the curriculum is perhaps not the decisive one. Let us ignore "culture"—"that which remains when all else is forgotten"—as a vestige of times past. Some still persist in thinking that, in one form or another, one of the goals of teaching is *selection*, that is to say, determining the aptitudes of each student and developing them to the maximum, with particular emphasis on the gifted student. I claim that it is impossible to carry out such a task in the framework of a discipline that does not include at least some gratuitous, nonuseful aspects. In order to judge fully the capabilities of a student, it is necessary to place him in an active role and to call on his individual initiative and enterprising spirit. None of this is conceivable within a framework of "useful" studies, where all the elements, included because of their technical utility, are dogmatically taught and where scholarly excellence is defined as exact and rapid memorization of given material. Only those topics which have a quality of "play" have educational value, and of all such games, Euclidean geometry, with its constant references to underlying intuitively understood fundamentals, is the least gratuitous and the richest in meaning.

By this line of reasoning, the contemporary trend to replace geometry with algebra is educationally baneful and should be reversed. There is a simple reason for this: while there are geometry problems, there are no algebra problems. A so-called algebra problem can only be a simple exercise requiring the blind application of arithmetical rules and of a preestablished procedure. With rare exceptions, one cannot ask a student to prove an algebra theorem; either the requested answer is almost obvious and can be arrived at by direct substitution of definitions, or the problem falls into the category of theoretical algebra and its solution exceeds the capacities of even the most gifted student. Exaggerating only slightly, one can say that any question in algebra is either trivial or impossible to solve. By contrast, the classic problems of geometry present a wide range of challenges.

Geometry problems require a combination of time, effort, concentration, and powers of association of which few students are capable. Perhaps Euclidean geometry, like Latin translation, is one of those lofty, obsolete exercises that are limited to the elite and incompatible with mass education. If such is the case, expelling geometry from the curriculum becomes essentially a sociological question that I do not wish to discuss here. Still, it would be a grave error to hope to simplify the learning of mathematics by replacing geometry with algebraic structures that are then widely and prematurely taught without adequate motivation.

Rigor

Let us now turn to the objection to Euclidean geometry that criticizes the axiomatics of the *Elements* as being flawed and lacking in rigor. One can point out, first of all, that geometry books long ago gave up the heavy, indigestible rhetoric of Euclid. Some cherished the hope of substituting an acceptable version of Hilbert's *Grundlagen*. Not surprisingly, this hope was defeated by the dreadful complexity of this work. One cannot take a stand on this issue without first attacking the philosophical question of what conception of mathematical rigor one should adopt. Three attitudes are possible: (1) the formal view. In a formal system *S*, a proposition *P* is true if it can be deduced from the axioms of *S* by a finite number of steps permitted within the system of *S*. (2) The realist or Platonic view. Mathematical entities exist independently of thought, as Platonic ideas. A proposition *P* is true when it expresses a relationship actually existing between ideas, i.e. when it is an idea of higher order, structuring a group of ideas that are subordinate to it. (3) The empirical or sociological view. A proof *P* is accepted as rigorous if it obtains the endorsement of the leading specialists of the time.

Of these three attitudes, mathematicians today favor the first. At first sight, it is the most tempting; it does not raise the ontological difficulties of the second, and it is not as vague and arbitrary as the third. Bertrand Russell has said that "mathematics is the subject in which we never know what we are talking about nor whether what we are saying is true."[2] Unfortunately, the purely formal view is difficult to uphold, paradoxically for formal reasons. We know the difficulties presented by the formalization of arithmetic associated with Gödel's Theorem. Professor Kreisel, in his recent article in *L'Age de la science*,[3] put the formal view on trial. For myself, I am content with the following illustration: Let us suppose that we have been able to construct for a formal theory *S* an electronic machine *M* capable of carrying out at a terrifying speed all the elementary steps in *S*. We wish to verify the correctness of one formula *F* of the theory. After a process totaling 10^{30} elementary operations, completed in a few seconds, the machine *M* gives us a positive reply. Now what mathematician would accept without hesitation the validity of such a "proof," given the impossibility of verifying all its steps?

"Meaning" in mathematics

Any mathematician endowed with a modicum of intellectual honesty will recognize that in each of his proofs he is capable of giving a *meaning* to the symbols he uses. Because of this, his work differs from that of the theoretical physicist, who very frequently does not hesitate to put his trust magically in the virtues of blind formalism in the hope (often deceived) that the light at the end of the tunnel will dispel the intervening darkness.

If one gives up the formal definition of rigor, one must of necessity choose between the two remaining alternatives. Everything considered, mathematicians should have the courage of their most profound convictions and thus affirm that mathematical forms indeed have an existence that is independent of the mind considering them. This existence is without doubt different from the concrete existence of the external world, but it is still subtly and deeply related to it. If mathematics is only an arbitrary game which is the random product of cerebral activity, how can one explain its unquestioned success in describing the universe? Mathematics is found not only in the mysterious fixed order of physical laws but also, in a more hidden though equally certain manner, in the infinite succession of animate and inanimate forms and in the formation and breaking up of their symmetries.

Despite appearance, this is why the hypothesis stating that Platonic ideas give shape to the universe is the most natural and, philosophically, the most economical.

Yet, at any given moment, mathematicians have only an incomplete and fragmentary vision of this world of ideas. As a result, each proof is, above all, the revelation of a new structure whose elements lie disconnected in man's intuition until reason joins them together. In this sense, each proof is a Socratic experience requiring the re-creation in the reader of the psychological processes necessary to elicit the implicit truth, all the elements of which he possessed but which had remained hidden in an unformulated state. In this sense, there is no contradiction between the second and third views. The world of ideas is not revealed to us in one stroke; we must both permanently and unceasingly re-create it in our consciousness.

The opponents of the ontological view would do well to reflect on the following: There is no case in the history of mathematics where the mistake of one man has thrown the entire field on the wrong track. Frequently, mathematics has become lost in the formal development of insignificant, uninteresting theories. It has done so in the past, does so today, and will certainly continue to do so in the future. But never has a significant error slipped into a conclusion without almost immediately being discovered. How could one explain such a consensus if it did not correspond to a general opinion that is the result of the mind's struggle with permanent, timeless, and universal constraints? With this confidence in the existence of an ideal universe, the mathematician need not worry unduly about the limits of formal procedure; likewise, he can forget the problem of noncontradiction, for the reason that the world of ideas infinitely exceeds our "technical possibilities." It is in the intuition that the *ultima ratio* of our faith in the truth of a theorem resides. And, according to a now-forgotten etymology, a theorem is above all the object of a vision.

Each must decide for himself. There is no rigorous definition of rigor. We will therefore affirm that any proof is rigorous if it wins acceptance by all readers who are adequately educated and prepared to understand it. Furthermore, the evidence leading to persuasion results from having a sufficiently clear understanding of each of the symbols involved, so that their combination convinces the reader. From this point of view, rigor (or its contrary, imprecision) is essentially a *local* property of mathematical reasoning. No elaborate axiomatic structure or refined conceptual machine is needed to judge the validity of a line of reasoning. It suffices merely to have an understanding of the meaning of each symbol involved and a clear idea of how to combine them.

Limits and necessity of axiomatization

Such a point of view suggests that we retreat somewhat from axiomatics. To formalize a theory means, starting with the material presented by the theory which is organized as an intuitive "morphology" T, to give a formal set of symbols and rules generating a formal system S isomorphic to the morphology T; the isomorphism $S \to T$ being precisely the correspondence which attaches to any symbol s belonging to S its "meaning," i.e. its intuitive content in T (its semantic realization, logicians would say). Can one reasonably hope that the intuitive material of the theory T can be fully covered by the symbolic expressions of S? An example immediately comes to mind, that of natural languages. Linguists of the formalist school have been trying strenuously to reduce natural language grammar and syntax to axioms. In doing so they have come up with a certain number of formal procedures—generative and transformational grammars—whose validity, on the level of formal description of the sentences contained in the corpus, cannot be denied. But if these procedures are systematized into a series of rules which are then pursued blindly to their logical conclusion, the resulting sentences soon become so long and complex that they lose all meaning.

I see no reason why a similar phenomenon could not happen in mathematics; in extrapolating a formal mechanism to the limit of its generative capacities, it does not take long to assemble formulas that are so long and complex that all possibility of intuitive interpretation disappears. The "theorems" thus obtained will probably be formally correct but semantically insignificant. Thus for a given intuitive theory T one must expect to have to use not one but several "local" axiomatizations; each local axiomatization S has a contact zone Z_S in the morphology for which S is valid; but as soon as one constructs formulas in S which are too long or involved, the intelligibility disappears. At the boundary of the zone Z_S the semantic link between S and Z_S breaks down; this prohibits the extension beyond Z_S of the isomorphism $S \rightarrow T$, defined by the meaning. The idea that a theory T could be generated by just one formal system S is, a priori, just as unlikely as the idea that the earth should be flat or that one could cover a surface by a single system of coordinates. It would be interesting to understand this semantic breakdown more clearly. Below, we shall see a striking example of what happens when the rules of combination are incompatible with the semantic qualities of the symbolized entities (in this case, Boolean formalism applied to ordinary language). In the case of mathematics, it appears that such a semantic breakdown occurs in a progressive, hazy manner (the case of "transfinite numbers" in set theory, for example).

The undeniable advantage of local formalization is frequently to make intuitively understood ideas more precise and, most indispensably, to permit communication between mathematicians. As all means of communication, spoken or written, use a one-dimensional morphology, it is necessary to code the intuitive morphology T (which in general is defined on a multidimensional space) into a formal system of one-dimensional symbols. During the past few years the importance of axiomatization as an instrument of systematization and discovery has been much emphasized. As a method of systematizing, it is certainly effective; as for discovery, the matter is more doubtful. It is characteristic that no new theorem of any importance came out of the immense effort at systematization of Nicolas Bourbaki (which in itself is not a true formalization because Bourbaki uses a nonformalized metalanguage). If mathematicians refer to Bourbaki, they usually find more food for thought in his exercises—to which the author relegated the concrete material—than in the deductive part of the text. One must say it clearly: axiomatization is the work of specialists and has no place in secondary or college teaching except for those professionals specializing in the study of foundations. All this explains why the reproaches of inconsistency directed at Euclidean geometry are irrelevant; they do not touch the validity of local intuitive reasoning.

"Genetic" importance of geometry: continuity precedes discontinuity

The foregoing considerations reveal the key to the historical success of Euclid's *Elements*. Euclidean geometry is the first example of the transcription of a two- or three-dimensional spatial procedure into the one-dimensional language of writing. In this, Euclidean geometry applies to a rigid, precise situation, a procedure which is already present in everyday language. The primary function of ordinary language is, after all, to describe the spatio-temporal processes which surround us, and whose topology is transparent in the syntax of the sentences describing them[4]. In Euclidean geometry we are dealing with the same function of language, but this time the group of equivalences operating on the forms is a Lie group, the metric group, in contrast to the groups describing the more topological invariance of the "gestalten" that permit us to recognize objects of the exterior world as described by their natural language names.

As such, geometry is a natural and possibly irreplaceable intermediary between ordinary language and mathematical formalism, where each object is reduced to a symbol and the group of equivalences is reduced to the identity of the written symbol with itself. From this point of view the stage of geometric thought may be a stage that it is impossible to omit in the normal development of man's rational activity. Much emphasis has been placed during the past fifty years on the reconstruction of the geometric continuum from the natural integers, using the theory of Dedekind cuts or the completion of the field of rational numbers. Under the influence of axiomatic and bookish traditions, man perceived in discontinuity the first mathematical Being: "God created the integers and the rest is the work of man." This maxim spoken by the algebraist Kronecker reveals more about his past as a banker who grew rich through monetary speculation than about his philosophical insight. There is hardly any doubt that, from a psychological and, for the writer, ontological point of view, the geometric continuum is the primordial entity. If one has any consciousness at all, it is consciousness of time and space; geometric continuity is in some way inseparably bound to conscious thought.

Gradually, however, this initially homogeneous, amorphous continuum takes on a structure, and the most important structuring tool is the metric group. It alone permits us to introduce discontinuity and discrete operations into the homogeneous expanse. This is, however, a very sophisticated procedure. To begin with, we had all the topological properties of the continuum, but only in modern times has mathematics returned to its sources in founding topology, thus freeing itself from the domination of the metric group. Such a theory, being neither metric nor quantitative, is basically qualitative and can rely only on the discrete symbolism of a semiformalized language. However, topological invariants, being more deeply rooted, are more difficult for the mind to conceive than the more superficial metric invariants. With this point in mind, we can see that the transition from everyday thought to formalized thought takes place naturally through geometric thinking. This has always been the case in the history of human thought and, insofar as one believes Haeckel's Law of recapitulation, which states that in his development the individual passes through all the stages of the species, it should be the case in the normal development of rational thought.

SET THEORY

I come now to my first point, set theory. This is the essential litany intoned by those who advocate the so-called modern mathematics. Some affirm that the use of set theory permits the entire renovation of mathematics teaching and that, thanks to this change, the average student will be able to achieve mastery of the curriculum. Needless to say, this is pure illusion. As long as it is a matter of handling the obvious facts of naive set theory, of course anyone can get by. But this is neither mathematics nor even logic. As soon as one comes face to face with real mathematics (i.e. real numbers, geometry, functions), one rediscovers that there is no royal road and that only a minority of students are capable of fully understanding the material.

Everything considered, the excessive optimism bred by the use of set theory symbols has its roots in a philosophical error. It was believed that by teaching the use of the symbols $\in$, $\subset$, $\cup$, $\cap$ it was possible to make explicit the mechanisms underlying all reasoning and deduction. Twentieth-century man has enthusiastically rediscovered the syllogisms Darapti and Celarent taught by the medieval scholastics. But what a deterioration has taken place! When, in the nineteenth century, Boole wrote the celebrated treatise on algebra that bears his name, he did not hesitate to entitle it "An Investigation into the Laws of Thought." The naive belief that every deduction finds its model in set theoretic manipulations was shared by such modern philosophers as the neopositivists. Neither Aristotle nor the medieval scholastics shared this illusion. As J. Vuillemin reminds us,[5] Aristotelian logic has its base in a rich and complex ontology of substance. Modern protagonists of set theory should realize that this theory is insufficient to account for even the most elementary deductive steps of ordinary thought. Permit me to give an example of this fact.

The Copulas or *and* and

Classically, it is taught that the grammatical equivalent of the symbol $\cup$ (union) is *or* and that of the symbol $\cap$ (intersection) is *and*. Let us apply this rule to two simple sentences whose subjects are proper names:

(1) Peter or John is coming.
(2) Peter and John are coming.

The first sentence can be paraphrased, "Peter is coming or John is coming." Here there is complete agreement of the symbol *or* with the logical union $\cup$, with the condition that the copula refers not to the subject but to the verb "to come."

The second sentence too can be paraphrased, "Peter is coming and John is coming." Having done this, one realizes that the original sentence is subtly ambiguous, for it implicitly contains what linguists term "presuppositions." For example, "Peter and John are coming" frequently presupposes, "Peter and John are coming *together.*" While the phrase "Peter or John" alone has no semantic interpretation, it is possible to conceive of "Peter and John" as an entity formed by a pair of individuals, Peter and John, who, spatially, are together. This fact explains the different grammatical treatments of the verbs in (1) and (2) : the copula *and* requires the plural because it presupposes a certain spatial contiguity of the subjects.

Let us consider some sentences in which copulas are used with qualities.

(3) Peter is short or intelligent.
(4) Peter is short and intelligent.
(5) Joan's hair is gray or brown.
(6) Joan's hair is gray and brown.

Sentences (4) and (5) are semantically acceptable whereas (3) and (6) may be dubious or unacceptable. One may extrapolate these remarks to the following principle:

Exclusion principle: If X and Y are two qualities, the sentences

A is X or Y	cannot both be
A is X and Y	semantically acceptable.

When "X or Y" may be preceded by a subject, one would say that X and Y belong to the same semantic field: for example, "gray" and "brown" in sentences (5) and (6). In this case, "X and Y" is, in principle, meaningless. There is, nevertheless, an important exception, the case where *and* designates not logical intersection but spatial contiguity. Thus it is perfectly possible to say:

(7) This flag is white or blue.
(8) This flag is white and blue.

The fact that in (8) the copula does not have the meaning $\cap$ explains why "This flag is white and blue" implies that "This flag is white" is false.

Indeed, the conditions necessary for the expression "X or Y" to be meaningful are extremely restricted; thus "Joan has red or auburn hair" is clearly more acceptable than "Joan has red or brown hair" because, in terms of the semantic category of hair colors, "red" and "auburn" are adjacent to one another whereas "red" and "brown" are not. The copula *or*, geometrically speaking, has the effect of lowering the threshold between the domains of attraction defined by the adjectives "red" and "auburn." When the semantic distance between two qualities X and Y is too large, in particular when these qualities belong to different semantic fields, as with a physical quality and a moral quality, then the phrase "X or Y" loses all meaning.

Although it is rather obvious, this fact seems to have escaped the authors of many set theory textbooks. They offer students exercises in Boolean algebra which discuss "cubes that are big or blue," and "Parisians who are bald or rich." Not only are these exercises outlandish and useless, but, if pursued too far, they can become harmful to the child's intellectual equilibrium. One of the fundamental constraints imposed by accurate thought is precisely the avoidance of mixing distinct semantic fields. This mixing has a name—delirium. In attempting to attach meaning to all the phrases constructed in ordinary languages, according to Boolean rules, the logician proceeds to a phantasmic, delirious reconstruction of the universe.

All these points show the narrow limits of set theory in describing ordinary thought. Everyday reasoning calls upon profound psychic mechanisms, such as analogy, which can never be reduced to the level of set theoretic operations. An important factor in such cases is the organizational isomorphism between semantic fields which are homologically associated.

In fact, Boolean schematizations hardly apply without some defect except in cases described by spatial inclusions of subsets in space, as in Venn diagrams. In such a case, no one will take the trouble to put the reasoning in a syllogistic form. The fox knows that if the hens are in the hen-house and the hen-house is in the yard, then the hens are in the yard; he does not bother with set theory. Everyone uses set theory from the moment he exists, just as M. Jourdain in Molière's *Le Bourgeois Gentilhomme* uses prose without knowing it. Some say that it is better to use it knowingly. The advantage here, if there be any at all, applies to the rhetoric. It is only to the extent that the technique of mathematical proof is a type of rhetoric that it becomes worthwhile to proceed by local formalizations—which actually are local "spatializations"—and to apply the set-theoretic formalism to them. The persuasive force of the logical scheme comes from spatial inclusions, and not vice versa. This indicates to us the attitude that reasonable educational thought should take toward set theory. In its simple, concrete form, it should be introduced in kindergarten, which is its natural habitat. In the early years of secondary school, students should learn the use of the symbols $\in$, $\cap$, $\cup$, $\subset$; later they should be introduced to the quantifiers, and that should be the end of it.

It is not certain that, even in pure mathematics, each deduction can have a set-theoretic model. Poorly resolved paradoxes that undermine formal set theory are there to remind the mathematician of the dangers that await him in the injudicious use of these seemingly innocent symbols. Perhaps, even in mathematics, quality subsists, and resists all reduction to sets. The old hope of Bourbaki, to see mathematical structures arise naturally from a hierarchy of sets, from their subsets, and from their combination, is, doubtless, only an illusion. No one can reasonably escape the impression that the most important mathematical structures (algebraic structures, topological structures) appear as fundamental data imposed by the exterior world, and that their irrational diversity finds its only justification in reality.

REFERENCES AND FOOTNOTES

1. Nicolas Bourbaki is the nom-de-plume adopted in the 1930s by a group of outstanding young French mathematicians who undertook the monumental task of reorganizing mathematics in terms of basic structural components. This enterprise is

an ongoing effort, whose members must resign at age fifty according to Bourbaki's bylaws.

2. Bertrand Russell, quoted in A. Hooper, 1948. *Makers of Mathematics.* N.Y.: Random House, p. 384.

3. G. Kreisel. 1970. The formalist-positivist doctrine of mathematical precision in the light of experience. *L'Age de la science* 3:17–46.

4. R. Thom. 1970. Topologie et linguistique. In *Essays on Topology and Related Topics,* André Haefliger and Raghavan Narasimham, eds. (Mémoires dédiés à Georges de Rham.) New York: Springer-Verlag, pp. 226–48.

5. J. Vuillemin. 1967. *De la logique à la théologie.* Paris: Flammarion.

NICHOLAS D. GOODMAN

Mathematics as an Objective Science

Goodman's article summarizes many of the issues raised by the preceding papers and serves as a fitting conclusion to this section of the anthology. The four most prominent candidates for foundations are considered; platonism, logicism, formalism and intuitionism. They are assessed with expertise, justice and an unusual amount of charity—and found wanting. Moreover, in the course of his critique, Goodman incorporates many of the suggestion for new directions in the philosophy of mathematics that have been presented, and adds to them.

Goodman's essay is organized about an abstract philosophical hypothesis, his principle of objectivity. "Anything which is practically real should be taken as objectively real." Roughly speaking, the principle of objectivity comes to this. If a concept X plays an important role in a theory and if failure to acknowledge the role of X severely limits the theory, then X is practically real. Moreover, "in the absence of a strong argument to the contrary . . . the presumption must be that anything practically real is objectively real."

Fortunately, we don't need any metaphysics to follow Goodman. In the case of mathematics, his principle amounts to the claim that what is practically real in the public experience of mathematicians should be an integral concern of the philosophy of mathematics. This standard allows Goodman to be charitable to the positive contributions of each foundational theory. Each is rooted in some deep aspect of mathematical experience: formalism in formal languages and symbol manipulations, intuitionism in the feasibility of certain constructions, logicism in the framework of logic, and platonism in the discovery of mathematical objects. However, as a foundation of mathematics each theory claims to be exhaustive. Goodman methodically shows that these claims require each theory not merely to ignore, but to rule out some practically real aspect of mathematical experience.

Reprinted from the American Mathematical Monthly, Vol. 86, No. 7, August-September 1979, pp. 540–551.

So the picture of 'foundations for mathematics' which so beguiled Frege and the other giants of foundationalism turns out, ironically, to be a castle in the sky. Goodman concludes this section of the anthology by advising us to look for a new vision of the philosophy of mathematics that "has yet to be formulated."

• • • • •

1 INTRODUCTION

Morris Kline has written that "mathematics is a body of knowledge. But it contains no truths." [13, p. 9] Views of this general kind, which deny that mathematics has objective scientific content, are widely held by mathematicians and are disseminated in classrooms and in popular books such as Kline's. I believe that such views are false and that their dissemination does no good for our own or others' respect for our subject. Below I shall examine four views which, though they do not exhaust the current range of opinion in the philosophy of mathematics, are nevertheless sufficiently representative to raise what seem to me to be the main issues about the objectivity of mathematics. I shall argue that each of these views arises from an oversimplification of what happens when we do mathematics.

2 SURFACISM

In order to bring out some of the features which the views I want to oppose have in common, let me begin with an imaginary analogous view in the philosophy of physics. Many of the qualities we associate with material objects—such as definite shape, hardness, color—can be thought of as qualities of their surfaces. Consider a philosopher who is misled by this simple observation and believes that *all* qualities of material objects are qualities of their surfaces. He holds, let us say, that material objects are not solid, as we usually suppose, but instead are infinitely thin surfaces. It is meaningless, on his view, to speak of the inside of a material object. Since no one would refer to his own position as "superficialism," we may imagine that our philosopher calls his view "surfacism." Asked to explain the fact that when we cut into an object we do not just find a void, our surfacist says that the edge of the knife pulls on the surface to which it is applied, thereby stretching that surface so as to create two new surfaces. Asked to give an account of a quality which is difficult to treat consistently as a quality of surfaces, such as weight, he asserts that the quality is illusory. What is actually going on, he claims, is that certain qualities of the surfaces of our bodies, or of our interactions with other surfaces, are being projected into the external world. For example, suppose we consider the case of weight more carefully. The weight of an object is really just the difficulty I have in lifting it. That difficulty must, strictly speaking, be located in those points at which the object and my body interact. Hence the weight must reside in the common surface of the object and my body. It is a gratuitous oversimplification to think of the weight as a quality of the material object in and of itself.

We need not suppose that our surfacist philosopher is always on the defensive. He may maintain, for instance, that the conventional view first violates the principle of parsimony by creating an entirely unnecessary entity—the inside of the object—and then goes on to give that entity absurd qualities. The inside, for one example, is supposed to be material but invisible. Why should insides be so different from outsides? Whence this asymmetry? If there really is space inside material objects, would it not be more reasonable to suppose that, like the space outside material objects, the space inside is filled with air? Occasionally, we may suppose, our surfacist complains about the unscientific and superstitious character of his opponents' views. Belief in the solid inside of a material object, he asserts, is a remnant of belief in the immortal soul, which was the "solid" inside of a human being. As a matter of fact, he argues, the usual account is simply incomprehensible. Who can visualize a material object except by visualizing its surface? Who, when visualizing a material object, can visualize anything in addition to its surface?

It seems to me that the views about the nature of mathematics that I wish to discuss are forms, more or less disguised, of surfacism. Hence it will be useful for me to consider how one might refute surfacism in the pure form just described.

The purpose of having a view about the nature of material objects is to order our experiences of those objects in a way which is useful in our dealings with them. Such a view is a social artifact which serves a variety of social functions. Material objects are themselves public in character, and most of my interactions with my material environment are, directly or indirectly, also interactions with my social environment. It follows that the most important function which such a view must serve is to facilitate both those of our interactions with material objects which have public significance and those of our interactions with each other which are mediated by material objects or which concern material objects. Hence a view about the nature of material objects which is intended to be more than a debating position should satisfy the following *Priniciple of Objectivity: Anything which is practically real should be taken as objectively real.*

Let me make this clearer. When I say that an attribute like weight is practically real, I mean that the attribute plays a role, and that there exists a consensus that the attribute does play a role and should play a role, in our interactions with the objects that have the attribute. It will follow that there is at least a rough consensus on the degree or kind of presence of the attribute in a particular object. For, to repeat what I said above, our interactions with objects are generally also interactions with each other. On the other hand, when I say that an attribute is taken as objectively real, I mean that it is taken to reside in the observed object rather than in the subjective experience of the observer or in the subjective relationship between the observer and the observed object. A theory about the nature of material objects, then, is only serious if it accepts as its data all those attributes which have a commonly accepted role in our ordinary social dealings with the objects. It must take those data and unite them into a coherent account, explaining some in terms of others no doubt, but not explaining any of them away. In particular, a theory will undermine our ordinary activities, rather than support them, if it treats attributes which are important in those activities as mere subjective illusion. Of course one can find examples in which entities that formerly appeared to play a role in our practical activities were later shown not to exist. Nevertheless, in an argument about the objective reality of something whose practical reality is evident, the whole burden of proof should fall on the proponent of the negative position. After all, the simplest explanation for the apparent practical importance of an entity is that the entity actually exists and actually plays a role in our practice. In the absence of a strong argument to the contrary, then, the presumption must be that anything practically real is objectively real.

To avoid possible misunderstandings, let me consider a case in which the principle of objectivity is satisfied. An argument one sometimes hears against taking physics literally is that in the world of the physicist there is no such thing as yellow. If that were true, it would be a powerful argument. Fortunately, it is not true.

First of all, it is important to distinguish our experience of yellow from the color itself. What is relevant to our public dealings with a material object is not how it appears to this observer or that observer under these conditions or those conditions. What is relevant is the actual color of the object—roughly speaking, how it appears to a normal observer under standard conditions. Thus it cannot be the task of physics, as opposed to psychology, to give an account of our experience of yellow.

It remains, however, that physics does not take color as an ingredient in its description of the world. Nevertheless, the usual account in terms of wave lengths of light does give objective content to talk about yellow. Colors are not denigrated or explained away. They are not made to reside in our eyes or in our minds. On the contrary, our ability to deal with color is enriched. Not only does the theory account for the observed properties of colors, but it makes possible their manipulation in new ways. The physicists have even found new colors (for example, in the infrared) which we cannot see.

Thus in this case the principle of objectivity is amply satisfied. The merely private aspects of our experience of color are dismissed as subjective. The practically real color itself, on the other hand, is supplied with objective content.

The principle of objectivity, then, may be used to refute surfacism as follows. The weight of a homogeneous material object is proportional to its volume and not to its surface area. It is reasonable to conclude that the weight of the object is distributed through it. Hence the surfacist must hold that weight is merely an illusion—not objectively real. But since weight is important in our dealings with material objects, and since it can be measured in a way which is interpersonally valid, the surfacist who declares weight to be illusory thereby trivializes his theory.

In order to apply these ideas to the philosophy of mathematics, we must observe that mathematics is a public activity. It occurs in a social context and has social consequences. Posing a problem, formulating a definition, proving a theorem are none of them private acts. They are all part of that larger social process we call science. A functioning mathematician is aware of the work of other mathematicians, publishes his own work, and expects other mathematicians to take his work into account. Thus a philosophy of mathematics is closely analogous to a view about the nature of material objects. Its main function should be to facilitate the ongoing social process of doing mathematics. It follows that a serious philosophy of mathematics must satisfy the principle of objectivity. That is, it must not deny objective reality to any aspects of mathematical activity which have practical reality.

3 FORMALISM

No one who observes the behavior of mathematicians can fail to notice that they manipulate symbols in accordance with rules. Thus our first attempt at a philosophy of mathematics might be to hold that mathematics is the rule-governed, or *formal*, manipulation of symbols and nothing else. (The phrase "and nothing else" is the mark of the surfacist.) This view is often called *formalism.* Positions more or less like this may be found in Haskell Curry [5], Abraham Robinson [17], and Paul Cohen [4]. (The views of David Hilbert, though often called "formalism," are quite different from the position we are discussing here, since Hilbert takes at least the finite, combinatorial part of mathematics to be meaningful and true. See, for example, Hilbert [12] or Kreisel [15].) An example of a different sort is provided by some computer scientists interested in artificial intelligence. They naturally want to think that human intelligence is not in principle different from what their computing machines are doing. Thus the human brain is assimilated to a computer, theories are assimilated to programs, and thought is assimilated to the operation of a Turing machine. After all, says the formalist, what else could mathematics be? Can you imagine a mathematician working in any way other than by manipulating symbols?

To make this somewhat more concrete, let us imagine asking a formalist what he takes to be the content of the fundamental theorem of arithmetic. If he is really a strict formalist, he must reply that, standing alone, it has no content at all. The theorem is, after all, just a string of symbols. What makes us feel that it has content is only that it plays a definite role in certain activities we engage in. It is like a frequently encountered position in chess. If we give a more precise description of our symbolic activities, say by giving a particular formal system which codifies some part of mathematics, then we can also give a precise account of the role of the fundamental theorem of arithmetic. We might specify one or more formal proofs of the theorem in our system, and we might give some examples of uses of the theorem in formal proofs of other theorems. For the formalist, however, the theorem has no meaning apart from its role in our symbolic activities. For the strict formalist, the theorem does not make any assertion about natural numbers, since for him no such objects exist.

Now I agree that mathematics almost always involves the formal manipulation of symbols. I agree that a mathematician can usually be viewed as working inside some formal system. This seems to me an important insight. There is a branch of mathematical logic whose subject is just this aspect of mathematical activity. I mean the theory of recursive functions. That theory has contributed more than any other part of mathematical logic to our understanding of the inherent limitations of mathematics. Let me state this quite strongly. I do not believe that mathematicians will ever compute a nonrecursive function, solve a recursively unsolvable problem, or work in a theory which is not recursively axiomatizable. But all of that is not to concede that human minds are algorithmic devices in the sense of recursive function theory. Rather, it is analogous to the harmless concession we might make to surfacism that no one will ever see a material object without a surface.

It is easy to understand how a philosopher who never actually did any mathematics might hold a formalistic view of its foundations. After all, what is there for him to see but the outer play of symbols? On the other hand, I must admit that I find it difficult to understand when, as happens occasionally, a creative mathematician is a formalist. Introspection shows that when I am actually doing mathematics, when I am wrestling with a problem that I do not know how to solve, then I am hardly dealing with symbols at all, but rather with ideas and constructions. Some of the hardest work a mathematician does occurs when he has an idea but is, for the moment, unable to express that idea in a formal way. Often such ideas first manifest themselves as visual or kinesthetic images. As the mathematician becomes clearer about them, as they become more formal, he may discover that they manifest considerable internal structure which is, so to speak, not yet symbolically encoded. This point is hard to discuss in a way which avoids purely psychological categories not directly relevant to the epistemological point I am trying to make. Still, mathematicians customarily talk about ideas, constructions, and proofs in a way which makes it clear that they have in mind something other than the symbols they use. Thus mathematicians may discuss whether two distinct papers embody the same idea, whether two distinct strings of symbols express the same construction, or whether two distinct lectures expound the same proof. Every mathematician knows that the same construction can be used in quite different parts of mathematics and that, if you find a new proof of an old theorem, you had better check that it is not just an old proof in a new form.

As has been customary since Brouwer, let me use the word "construction" to refer generically to all of these entities which lie behind the symbols the mathematician writes and which give those symbols life and content. I think there can be no doubt that constructions are practically real in the sense I introduced above. Mathematicians discuss them constantly, agree on their general properties, and agree that they are what is important in mathematical creation. It follows that an adequate philosophy of mathematics cannot just treat constructions as subjective illusion. Most formalist philosophers, however, either do not mention them at all or else dismiss them under some such name as "heuristics" without giving any account that would explain the properties that mathematicians agree constructions have. Indeed, the formalist cannot give a theory of constructions, since he denies they exist. For example, even if there could be a program which could recursively recognize whether or not two strings of symbols embody the same idea, the formalist could not admit that that is what the program does. What could it even mean to say that a computing machine had an idea for a proof but was having trouble formalizing it?

In order to state this argument more carefully, let me introduce the word "intuitive." In the sense that is relevant here, "intuitive" is used to contrast with the word "formal." Thus an argument may be called intuitive if it is natural and easy to follow. This is roughly the sense in which the word "intuitive" seems to be used in intuitionism. Thus an intuitive proof, in that context, is one which is unformalized, independent of symbols, and perhaps not even entirely communicable. At any rate, there certainly are constructions which are *intuitive*, in the sense that they are not formal and not symbolic, but which do have internal structure, do enable us to see new facts, and can be formalized so as to give correct proofs.

Now my argument may be summarized as follows. Intuitive constructions are practially real. They are vital to the practice of mathematics. It is of the essence of formalism that it denies their objective reality. Therefore, by the principle of objectivity, formalism cannot be an adequate philosophy of mathematics.

4 INTUITIONISM

If formalism must be rejected because it neglects the intuitive content of mathematics, then it is natural to make a second attempt at a philosophy of mathematics as follows. Let us hold that mathematics consists of intuitive constructions, of the formal manipulation of symbols which is their external expression, and of nothing else. This seems to me to be the essence of the view usually called *intuitionism.* It was worked out by L.E.J. Brouwer and Arend Heyting. A good introduction is Heyting [11]. A more recent introduction is Dummet [6]. Perhaps the clearest general statement by Brouwer himself is his [3]. A related, but definitely distinct, point of view is that of Errett Bishop [2]. I should say that very few of my remarks about intuitionism apply directly to Bishop's philosophy of mathematics, since Bishop has little of Brouwer's subjectivistic tendency.

It is characteristic of intuitionism that it denies the existence of any mathematical reality external to the mathematician or even of any mathematical truth beyond what the mathematician has actually proved or could actually prove. Mathematical objects exist for me only as the results of my constructions, and mathematical facts are true for me only insofar as they are the conclusions of arguments I can make. Thus the sequence of natural numbers, being infinite and hence not surveyable, is only potentially real. Statements which have so far been neither proved nor refuted, like Fermat's conjecture, have no definite truth-value. The logical law of the excluded middle, which asserts that every statement is either true or false, is rejected as inapplicable to statements about infinite sets, and indirect proofs of such statements are rejected as invalid.

To take an example, let us again consider the fundamental theorem of arithmetic. The intuitionist, unlike the formalist, does not take this to be a mere string of symbols. The theorem has a meaning. Nevertheless, he also does not take the theorem to be a truth about an externally existing domain of natural numbers. Rather he thinks of it as expressing a certain ability that we have—namely, our ability to factor an arbitrary natural number into primes and to see, given two such decompositions, that they consist of the same primes with the same multiplicities. Like the formalist, the intuitionist takes the meaning of the theorem to reside in our practice, not in any external reality to which the statement might refer.

Let us examine Brouwer's rejection of the law of the excluded middle somewhat more closely. Brouwer does not have available any concept of truth which could be used to justify, or even to explain, a truth-functional interpretation of the logical connectives. Moreover, for Brouwer it only makes sense to assert a mathematical statement as the conclusion of an intuitive proof. But a proof that either A is true or B is true ought to contain an indication as to which of the two alternatives is being proved. Otherwise we could assert the existence of a number n such that if $n = 0$ then A, and if $n = 1$ then B; but we would not know the value of any such number. Surely, however, we know the value of a number we have actually constructed. Thus we would be asserting the existence of a number without having constructed it. Hence a proof that the Fermat conjecture is either true or false would have to contain either a proof or a refutation of the conjecture. Since I can supply neither, it follows from Brouwer's point of view that I am not in a position to assert that the conjecture is either true or false. Thus the law of the excluded middle is "refuted" not by finding a third possibility but by making an additional demand. An assertion is only to be considered justified if an intuitive construction can be supplied which justifies it.

As an intellectual movement, mathematical intuitionism is similar to other positions, like existentialism, which emphasizes our isolation from each other and which conclude from that isolation that we are epistemically reduced to our own individual resources. That is to say, it is characteristic of all of these views that they hold that our inner experience, as such, is the only source of knowledge available to us and that they deny that our inner experience essentially entails an external reality to which it refers. In consequence, these views tend to collapse into irrationalism and solipsism. When Brouwer emphasizes the absolute freedom of the creative subject in mathematics, he is taking a stance related to that of the existentialist emphasizing the absolute freedom of that same creative subject in aesthetics, in ethics, or in politics.

Looked at in our context, however, intuitionism is a fairly typical form of surfacism. Its characteristic rhetorical gesture is to ask what a mathematician could possibly have access to other than his own constructions. Put differently, try to think something other than one of your own thoughts, or try to visualize something other than one of your images.

As in the case of formalism, it seems to me important not to overlook the contributions that intuitionism has made to our understanding of the practice of mathematics. The writings of the intuitionists are a rich source of ideas about the internal process of mathematical creation. Here again there is a branch of mathematical logic devoted to trying to extract and develop the precise content of these insights. The various realizability notions, functional interpretations, Kripke structures, and the like, seem to me to give promise of a mathematical theory, perhaps yet to come, of the experience of doing mathematics.

I myself have been attracted by intuitionism. But I have gradually come to see that, in the long term, strong intuitionistic convictions undermine one's actually doing mathematics. By embracing intuitionism the mathematician is giving up the most powerful motivation for his work—the search for publicly validated truth. Mathematics, after all, is a part of science. The main purpose of doing mathematics is to discover new truths. If that conception is given up, as it is in intuitionism, then mathematics is reduced to an esoteric art form—to a kind of play. There is a sense in which intuitionism is inadequate in its own terms, for it overlooks what is introspectively obvious: that I am interested in my constructions not for their own sake but for the new truths they enable me to find. The constructions derive their significance from their epistemic role. Who would be interested in a proof that established nothing? Just as the constructions lie behind the symbols and give them their interest and meaning, so there is something behind the constructions—mathematical truth.

In this respect mathematical creation is not at all free. A mathematical argument often gives a feeling of inevitability. The concept of rigor, which plays such a great role in the mathematician's talking and thinking about his work, is a restriction on his freedom which he accepts in order that his theorems may be true and in order that his arguments may genuinely establish their truth.

Mathematical truth, unlike a mathematical construction, is not something I can hope to find by introspection. It does not exist in my mind. A mathematical theory, like any other scientific theory, is a social product. It is created and developed by the dialectical interplay of many minds, not just one mind. When we study the history of mathematics, we do not find a mere accumulation of new definitons, new techniques, and new theorems. Instead, we find a repeated refinement and sharpening of old concepts and old formulations, a gradually rising standard of rigor, and an impressive secular increase in generality and depth. Each generation of mathematicians rethinks the mathematics of the previous generation, discarding what was faddish or superficial or false and recasting what is still fertile into new and sharper forms. What guides this entire process is a common conception of truth and a common faith that, just as we clarified and corrected the work of our teachers, so our students will clarify and correct our work.

In order to formulate a more careful argument, I need to say a few words about the concept of *rigor*. It is widely believed that this notion changes. Arguments that seemed rigorous to Euler seemed inadequate to Cauchy. Arguments that seemed rigorous to Cauchy seem to us to contain obvious gaps. But it is not really the case that the concept of rigor has changed—only the standard of rigor. That is to say, a rigorous argument is always an argument which suffices to establish the truth of its conclusion. As our insight grows, we see that more is required to establish truth, and therefore arguments that once seemed rigorous are now seen to have gaps. But the concept of rigor itself has not changed since at least the time of Euclid.

More is true than that the concept of rigor presupposes the concept of truth. Actually, when we evaluate a mathematical argument, we do not check to see whether it accords with some set of rules taken, let us say, from a logic text. Rather, we try to determine whether the argument works—that is, whether it convinces us, and ought to convince us, of the truth of its conclusion. Thus the concept of mathematical truth is directly involved in the practice of mathematical rigor. It functions as an indispensable ingredient in the very criterion of rigor.

Now I may formulate my argument against intuitionism as follows. Mathematical truth is practically real. Indeed, without the practical reality of mathematical truth, there would be no such thing as mathematical rigor. But it is of the essence of intuitionism that it denies the objective reality of mathematical truth. Therefore, by the principle of objectivity, intuitionism cannot be an adequate philosophy of mathematics.

5 LOGICISM

If we reject intuitionism because it neglects mathematical truth, then we may be led to make a third attempt at a philosophy of mathematics as follows. Let us hold that mathematics consists of certain truths, of the arguments that establish these truths, of the constructions underlying those arguments, of the formal manipulation of symbols that expresses those arguments and truths, and of nothing else. It seems to me that this is the central thrust of what has traditionally been called *logicism.* Views of this sort have been advocated most prominently by Gottlob Frege and by Bertrand Russell. Classical statements of logicism may be found, for example, in Frege [7] or Russell [18]. A somewhat more recent statement is in Hempel [9].

A logicist, unlike a formalist or an intuitionist, would take the fundamental theorem of arithmetic as a truth whose content is quite independent of our activity. For the logicist, however, there are no natural numbers which exist as independent entities and which happen to have the property expressed by the theorem. Instead, the theorem is to be understood on the basis of a long sequence of definitions. When all the expressions used in the theorem are expanded out in accordance with these definitions, then, according to the logicist, the theorem will turn out to be merely a very complex logical truth. The fundamental theorem of arithmetic, for a logicist, is on a par with an assertion like, "if all A's are both B's and C's, then all A's are C's."

What the logicist denies is that there is any subject matter for mathematical truths to be about. Mathematical terms, for the logicist, do not refer—or at least do not refer uniquely. It follows that mathematical truths are not true by virtue of successfully describing any actual state of affairs. They are empty of factual content. Hence mathematical truths must be true solely by virtue of their own internal structure and of their relations to one another. That is the way in which logical truths are true: Hence the logicist thesis that mathematics is merely logic. In practice, of course, logicists have tended to use the term "logic" rather loosely, sometimes including all of set theory under that name. But the basic idea is always to deny that mathematical assertions have factual content—that is, to deny that their truth rests on anything outside of the structure of the mathematical statements themselves. That is presumably also what Kline means to deny by the words quoted at the beginning of this essay. (For an explicit statement of Kline's views, see [13, pp. 424–431]. For more details, see Kline [14, pp. 1028–1039].)

Logicism motivated much of the early work in mathematical logic. I think that logicism has made greater contributions than any other philosophy of mathematics to our understanding, not so much of the practice of mathematics, but of its foundations. The desire to reduce all of mathematics to "logic"—that is, to merely conceptual reasoning—has provided a strong impetus to simplify and unify the basic mathematical notions and to find and make explicit the fundamental principles upon which mathematics is based. Moreover, logicism is still making such contributions today. Much of what is now called proof theory can be seen as an effort to view larger and larger parts of mathematics as consisting of logical truths by extending the concept of logic in various directions. To mention only one example, the past twenty-five years have seen the development of a theory of infinitely long formulas and proofs so as to give a "logical" analysis of arithmetic and of increasingly extensive fragments of mathematical analysis.

Unlike formalism or intuitionism, logicism does provide an adequate account of a significant part of actual mathematical practice. Much of mathematics really is just logic. We reason from clearly formulated premises, trying to find an argument that will settle some previously formulated question. I doubt, however, that any work a mathematician would consider deep can be accounted for in terms the logicist would accept. Every mathematician knows that his best work is based not on mere reasoning but on the characteristic kind of insight he calls "intuition." In this sense, the word "intuition" refers to a faculty by which the mathematician is able to perceive properties of a structure which, at the time, he is not in a position to deduce. This perception can be trained, and is often quite reliable. Sometimes, when trying to work deductively, one feels like a man trying to find his way around an unfamiliar room in the dark. The mind is full of details that fail to cohere into a pattern. But then, either gradually or suddenly, one's eyes adjust to the dark, one sees dimly how the room is arranged, one knows about chairs one has not yet bumped into, and one is able to get about comfortably. It is an everyday occurrence that a mathematician "knows intuitively" that thus and so must be the case but does not have the vaguest idea how to go about proving it. Often, of course, he is wrong. But far more often than not he is right. Certainly, if I respect a particular mathematician and if he has had extensive experience with a particular structure, I will be willing to rely on his intuitions about the structure even in the absence of a proof—not absolutely, but to a very large extent.

Let me say at once that I am not urging the existence of an occult faculty whereby we have direct knowledge of platonic objects. Rather, I think that the mathematician's intuition is a special case of the general human ability to recognize patterns or, more specifically, to synthesize complex structures from scattered cues. Thus I think the mathematician's intuition about a particular structure is simply the result of long experience with that structure. It is not different in kind from a carpenter's "feel" for his wood. The fact is that mathematicians are able to arrive at more or less reliable conclusions about mathematical objects without having to deduce those conclusions. Indeed, mathematical creativity is much more a matter of intuition than it is of logic. (For essentially the same view, see Wilder [19] or Resnick [16].) It follows that a logicist account of mathematics cannot be adequate.

But what is missing? The logicist holds that mathematics is a body of truths that are not about anything. They are true just by virtue of their internal logical structure, not by virtue of any external objects to which they refer. But if that were true, then the phenomenon of mathematical intuition would be incomprehensible. For if the logicist is right, then there are no structures for the mathematician to become familiar with or to have insight into.

An interesting special case of this difficulty is the problem, from a logicist point of view, of the status of axioms. A principle which is neither a logical truth nor deduced from antecedently accepted principles is not being accepted merely by virtue of reasoning. Logicists, therefore, often deny that such principles are being accepted at all. Thus they tend to think of geometry, for example, as a hypothetical discipline. If physical space satisfies the axioms, then it satisfies the theorems. (For this opinion see the references to Kline above, or see Hempel [10].) But, as a matter of fact, we have a clear intuition of Euclidean space, and the theorems of Euclidean geometry are outright true about that structure. It is generally held that the earliest geometrical knowledge was arrived at empirically. If so, then that knowledge does not have a hypothetical character. The non-Euclidean geometries only show the logical consistency of denying the parallel postulate. They do not show that the parallel postulate is false. The general theory of relativity shows that certain esoteric observations are well described by treating space-time as a four-dimensional manifold of non-constant curvature. It may follow from this, though I am not sure that it does, that the space of our intuition does not correspond perfectly to physical space. It certainly does not follow that we do not have a clear spatial intuition. Moreover, Euclidean geometry remains an excellent description of the space we actually live in and actually experience. It is not as though the use of figures in geometrical demonstrations were derivative from purely logical proofs based on the axioms. On the contrary, some of the axioms, such as the axioms of order, are so evident to the intuition that the need for them was not noticed until the nineteenth century. It seems implausible that all the geometers before Moritz Pasch were guilty of the same systematic logical errors. It seems much more likely that they were engaged in some activity other than deducing the logical consequences of a set of axioms. I think they were studying space.

Let me summarize the argument. Mathematical intuition is practically real. It is only comprehensible as a non-deductive insight into structures external to the mathematics itself. Hence such external mathematical structures are practically real. But it is essential to logicism that it denies the objective reality of any such structure. Therefore, by the principle of objectivity, logicism cannot be an adequate philosophy of mathematics.

6 PLATONISM

Logicism, in other words, must be rejected as an incomplete philosophy of mathematics because it omits the objects that mathematics is about. Thus we may make a fourth attempt at a philosophy of mathematics as follows: Mathematics consists of truths about abstract structures existing independently of us, of the logical arguments that establish those truths, of the constructions underlying those arguments, of the formal manipulation of symbols that expresses those arguments and truths, and of nothing else. This is the philosophy of mathematics that I think ought properly to be called *platonism*. Its most distinguished contemporary proponent was Kurt Gödel. (For example in his [8].)

A platonist would interpret the fundamental theorem of arithmetic literally. For the platonist there are such things as natural numbers existing independently of us, and it is as a matter of fact true that they are all uniquely decomposable into prime factors.

The most characteristic expression of platonism within mathematical logic is model theory. This discipline is the study of the semantic content of mathematical theories. Of course, formalism, intuitionism, and logicism all deny that mathematical theories have semantic content. The central problem of model theory is the question of what properties of structures can be expressed in particular languages. This question only arises if structures are assumed to exist and to have properties independently of their description.

Let me try to summarize quickly the picture of mathematical activity that platonism offers. The mathematician, on this view, is confronted by a wide variety of abstract structures which themselves precede his mathematical activity. He does not create these structures; he finds them. In the course of his training, and then as he develops his powers, he forms and refines an intuition about these structures. Typically, of course, he will have much more insight into some of them than into others. His intuition is formed by the truths about the mathematical world that have been discovered by his predecessors and by his colleagues, and then his intuition, in turn, enables him to find new structures and to make new conjectures about the old structures. In order to verify these conjectures, to answer the questions that occur to him, he performs constructions, makes arguments, defines new concepts. These constructions, in turn, get expressed in mathematical English, are bolstered by computations, are made rigorous and formal. Thereby they are made publicly accessible and verifiable and become part of the larger social dialectic through which mathematics develops.

This seems to me a fairly satisfactory account of what the pure mathematician is doing. Indeed, I think that most contemporary mathematicians, even if they have not bothered to articulate it for themselves, would accept some variant of this view. So satisfactory is platonism that very few recent mathematicians or philosophers of mathematics have felt any need to go beyond it. Just in the past few years, however, there have been signs of discontent. To indicate their source, let me pause for some brief historical remarks.

In the eighteenth century, mathematics was considered a science distinguished from the other sciences only in being more certain and more fundamental. Its special province was the laws governing space and quantity. In the course of the nineteenth century, this conception of the nature of mathematics was strongly undermined. First the non-Euclidean geometries were used to deny the existence of a unique spatial structure for our intuitions to be about. Then analytic geometry was used to undercut the view that there was an intuition of space at all apart from our intuition of the numerical continuum. The end product of this development is the contemporary mathematician who tells his undergraduate students that by three-dimensional Euclidean space he *means* the set of all ordered triples of real numbers. Obviously, that is not what Euclid meant. Toward the end of the nineteenth century, even the intuitive conception of quantity or magnitude was replaced, at least officially, by the purely conceptual structures introduced by Weierstrass, Dedekind, and Cantor. Again, a contemporary mathematician is likely to tell his students that by a real number he *means* a Dedekind cut. Obviously, that is not what Euler meant.

One effect of these changes was to produce what might be called a foundational vacuum—a situation in which mathematicians were without any systematic account of the nature of the structures they were dealing with. Axiomatic set theory rushed in to fill this void. The set-theoretic view of foundations, however, is platonism in its most narrowly reductionistic form. All the objects of the set-theorist's world are abstract. Even if individuals are allowed, and they are usually excluded, these individuals are taken to have neither internal structure nor intensional relationships. They are mere abstract points. Thus the reduction of all of mathematics to set theory entails a narrowing of the subject matter of mathematics so as to exclude all of concrete reality.

For about two generations axiomatic set theory was a great success. I think there can be little doubt that set theory provides an elegant and convenient framework within which to do pure mathematics. It is wonderfully simple in conception, almost never gets in the way of mathematical practice, gives smoothly reassuring answers to questions like "But what are numbers, really?" and provides a wealth of interesting structures of which no one before Cantor could have dreamed.

In the past decade, however, set theory has been undermined roughly in the same way that geometry was undermined about a hundred years earlier. The independence results, the proliferation of large cardinal axioms, and the construction of increasingly bizarre models for set theory have made mathematicians realize how weak their set-theoretic intuition actually is. In the absence of new insight, the views of set-theorists begin to diverge. Some still follow Cantor in thinking the continuum hypothesis plausible, but others follow Gödel in believing more and more strongly that it must be false. It is becoming truistic that we need a new concept, one more fundamental than that of a set. Unfortunately, no one can imagine where to look for such a concept.

None of this is incompatible with a sufficiently liberal platonism. Increasingly one hears the suggestions that there is not just one set-theoretic universe, but many. You work in a world in which the continuum hypothesis holds, and I will work in one in which Martin's axiom holds but the continuum hypothesis fails. He will work in a universe containing a measurable cardinal, and she will work in one in which, since all sets are constructible, a measurable cardinal is impossible. These are all just different structures, all equally entitled to be considered interesting and worthy of study. Where is the problem?

The problem, of course, is the same as it was in 1890. How do these diferent structures interact? What are they? What are the laws that govern the mathematical universe as a whole, if none of these set-theoretic "universes" can any longer be regarded as including all of the structures mathematicians concern themselves with? None of these questions have generally accepted answers. I think it is out of despair at this situation that some mathematicians retreat to formalism, intuitionism, or logicism—positions from which such questions cannot arise.

Let me put the problem differently. It seems to me that mathematics can only flourish if there is a common conception of what we are about, if there is an agreement that the different structures we study are aspects of one reality. Without a foundational consensus, it seems to me, mathematics will tend to break apart into schools.

Actually, not only is set theory tending to split into pieces, but mathematical platonism itself is the result of a split in the larger structure of science. The traditional view of the nature of science, for example in the time of Newton, was that there is only one reality and therefore only one science. On this view the several special sciences—mathematics, physics, chemistry, biology—share a common reality but ask different questions about it and use different methods to study it. Of course, each special science will reveal its own particular aspect of the world; it remains a fundamental assumption of science as traditionally conceived that these various aspects are complementary, mutually illuminating aspects of one world. As a matter of fact, most branches of mathematics cast light fairly directly on some part of nature. Geometry concerns space. Probability theory teaches us about random processes. Group theory illuminates symmetry. Logic describes rational inference. Many parts of analysis were created to study particular physical processes and are still indispensable for the study of those processes. The list could be extended almost indefinitely. From the point of view of the platonist, however, only pure mathematics is really mathematics. For, according to platonism, the objects which mathematics studies are necessarily abstract. How can the theory of finite groups tell us about the structure of crystals if the only groups we consider are built up out of sets of sets of sets?

When the foundations of mathematics became completely abstract and ceased to have anything to do with the world of the senses, the connection between mathematics and the other sciences became obscure. Recently, as economic circumstances have forced mathematicians to look around for new means of support, this divorce of mathematics from the other sciences has ceased to be a matter for pride and become a matter of concern. Set theory, however, provides no clue as to how a reconciliation with the rest of science is to be effected.

Thus I think that mathematical platonism is again a form of surfacism. It is a practical reality that our best theorems give information about the concrete world. It is a practical reality that there is no clear boundary between pure and applied mathematics. There is only one science. It follows from the principle of objectivity that an adequate philosophy of mathematics would identify the objective content of these facts. Such a philosophy of mathematics would be only one chapter in a larger philosophy of science. That philosophy would make it clear in what sense there is only one objective world and how it is that the objects studied by the mathematician, many of which are not realized in physical reality, can nevertheless be seen as part of that world. Unfortunately, that philosophy has yet to be formulated.

ACKNOWLEDGMENTS

An early version of this paper was presented to the Buffalo Logic Colloquium on February 15, 1977. I am grateful to my colleagues who participated in the discussion, which led me to clarify my ideas on several issues. A later version was read by John Corcoran, Emily Hartshorne Goodman, John Josephson, Susan Josephson, and Jane Terry Nutter, each of whom made useful suggestions. I am particularly grateful to John Corcoran, whose perceptive criticisms added appreciably to the coherence of my argument.

REFERENCES

[1] Paul Benacerraf and Hilary Putnam, eds., Philosophy of Mathematics: Selected Readings, Prentice-Hall, Englewood Cliffs, N.J., 1964.

[2] Errett Bishop, Foundations of Constructive Analysis, McGraw-Hill, New York, 1967.

[3] L.E.J. Brouwer, Intuitionism and formalism, trans. by A. Dresden, in Benacerraf and Putnam [1, pp. 66–77].

[4] Paul J. Cohen, Comments on the foundations of set theory, in Dana S. Scott, ed., Axiomatic Set Theory, Proceedings of Symposia in Pure Mathematics 13, Part I, American Mathematical Society, Providence, R.I., 1971, pp. 9–15.

[5] Haskell B. Curry, Outlines of a Formalist Philosophy of Mathematics, North-Holland, Amsterdam, 1958.

[6] Michael Dummett, Elements of Intuitionism, Clarendon Press, Oxford, 1977.

[7] Gottlob Frege, The concept of number, in Benacerraf and Putnam [1, pp. 85–112).

[8] Kurt Gödel, What is Cantor's continuum problem?, in Benacerraf and Putnam [1, pp. 258–273].

[9] Carl G. Hempel, On the nature of mathematical truth, in Benacerraf and Putnam [1, pp. 366–381].

[10] ———, Geometry and empirical science, this MONTHLY, 52 (1945) 7–17.

[11] Arend Heyting, Intuitionism: An Introduction, 2nd. rev. ed., North-Holland, Amsterdam, 1966.

[12] David Hilbert, On the infinite, in Benacerraf and Putnam [1, pp. 134–151].

[13] Morris Kline, Mathematics in Western Culture, Oxford University Press, New York, 1953.

[14] ———, Mathematical Thought from Ancient to Modern Times, Oxford University Press, New York, 1972.

[15] Georg Kreisel, Hilbert's programme, in Benacerraf and Putnam [1, pp. 157–180].

[16] Michael D. Resnik, Mathematical knowledge and pattern cognition, Canad. J. Philos., 5 (1975) 25–39.

[17] Abraham Robinson, Formalism 64, in Yehoshua Bar-Hillel, ed., Logic, Methodology and Philosophy of Science, North-Holland, Amsterdam, 1965, pp. 228–246.

[18] Bertrand Russell, Selections from Introduction to Mathematical Philosophy, in Benacerraf and Putnam [1, pp. 113–133].

[19] R.L. Wilder, The role of intuition, Science, 156 (1967) 605–610.

Interlude

If the preceding essays reveal the ultimate implausibility of foundationalism along with its supporting dogmas, they also remind us of how plausible foundationalism is on the surface. After all, it has been the dominant force in the philosophy of mathematics for over half a century. Nevertheless, there has always been a small (very small) minority of investigators who were skeptical of the myth of foundations. I would like to mention three: the philosophers Ludwig Wittgenstein and Willard Quine, and the mathematician George Polya.

By the late 1930s, Wittgenstein had developed a view of philosophy that simultaneously eliminated the idea of foundations of mathematics and focused philosophical concern on the actual practice of mathematics. The following quotation, taken from his last work, *Philosophical Investigations*, summarizes his view.[1]

> 124. Philosophy may in no way interfere with the actual use of language; it can in the end only describe it.
>
> For it cannot give it any foundation either.
>
> It leaves everything as it is.
>
> It also leaves mathematics as it is, and no mathematical discovery can advance it. A "leading problem of mathematical logic" is for us a problem of mathematics like any other.
>
> 125. It is the business of philosophy, not to resolve a contradiction by means of a mathematical or logico-mathematical discovery, but to make it possible for us to get a clear view of the state of affairs *before* the contradiction is resolved. (And this does not mean that one is sidestepping a difficulty.)

However, even in his earliest work, *Tractatus Logico-Philosophicus,* Wittgenstein drew a sharp distinction between mathematics and science, and this distinction he never abandoned. While he would admit to subtle and important connections between proofs and calculations on the one hand and experiments on the other, nevertheless Wittgenstein regarded the two processes as fundamentally different. "I can *calculate* in the medium of imagination," he said, "but not experiment."[2]

By 1950, Quine had become skeptical of the very possibility of drawing a satisfactory distinction between mathematics and science. His point was not the obvious one that any such distinction would be fuzzy—that, for example, applied mathematics and theoretical physics are hard to disentangle. His point was rather that the philosophical contrast underlying the distinction was misguided. That contrast was between analytic truths, statements true solely in virtue of their form or meaning, and synthetic truths, statements true in part because of facts about experienced reality. Quine's argument was that the analytic-synthetic distinction was not just fuzzy, but incoherent.[3] As he puts the matter in his more recent work, *The Philosophy of Logic,*

> Because of these . . . two traits of logic and mathematics—their relevance to all science and their partiality toward none—it is customary to draw an emphatic boundary separating them from the natural sciences. These latter are seen as monopolizing the information; logic and mathematics serve only in processing it. This account is an arresting one, but the trouble comes in pressing it beyond the stage of metaphor. What clear notion of information would fit the account? ["Two august notions of information" are the cosmological, "the distribution of elementary particles", and the epistemological, "the distribution of sensory elements".] If each sentence of science could be assigned its individual share of information in either of these senses, the doctrine of analyticity would be sustained: the analytic sentences would include the truths of logic and mathematics, and would be distinguished from the truths of nature by their lack of information. Where the myth lies, however, is in the notion of any such general sorting of information over sentences.
>
> Logic is in principle no less open to revision than quantum mechanics or the theory of relativity.[4]

Nevertheless, while he was establishing a kinship between mathematics and science, Quine was quick to add that "The kinship I speak for is rather a kinship with the most general and systematic aspects of natural science, farthest from observation."[5]

In contrast, the mathematician Polya argued that observation impinged on mathematics in a more direct way than Quine allowed; Polya maintained that observation was an everyday feature of mathematical practice. Moreover, Polya continued, the practice of mathematics had many other features in common with natural science, features such as induction, plausible reasoning, guesses, and analogies. In a series of books he tried to present mathematics as it is actually done, emphasizing its kinship with science and, incidentally, undermining foundationalism's dichotomy between mathematics and science.[6]

Polya was an early advocate of many of the theses argued for elsewhere in this anthology. Among his contentions are the principles:

> Mathematical practice provides important material for a philosophical understanding of mathematics.
>
> The questions of mathematical discovery and development are essential to a philosophy of mathematics.
>
> There is a fundamental similarity between the practices of mathematics and the practices of science.
>
> Pedagogy is an important topic in the philosophy of mathematics.

In order to provide the reader with a sense of Polya's approach to mathematics, I include the following selection, which is the second chapter of his book, *Induction and Analogy in Mathematics*

For all of his innovations, however, Polya remains a transitional figure in the philosophy of mathematics. He paved the way for quasi-empiricism without ever taking the final step towards it. He prefaced his major work by acceding to the ultimate contrast between mathematics and science that is postulated by foundationalism. Plausible reasoning, common to mathematics and science, was, he granted, fundamentally distinct from demonstrative reasoning, the special property of mathematics and logic. In that preface he maintained that "Finished mathematics presented in a finished form appears as purely demonstrative, consisting of proofs only," such proofs being "safe, beyond controversy, and final." No foundationalist could ask for anything more. The *philosophy* of mathematics, foundationalists would assert, consists in the explanation of demonstrative reasoning. To foundational eyes, Polya's work seems to pertain only to the development of mathematical proofs and so is interesting to the sociology or history or pedagogy of mathematics, but not to its philosophy.

Consequently, Polya's work had little impact on the philosophy of mathematics until it was taken up by the more radical quasi-empiricists. They push his analysis one step further by questioning the assumption of completely safe proofs, "beyond controversy and final." Indeed, the more we insist on the safety of demonstrative formal reasoning, the more our proofs rely on higher-level assumptions that our formalizations are at least consistent. According to the quasi-empiricists, as we shall see, it is our informal proofs, the kind investigated by Polya, that are often safer than any derivative formalizations of them. Once this extra step is taken, Polya's work ceases to be a mere gloss on the foundational conception of mathematics but instead becomes a genuine alternative to it. I have prefaced Polya's chapter on "Generalization, Specialization, Analogy," with an excerpt from his own preface to *Induction and Analogy in Mathematics,* which makes clear his own motives and his relation to foundationalism.

Incidentally, Polya begins the essay (chapter 2 of his text) by alluding to an example drawn from the first chapter. There he developed the observation that

$$3 + 7 = 10, \qquad 3 + 17 = 20, \qquad 13 + 17 = 30,$$

by successive criticisms and refinements, into the conjecture that "any even number that is neither a prime nor the square of a prime, is the sum of two odd primes." This is known as Goldbach's Conjecture, and as Polya notes, Goldbach had not much better evidence for it than Polya elicits. To understand mathematics, it is not enough to understand how mathematicians prove theorems, according to Polya. One must also understand how they discover conjectures to prove. As an aid to that understanding, I've included many of the fascinating exercises of Polya's that are such an important part of his work.

FOOTNOTES

1. *Philosophical Investigations,* MacMillan, New York (1953), 49–50.
2. *Remarks on the Foundations of Mathematics,* Basil Blackwell, Oxford (1964), 29.
3. "Two Dogmas of Empiricism", *Philosophical Review,* 60 (1951).
4. *Philosophy of Logic,* Prentice Hall, Englewood Cliffs (1970), 98–99.
5. Ibid., 100.
6. *How to Solve It* (1945), *Induction and Analogy in Mathematics* (1954), and *Patterns of Plausible Inference* (1954), all published by Princeton University Press, Princeton, New Jersey.

GEORGE POLYA

From the Preface of *Induction and Analogy in Mathematics*

This book has various aims, closely connected with each other. In the first place, this book intends to serve students and teachers of mathematics in an important but usually neglected way. Yet in a sense the book is also a philosophical essay. It is also a continuation and requires a continuation. I shall touch upon these points, one after the other.

1. Strictly speaking, all our knowledge outside mathematics and demonstrative logic (which is, in fact, a branch of mathematics) consists of conjectures. There are, of course, conjectures and conjectures. There are highly respectable and reliable conjectures as those expressed in certain general laws of physical science. There are other conjectures, neither reliable nor respectable, some of which may make you angry when you read them in a newspaper. And in between there are all sorts of conjectures, hunches, and guesses.

We secure our mathematical knowledge by *demonstrative reasoning,* but we support our conjectures by *plausible reasoning.* A mathematical proof is demonstrative reasoning, but the inductive evidence of the physicist, the circumstantial evidence of the lawyer, the documentary evidence of the historian, and the statistical evidence of the economist belong to plausible reasoning.

The difference between the two kinds of reasoning is great and manifold. Demonstrative reasoning is safe, beyond controversy, and final. Plausible reasoning is hazardous, controversial, and provisional. Demonstrative reasoning penetrates the sciences just as far as mathematics does, but it is in itself (as mathematics is in itself) incapable of yielding essentially new knowledge about the world around us. Anything new that we learn about the world involves plausible reasoning, which is the only kind of reasoning for which we care in everyday affairs. Demonstrative reasoning has rigid standards, codified and clarified by logic (formal or demonstrative logic), which is the theory of demonstrative reasoning. The standards of plausible reasoning are fluid, and there is no theory of such reasoning that could be compared to demonstrative logic in clarity or would command comparable consensus.

2. Another point concerning the two kinds of reasoning deserves our attention. Everyone knows that mathematics offers an excellent opportunity to learn demonstrative reasoning, but I contend also that there is no subject in the usual curricula of the schools that affords a comparable opportunity to learn plausible reasoning. I address myself to all interested students of mathematics of all grades and I say: Certainly, let us learn proving, but also *let us learn guessing.*

This sounds a little paradoxical and I must emphasize a few points to avoid possible misunderstandings.

Mathematics is regarded as a demonstrative science. Yet this is only one of its aspects. Finished mathematics presented in a finished form appears as purely demonstrative, consisting of proofs only. Yet mathematics in the making resembles any other human knowledge in the making. You have to guess a mathematical theorem before you prove it; you have to guess the idea of the proof before you carry through the details. You have to combine observations and follow analogies; you have to try and try again. The result of the mathematician's creative work is demonstrative reasoning, a proof; but the proof is discovered by plausible reasoning, by guessing. If the learning of mathematics reflects to any degree the invention of mathematics, it must have a place for guessing, for plausible inference.

There are two kinds of reasoning, as we said: demonstrative reasoning and plausible reasoning. Let me observe that they do not contradict each other; on the contrary, they complete each other. In strict reasoning the principal thing is to distinguish a proof from a guess, a valid demonstration from an invalid attempt. In plausible reasoning the principal thing is to distinguish a guess from a guess, a more reasonable guess from a less reasonable guess. If you direct your attention to both distinctions, both may become clearer.

A serious student of mathematics, intending to make it his life's work, must learn demonstrative reasoning; it is his profession and the distinctive mark of his science. Yet for real success he must also learn plausible reasoning; this is the kind of reasoning on which his creative work will depend. The general or amateur student should also get a taste of demonstrative reasoning: he may have little opportunity to use it directly, but he should acquire a standard with which he can compare alleged evidence of all sorts aimed at him in modern life. But in all his endeavors he will need plausible reasoning. At any rate, an ambitious student of mathematics, whatever his further interests may be, should try to learn both kinds of reasoning, demonstrative and plausible.

3. I do not believe that there is a foolproof method to learn guessing. At any rate, if there is such a method, I do not know it, and quite certainly I do not pretend to offer it on the following pages. The efficient use of plausible reasoning is a practical skill and it is learned, as any other practical skill, by imitation and practice. I shall try to do my best for the reader who is anxious to learn plausible reasoning, but what I offer are only examples for imitation and opportunity for practice.

In what follows, I shall often discuss mathematical discoveries, great and small. I cannot tell the true story how the discovery did happen, because nobody really knows that. Yet I shall try to make up a likely story how the discovery could have happened. I shall try to emphasize the motives underlying the discovery, the plausible inferences that led to it, in short, everything that deserves imitation. Of course, I shall try to impress the reader; this is my duty as teacher and author. Yet I shall be perfectly honest with the reader in the point that really matters: I shall try to impress him only with things which seem genuine and helpful to me. . . .

GEORGE POLYA

Generalization, Specialization, Analogy

1. GENERALIZATION, SPECIALIZATION, ANALOGY, AND INDUCTION. Let us look again at the example of inductive reasoning that we have discussed in some detail (sect. 1.2, 1.3). We started from observing the *analogy* of the three relations

$$3 + 7 = 10, \qquad 3 + 17 = 20, \qquad 13 + 17 = 30,$$

we *generalized* in ascending from 3, 7, 13, and 17 to all primes, from 10, 20, and 30 to all even numbers, and then we *specialized* again, came down to test particular even numbers such as 6 or 8 or 60.

This first example is extremely simple. It illustrates quite correctly the role of generalization, specialization, and analogy in inductive reasoning. Yet we should examine less meager, more colorful illustrations and, before that, we should discuss generalization, specialization, and analogy, these great sources of discovery, for their own sake.

2. GENERALIZATION is passing from the consideration of a given set of objects to that of a larger set, containing the given one. For example, we generalize when we pass from the consideration of triangles to that of polygons with an arbitrary number of sides. We generalize also when we pass from the study of the trigonometric functions of an acute angle to the trigonometric functions of an unrestricted angle.

It may be observed that in these two examples the generalization was effected in two characteristically different ways. In the first example, in passing from triangles to polygons with n sides, we replace a constant by a variable, the fixed integer 3 by the arbitrary integer n (restricted only by the inequality $n \geq 3$). In the second example, in passing from acute angles to arbitrary angles α, we remove a restriction, namely the restriction that $0° < \alpha < 90°$.

We often generalize in passing from just one object to a whole class containing that object.

3. SPECIALIZATION is passing from the consideration of a given set of objects to that of a smaller set, contained in the given one. For example, we specialize when we pass from the consideration of polygons to that of regular polygons, and we specialize still further when we pass from regular polygons with n sides to the regular, that is, equilateral, triangle.

These two subsequent passages were effected in two characteristically different ways. In the first passage, from polygons to regular polygons, we introduced a restriction, namely that all sides and all angles of the polygon be equal. In the second passage we substituted a special object for a variable, we put 3 for the variable integer n.

Very often we specialize in passing from a whole class of objects to just one object contained in the class. For example, when we wish to check some general assertion about prime numbers we pick out some prime number, say 17, and we examine whether that general assertion is true or not for just this prime 17.

4. ANALOGY. There is nothing vague or questionable in the concepts of generalization and specialization. Yet as we start discussing analogy we tread on a less solid ground.

Analogy is a sort of similarity. It is, we could say, similarity on a more definite and more conceptual level. Yet we can express ourselves a little more accurately. The essential difference between analogy and other kinds of similarity lies, it seems to me, in the intentions of the thinker. Similar objects agree with each other in some aspect. If you intend to reduce the aspect in which they agree to definite concepts, you regard those similar objects as *analogous*. If you succeed in getting down to clear concepts, you have *clarified* the analogy.

Comparing a young woman to a flower, poets feel some similarity, I hope, but usually they do not contemplate analogy. In fact, they scarcely intend to leave the emotional level or reduce that comparison to something measurable or conceptualy definable.

Looking in a natural history museum at the skeletons of various mammals, you may find them all frightening. If this is all the similarity you can find between them, you do not see much analogy. Yet you may perceive a wonderfully suggestive analogy if you consider the hand of a man, the paw of a cat, the foreleg of a horse, the fin of a whale, and the wing of a bat, these organs so differently used, as composed of similar parts similarly related to each other.

The last example illustrates the most typical case of clarified analogy; two *systems* are analogous, if they *agree in clearly definable relations of their respective parts.*

For instance, a triangle in a plane is analogous to a tetrahedron in space. In the plane, 2 straight lines cannot include a finite figure, but 3 may include a triangle. In space, 3 planes cannot include a finite figure but 4 may include a tetrahedron. The relation of the triangle to the plane is the same as that of the tetrahedron to space in so far as both the triangle and the tetrahedron are bounded by the minimum number of simple bounding elements. Hence the analogy.

One of the meanings of the Greek word "analogia," from which the word "analogy" originates, is "proportion." In fact, the system of the two numbers 6 and 9 is "analogous" to the system of the two numbers 10 and 15 in so far as the two systems agree in the ratio of their corresponding terms,

$$6 : 9 = 10 : 15.$$

Proportionality, or agreement in the ratios of corresponding parts, which we may see intuitively in geometrically similar figures, is a very suggestive case of analogy.

Here is another example. We may regard a triangle and a pyramid as analogous figures. On the one hand take a segment of a straight line, and on the other hand a polygon. Connect all points of the segment with a point outside the line of the segment, and you obtain a triangle. Connect all points of the polygon with a point outside the plane of the polygon, and you obtain a pyramid. In the same manner, we may regard a parallelogram and a prism as analogous figures. In fact, move a segment or a polygon parallel to itself, across the direction of its line or plane, and the one will describe a parallelogram, the other a prism. We may be tempted to express these corresponding relations between plane and solid figures by a sort of proportion and if, for once, we do not resist temptation, we arrive at fig. 2.1. This figure modifies the usual meaning of certain symbols (: and =) in the same way as the meaning of the word "analogia" was modified in the course of linguistic history: from "proportion" to "analogy."

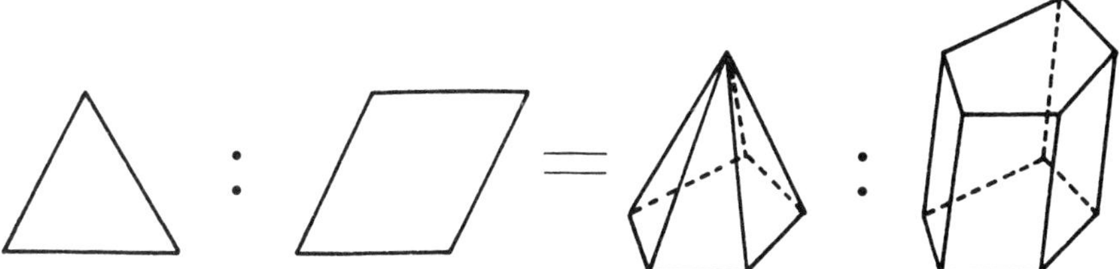

FIG. 2.1. Analogous relations in plane and space.

The last example is instructive in still another respect. Analogy, especially incompletely clarified analogy, may be ambiguous. Thus, comparing plane and solid geometry, we found first that a triangle in a plane is analogous to a tetrahedron in space and then that a triangle is analogous to a pyramid. Now, both analogies are reasonable, each is valuable at its place. There are several analogies between plane and solid geometry and not just one privileged analogy.

Fig. 2.2 exhibits how, starting from a triangle, we may ascent to a polygon by generalization, descend to an equilateral triangle by specialization, or pass to different solid figures by analogy—there are analogies on all sides.

And, remember, do not neglect vague analogies. Yet, if you wish them respectable, try to clarify them.

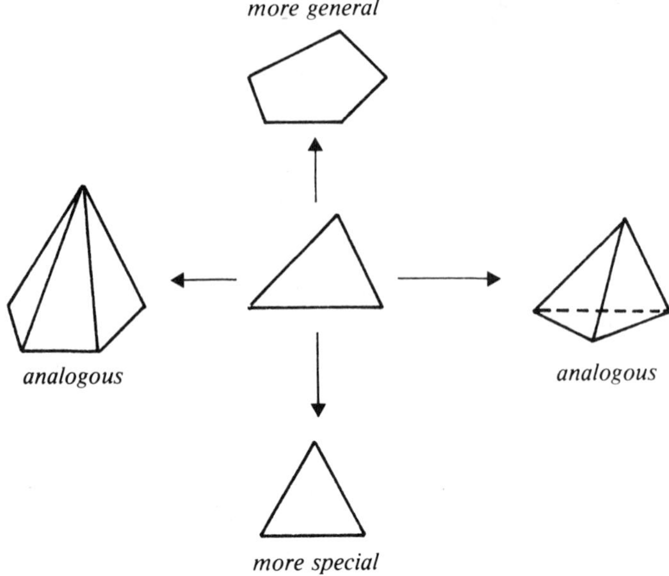

FIG. 2.2. Generalization, specialization, analogy.

5. GENERALIZATION, SPECIALIZATION, AND ANALOGY often concur in solving mathematical problems.[1] Let us take as an example the proof of the best known theorem of elementary geometry, the theorem of Pythagoras. The proof that we shall discuss is not new; it is due to Euclid himself (Euclid VI, 31).

(1) We consider a right triangle with sides *a, b,* and *c,* of which the first, *a,* is the hypotenuse. We wish to show that

(A) $a^2 = b^2 + c^2$.

This aim suggests that we describe squares on the three sides of our right triangle. And so we arrive at the not unfamiliar part I of our compound figure, fig. 2.3. (The reader should draw the parts of this figure as they arise, in order to see it in the making.)

(2) Discoveries, even very modest discoveries, need some remark, the recognition of some relation. We can discover the following proof by observing the *analogy* between the familiar part I of our compound figure and the scarcely less familiar part II: the same right triangle that arises in I is divided in II into two parts by the altitude perpendicular to the hypotenuse.

(3) Perhaps, you fail to perceive the analogy between I and II. This analogy, however, can be made explicit by a common *generalization* of I and II which is expressed in III. There we find again the same right triangle, and on its three sides three polygons are described which are similar to each other but arbitrary otherwise.

(4) The area of the square described on the hypotenuse in I is a^2. The area of the irregular polygon described on the hypotenuse in III can be put equal to λa^2; the factor λ is determined as the ratio of two given areas. Yet then, it follows from the similarity of the three polygons described on the sides *a, b,* and *c* of the triangle in III that their areas are equal to λa^2, λb^2, and λc^2, respectively.

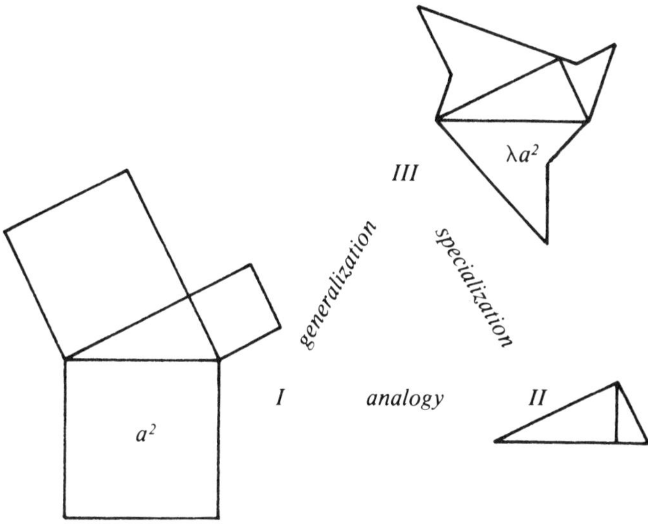

FIG. 2.3

Now, if the equation (A) should be true (as stated by the theorem that we wish to prove), then also the following would be true:

(B) $\lambda a^2 = \lambda b^2 + \lambda c^2.$

In fact, very little algebra is needed to derive (B) from (A). Now, (B) represents a *generalization* of the original theorem of Pythagoras: *If three similar polygons are described on three sides of a right triangle, the one described on the hypotenuse is equal in area to the sum of the two others.*

It is instructive to observe that this generalization is *equivalent* to the special case from which we started. In fact, we can derive the equations (A) and (B) from each other, by multiplying or dividing by λ (which is, as the ratio of two areas, different from 0).

(5) The general theorem expressed by (B) is equivalent not only to the special case (A), but to any other special case. Therefore, if any such special case should turn out to be obvious, the general case would be demonstrated.

Now, trying to *specialize* usefully, we look around for a suitable special case. Indeed II represents such a case. In fact, the right triangle described on its own hypotenuse is similar to the two other triangles described on the two legs, as is well known and easy to see. And, obviously, the area of the whole triangle is equal to the sum of its two parts. And so, the theorem of Pythagoras has been proved.

The foregoing reasoning is eminently instructive. A case is instructive if we can learn from it something applicable to other cases, and the more instructive the wider the range of possible applications. Now, from the foregoing example we can learn the use of such fundamental mental operations as generalization, specialization, and the perception of analogies. There is perhaps no discovery either in elementary or in advanced mathematics or, for that matter, in any other subject that could do without these operations, especially without analogy.

The foregoing example shows how we can ascend by generalization from a special case, as from the one represented by I, to a more general situation as to that of III, and redescend hence by specialization to an analogous case, as to that of II. It shows also the fact, so usual in mathematics and still so surprising to the beginner, or to the philosopher who takes himself for advanced, that the general case can be logically equivalent to a special case. Our example shows, naïvely and suggestively, how generalization, specialization, and analogy are naturally combined in the effort to attain the desired solution. Observe that only a minimum of preliminary knowledge is needed to understand fully the foregoing reasoning.

6. DISCOVERY BY ANALOGY. Analogy seems to have a share in all discoveries, but in some it has the lion's share. I wish to illustrate this by an example which is not quite elementary, but is of historic interest and far more impressive than any quite elementary example of which I can think.

Jacques Bernoulli, a Swiss mathematician (1654–1705), a contemporary of Newton and Leibnitz, discovered the sum of several infinite series, but did not succeed in finding the sum of the reciprocals of the squares,

$$1 + \frac{1}{4} + \frac{1}{9} + \frac{1}{25} + \frac{1}{36} + \frac{1}{49} + \dots .$$

"If somebody should succeed," wrote Bernoulli, "in finding what till now withstood our efforts and communicate it to us, we shall be much obliged to him."

The problem came to the attention of another Swiss mathematician, Leonhard Euler (1707–1783), who was born at Basle as was Jacques Bernoulli and was a pupil of Jacques' brother, Jean Bernoulli (1667–1748). He found various expressions for the desired sum (definite integrals, other series), none of which satisfied him. He used one of these expressions to compute the sum numerically to seven places (1.644934). Yet this is only an approximate value and his goal was to find the exact value. He discovered it, eventually. Analogy led him to an extremely daring conjecture.

(1) We begin by reviewing a few elementary algebraic facts essential to Euler's discovery. If the equation of degree n

$$a_0 + a_1x + a_2x^2 + \dots + a_nx^n = 0$$

has n different roots

$$\alpha_1, \alpha_2, \dots \alpha_n$$

the polynomial on its left hand side can be represented as a product of n linear factors,

$$a_0 + a_1x + a_2x^2 + \dots + a_nx^n = a_n(x - \alpha_1)(x - \alpha_2) \cdots (x - \alpha_n).$$

By comparing the terms with the same power of x on both sides of this identity, we derive the well known relations between the roots and the coefficients of an equation, the simplest of which is

$$a_{n-1} = -a_n(\alpha_1 + \alpha_2 + \dots + \alpha_n);$$

we find this by comparing the terms with x^{n-1}.

There is another way of presenting the decomposition in linear factors. If none of the roots $\alpha_1, \alpha_2, \ldots \alpha_n$ is equal to 0, or (which is the same) if a_0 is different from 0, we have also

$$\begin{aligned} &a_0 + a_1x + a_2x^2 + \ldots + a_nx^n \\ &= a_0\left(1 - \frac{x}{\alpha_1}\right)\left(1 - \frac{x}{\alpha_2}\right)\ldots\left(1 - \frac{x}{\alpha_n}\right) \end{aligned}$$

and

$$a_1 = -a_0\left(\frac{1}{\alpha_1} + \frac{1}{\alpha_2} + \ldots + \frac{1}{\alpha_n}\right).$$

There is still another variant. Suppose that the equation is of degree $2n$, has the form

$$b_0 - b_1x^2 + b_2x^4 - \ldots + (-1)^n b_n x^{2n} = 0$$

and $2n$ different roots

$$\beta_1, \quad -\beta_1, \quad \beta_2, \quad -\beta_2, \quad \ldots \quad \beta_n, \quad -\beta_n.$$

Then

$$\begin{aligned} &b_0 - b_1x^2 + b_2x^4 - \ldots + (-1)^n b_n x^{2n} \\ &= b_0\left(1 - \frac{x^2}{\beta_1^2}\right)\left(1 - \frac{x^2}{\beta_2^2}\right)\ldots\left(1 - \frac{x^2}{\beta_n^2}\right) \end{aligned}$$

and

$$b_1 = b_0\left(\frac{1}{\beta_1^2} + \frac{1}{\beta_2^2} + \ldots + \frac{1}{\beta_n^2}\right).$$

(2) Euler considers the equation

$$\sin x = 0$$

or

$$\frac{x}{1} - \frac{x^3}{1\cdot 2\cdot 3} + \frac{x^5}{1\cdot 2\cdot 3\cdot 4\cdot 5} - \frac{x^7}{1\cdot 2\cdot 3\ldots 7} + \ldots = 0.$$

The left hand side has an infinity of terms, if of "infinite degree." Therefore, it is no wonder, says Euler, that there is an infinity of roots

$$0, \quad \pi, \quad -\pi, \quad 2\pi, \quad -2\pi, \quad 3\pi, \quad -3\pi, \quad \ldots \; .$$

Euler discards the root 0. He divides the left hand side of the equation by x, the linear factor corresponding to the root 0, and obtains so the equation

$$1 - \frac{x^2}{2\cdot 3} + \frac{x^4}{2\cdot 3\cdot 4\cdot 5} - \frac{x^6}{2\cdot 3\cdot 4\cdot 5\cdot 6\cdot 7} + \ldots = 0$$

with the roots

$$\pi, \quad -\pi, \quad 2\pi, \quad -2\pi, \quad 3\pi, \quad -3\pi, \quad \ldots \; .$$

We have seen an analogous situation before, under (1), as we discussed the last variant of the decomposition in linear factors. Euler concludes, by analogy, that

$$\frac{\sin x}{x} = 1 - \frac{x^2}{2 \cdot 3} + \frac{x^4}{2 \cdot 3 \cdot 4 \cdot 5} - \frac{x^6}{2 \cdot 3 \cdots 7} + \ldots ,$$

$$= \left(1 - \frac{x^2}{\pi^2}\right)\left(1 - \frac{x^2}{4\pi^2}\right)\left(1 - \frac{x^2}{4\pi^2}\right)\ldots ,$$

$$\frac{1}{2 \cdot 3} = \frac{1}{\pi^2} + \frac{1}{4\pi^2} + \frac{1}{9\pi^2} + \ldots ,$$

$$1 + \frac{1}{4} + \frac{1}{9} + \frac{1}{16} + \ldots = \frac{\pi^2}{6}.$$

This is the series that withstood the efforts of Jacques Bernoulli—but it was a daring conclusion.

(3) Euler knew very well that his conclusion was daring. "The method was new and never used yet for such a purpose," he wrote ten years later. He saw some objections himself and many objections were raised by his mathematical friends when they recovered from their first admiring surprise.

Yet Euler had his reasons to trust his discovery. First of all, the numerical value for the sum of the series which he has computed before, agreed to the last place with $\pi^2/6$. Comparing further coefficients in his expression of sin x as a product, he found the sum of other remarkable series, as that of the reciprocals of the fourth powers,

$$1 + \frac{1}{16} + \frac{1}{81} + \frac{1}{256} + \frac{1}{625} + \ldots = \frac{\pi^4}{90}.$$

Again, he examined the numerical value and again he found agreement.

(4) Euler also tested his method on other examples. Doing so he succeeded in rederiving the sum $\pi^2/6$ for Jacques Bernoulli's series by various modifications of his first approach. He succeeded also in rediscovering by his method the sum of an important series due to Leibnitz.

Let us discuss the last point. Let us consider, following Euler, the equation

$$1 - \sin x = 0.$$

It has the roots

$$\frac{\pi}{2}, \quad -\frac{3\pi}{2}, \quad \frac{5\pi}{2}, \quad -\frac{7\pi}{2}, \quad \frac{9\pi}{2}, \quad -\frac{11\pi}{2} \quad \ldots .$$

Each of these roots is, however, a double root. (The curve $y = \sin x$ does not intersect the line $y = 1$ at these abscissas, but is tangent to it. The derivative of the left hand side vanishes for the same values of x, but not the second derivative.) Therefore, the equation

$$1 - \frac{x}{1} + \frac{x^3}{1 \cdot 2 \cdot 3} - \frac{x^5}{1 \cdot 2 \cdot 3 \cdot 5} + \ldots = 0$$

has the roots

$$\frac{\pi}{2}, \quad \frac{\pi}{2}, \quad -\frac{3\pi}{2}, \quad -\frac{3\pi}{2}, \quad \frac{5\pi}{2}, \quad \frac{5\pi}{2}, \quad -\frac{7\pi}{2}, \quad -\frac{7\pi}{2}, \quad \ldots$$

and Euler's analogical conclusion leads to the decomposition in linear factors

$$1 - \sin x = 1 - \frac{x}{1} + \frac{x^3}{1 \cdot 2 \cdot 3} - \frac{x^5}{1 \cdot 2 \cdot 3 \cdot 4 \cdot 5} + \dots$$

$$= \left(1 - \frac{2x}{\pi}\right)^2 \left(1 + \frac{2x}{3\pi_1}\right)^2 \left(1 - \frac{2x}{5\pi_1}\right)^2 \left(1 + \frac{2x}{7\pi_1}\right)^2 \dots \quad .$$

Comparing the coefficient of x on both sides, we obtain

$$-1 = -\frac{4}{\pi} + \frac{4}{3\pi} - \frac{4}{5\pi} + \frac{4}{7\pi} - \dots \; ,$$

$$\frac{\pi}{4} = 1 - \frac{1}{3} + \frac{1}{5} - \frac{1}{7} + \frac{1}{9} - \frac{1}{11} + \dots \; .$$

This is Leibnitz's celebrated series; Euler's daring procedure led to a known result. "For our method," says Euler, "which may appear to some as not reliable enough, a great confirmation comes here to light. Therefore, we should not doubt at all of the other things which are derived by the same method."

(5) Yet Euler kept on doubting. He continued the numerical verifications described above under (3), examined more series and more decimal places, and found agreement in all cases examined. He tried other approaches, too, and, finally, he succeeded in verifying not only numerically, but exactly, the value $\pi^2/6$ for Jacques Bernoulli's series. He found a new proof. This proof, although hidden and ingenious was based on more usual considerations and was accepted as completely rigorous. Thus, the most conspicuous consequence of Euler's discovery was satisfactorily verified.

These arguments, it seems, convinced Euler that his result was correct.[2]

7. ANALOGY AND INDUCTION. We wish to learn something about the nature of inventive and inductive reasoning. What can we learn from the foregoing story?

(1) Euler's decisive step was daring. In strict logic, it was an outright fallacy: he applied a rule to a case for which the rule was not made, a rule about algebraic equations to an equation which is not algebraic. In strict logic, Euler's step was not justified. Yet it was justified by analogy, by the analogy of the most successful achievements of a rising science that he called himself a few years later the "Analysis of the Infinite." Other mathematicians, before Euler, passed from finite differences to infinitely small differences, from sums with a finite number of terms to sums with an infinity of terms, from finite products to infinite products. And so Euler passed from equations of finite degree (algebraic equations) to equations of infinite degree, applying the rules made for the finite to the infinite.

This analogy, this passage from the finite to the infinite, is beset with pitfalls. How did Euler avoid them? He was a genius, some people will answer, and of course that is no explanation at all. Euler had shrewd reasons for trusting his discovery. We can understand his reasons with a little common sense, without any miraculous insight specific to genius.

(2) Euler's reasons for trusting his discovery, summarized in the foregoing,[3] are *not* demonstrative. Euler does not reexamine the grounds for his conjecture,[4] for his daring passage from the finite to the infinite; he examines only its consequences. He regards the verification of any such consequence as an argument in favor of his conjecture. He accepts both approximative and exact verifications, but seems to attach more weight to the latter. He examines also the consequences of closely related analogous conjectures[5] and he regards the verification of such a consequence as an argument for his conjecture.

Euler's reasons are, in fact, inductive. It is a typical inductive procedure to examine the consequences of a conjecture and to judge it on the basis of such an examination. In scientific research as in ordinary life, we believe, or ought to believe, a conjecture more or less according as its observable consequences agree more or less with the facts.

In short, Euler seems to think the same way as reasonable people, scientists or non-scientists, usually think. He seems to accept certain principles: *A conjecture becomes more credible by the verification of any new consequence.* And: *A conjecture becomes more credible if an analogous conjecture becomes more credible.*

Are the principles underlying the process of induction of this kind?

EXAMPLES AND COMMENTS ON CHAPTER II

First part

1. *The right generalization.*

A. Find three numbers x, y, and z satisfying the following system of equations:

$$\begin{aligned} 9x - 6y - 10z &= 1, \\ -6x + 4y + 7z &= 0, \\ x^2 + y^2 + z^2 &= 9. \end{aligned}$$

If you have to solve A, which one of the following three generalizations does give you a more helpful suggestion, B or C or D?

B. Find three unknowns from a system of three equations.

C. Find three unknowns from a system of three equations the first two of which are linear and the third quadratic.

D. Find n unknowns from a system of n equations the first $n - 1$ of which are linear.

2. A point and a "regular" pyramid with hexagonal base are given in position. (A pyramid is termed "regular" if its base is a regular polygon the center of which is the foot of the altitude of the pyramid.) Find a plane that passes through the given point and bisects the volume of the given pyramid.

In order to help you, I ask you a question: What is the right generalization?

3. A. Three straight lines which are not in the same plane pass through the same point O. Pass a plane through O that is equally inclined to the three lines.

B. Three straight lines which are not in the same plane pass through the same point. The point P is on one of the lines; pass a plane through P that is equally inclined to the three lines.

Compare the problems A and B. Could you use the solution of one in solving the other? What is their logical connection?

4. A. Compute the integral

$$\int_{-\infty}^{\infty} (1 + x^2)^{-3}\, dx.$$

B. Compute the integral

$$\int_{-\infty}^{\infty} (p + x^2)^{-3}\, dx$$

where p is a given positive number.

Compare the problems A and B. Could you use the solution of one in solving the other? What is their logical connection?

5. *An extreme special case.* Two men are seated at a table of usual rectangular shape. One places a penny on the table, then the other does the same, and so on, alternately. It is understood that each penny lies flat on the table and not on any penny previously placed. The player who puts the last coin on the table takes the money. Which player should win, provided that each plays the best possible game?

This is a time-honored but excellent puzzle. I once had the opportunity to watch a really distinguished mathematician when the puzzle was proposed to him. He started by saying, "Suppose that the table is so small that it is covered by one penny. Then, obviously, the first player must win." That is, he started by picking out an *extreme special case* in which the solution is obvious.

From this special case, you can reach the full solution when you imagine the table gradually extending to leave place to more and more pennies. It may be still better to *generalize* the problem and to think of tables of various shapes and sizes. If you observe that the table has a center of symmetry and that the *right generalization* might be to consider tables with a center of symmetry, then you have got the solution, or you are at least very near to it.

6. Construct a common tangent to two given circles.

In order to help you, I ask you a question: Is there a more accessible extreme special case?

7. *A leading special case.* The area of a polygon is A, its plane includes with a second plane the angle α. The polygon is projected orthogonally onto the second plane. Find the area of the projection.

Observe that the shape of the polygon is not given. Yet there is an endless variety of possible shapes. Which shape should we discuss? Which shape should we discuss first?

There is a particular shape especially easy to handle: a rectangle, the base of which is parallel to the line l, intersection of the plane of the projected figure with the plane of the projection. If the base of such a rectangle is a, its height b, and therefore its area is ab, the corresponding quantities for the projection are a, b cos α, and ab cos α. If the area of such a rectangle is A, the area of its projection is A cos α.

This special case of the rectangle with base parallel to l is not only particularly accessible; it is a *leading special case.* The other cases follow; *the solution of the problem in the leading special case involves the solution in the general case.* In fact, starting from the rectangle with base parallel to l, we can extend the rule "area of the projection equals A cos α" successively to all other figures. First to right triangles with a leg parallel to l (by bisecting the rectangle we start from); then to any triangle with a side parallel to l (by combining two right triangles); finally to a general polygon (by disecting it into triangles of the kind just mentioned). We could even pass to figures with curvilinear boundaries (by considering them as limits of polygons).

8. The angle at the center of a circle is double the angle at the circumference on the same base, that is, on the same arc. (Euclid III, 20.)

If the angle at the center is given, the angle at the circumference is not yet determined, but can have various positions. In the usual proof of the theorem (Euclid's proof), which is the "leading special position"?

9. Cauchy's theorem, fundamental in the theory of analytic functions, asserts that the integral of such a function vanishes along an arbitrary closed curve in the interior of which the function is regular. We may consider the special case of Cauchy's theorem in which the closed curve is a triangle as a leading special case: having proved the theorem for a triangle, we can easily extend it successively to polygons (by combining triangles) and to curves (by considering them as limits of polygons). Observe the analogy with ex. 7 and 8.

10. *A representative special case.* You have to solve some problem about polygons with n sides. You draw a pentagon, solve the problem for it, study your solution, and notice that it works just as well in the general case, for any n, as in the special case $n = 5$. Then you may call $n = 5$ a *representative* special case: it represents to you the general case. Of course, in order to be really representative, the case $n = 5$ should have no particular simplification that could mislead you. The representative special case should *not* be simpler than the general case.

Representative special cases are often convenient in teaching. We may prove a thorem on determinants with n rows in discussing carefully a determinant with just 3 rows.

11. *An analogous case.* The problem is to design airplanes so that the danger of skull fractures in case of accident is minimized. A medical doctor, studying this problem, experiments with eggs which he smashes under various conditions. What is he doing? He has *modified* the original problem, and is

studying now an *auxiliary problem,* the smashing of eggs instead of the smashing of skulls. The link between the two problems, the original and the auxiliary, is *analogy.* From a mechanical viewpoint, a man's head and a hen's egg are roughly analogous: each consists of a rigid, fragile shell containing gelatinous material.

12. If two straight lines in space are cut by three parallel planes, the corresponding segments are proportional.

In order to help you to find a proof, I ask you a question: Is there a simpler analogous theorem?

13. The four diagonals of a parallelepiped have a common point which is the midpoint of each.

Is there a simpler analogous theorem?

14. The sum of any two face angles of a trihedral angle is greater than the third face angle.

Is there a simpler analogous theorem?

15. Consider a tetrahedron as the solid that is analogous to a triangle. List the concepts of solid geometry that are analogous to the following concepts of plane geometry: *parallelogram, rectangle, square, bisector of an angle.* State a thorem of solid geometry that is analogous to the following theorem of plane geometry: *The bisectors of the three angles of a triangle meet in one point which is the center of the circle inscribed in the triangle.*

16. Consider a pyramid as the solid that is analogous to a triangle. List the solids that are analogous to the following plane figures: *parallelogram, rectangle, circle.* State a theorem of solid geometry that is analogous to the following theorem of plane geometry: *The area of a circle is equal to the area of a trinagle the base of which has the same length as the perimeter of the circle and the altitude of which is the radius.*

17. Invent a theorem of solid geometry that is analogous to the following theorem of plane geometry: *The altitude of an isosceles trinagle passes through the midpoint of the base.*

What solid figure do you consider as analogous to an isosceles triangle?

18. *Great analogies.*

(1) The foregoing ex. 12–17 insisted on the analogy between *plane geometry* and *solid geometry.* This analogy has many aspects and is therefore often ambiguous and not always clearcut, but it is an inexhaustible source of new suggestions and new discoveries.

(2) Numbers and figures are not the only objects of mathematics. Mathematics is basically inseparable from logic, and it deals with all objects which may be objects of an exact theory. Numbers and figures are, however, the most usual objects of mathematics, and the mathematician likes to illustrate facts about numbers by properties of figures and facts about figures by properties of numbers. Hence, there are countless aspects of the analogy between *numbers* and *figures.* Some of these aspects are very clear. Thus, in analytic geometry we study well-defined correspondences between algebraic and geometric objects and relations. Yet the variety of

geometric figures is inexhaustible, and so is the variety of possible operations on numbers, and so are the possible correspondences between these varieties.

(3) The study of limits and limiting processes introduces another kind of analogy which we may call the analogy between the *infinite* and the *finite*. Thus, infinite series and integrals are in various ways analogous to the finite sums whose limits they are; the differential calculus is analogous to the calculus of finite differences; differential equations, especially linear and homogeneous differential equations, are somewhat analogous to algebraic equations, and so forth. An important, relatively recent, branch of mathematics is the theory of integral equations; it gives a surprising and beautiful answer to the qustion: What is the analogue, in the integral calculus, of a system of n linear equations with n unknowns? The analogy between the infinite and the finite is particularly challenging because it has characteristic difficulties and pitfalls. It may lead to discovery or error; see ex. 46.

(4) Galileo, who discovered the parabolic path of projectiles and the quantitative laws of their motion, was also a great discoverer in astronomy. With his newly invented telescope, he discovered the satellites of Jupiter. He noticed that these satellites circling the planet Jupiter are analogous to the moon circling the earth and also analogous to the planets circling the sun. He also discovered the phases of the planet Venus and noticed their similarity with the phases of the moon. These discoveries were received as a great conformation of Copernicus's heliocentric theory, hotly debated at that time. It is strange that Galileo failed to consider the analogy between the motion of heavily bodies and the motion of projectiles, which can be seen quite intuitively. The path of a projectile turns its concave side towards the earth, and so does the path of the moon. Newton insisted on this analogy: " . . . a stone that is projected is by the pressure of its own weight forced out of the rectilinear path, which by the initial projection alone it should have pursued, and made to describe a curved line in the air, and . . . at last brought down to the ground; and the greater the velocity is with which it is projected, the farther it goes before it falls to the earth. We may therefore suppose the velocity to be so increased, that it would describe an arc of 1, 2, 5, 10, 100, 1000 miles before it arrived at the earth, till at last, exceeding the limits of the earth, it should pass into space without touching it."[6] See fig. 2.4.

Varying continuously, the path of the stone goes over into the path of the moon. And as the stone and the moon are to the earth, so are the satellites to Jupiter, or Venus and the other planets to the sun. Without visualizing this analogy, we can only very imperfectly understand Newton's discovery of universal gravitation, which we may still regard as the greatest scientific discovery ever made.

19. *Clarified analogies.* Analogy is often vague. The answer to the question, what is analogous to what, is often ambiguous. The vagueness of analogy need not diminish its interest and usefulness; those cases, however, in which the concept of analogy attains the clarify of logical or mathematical concepts deserve special consideration.

(1) Analogy is similarity of relations. The similarity has a clear meaning if the *relations are governed by the same laws.* In this sense, the addition of

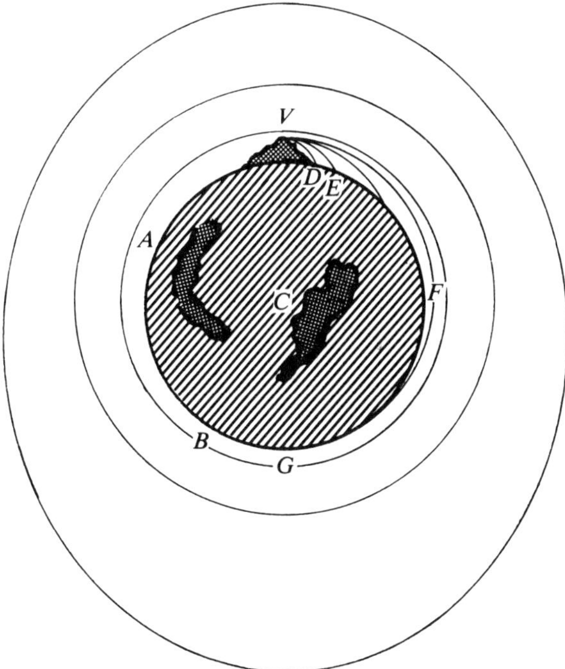

FIG. 2.4. From the path of the stone to the path of the moon.
From Newton's *Principia*.

numbers is analogous to the multiplication of numbers, in so far as addition and multiplication are subject to the same rules. Both addition and multiplication are commutative and associative,

$$a + b = b + a, \qquad ab = ba,$$

$$(a + b) + c = a + (b + c), \qquad (ab)c = a(bc).$$

Both admit an inverse operation; the equations

$$a + x = b, \qquad ax = b$$

are similar, in so far as each admits a solution, and no more than one solution. (In order to be able to state the last rule without exceptions we must admit negative numbers when we consider addition, and we must exclude the case $a = 0$ when we consider multiplication.) In this connection subtraction is analogous to division; in fact, the solutions of the above equations are

$$x = b - a, \qquad x = \frac{b}{a},$$

respectively. Then, the number 0 is analogus to the number 1; in fact, the addition of 0 to any number, as the multiplication by 1 of any number, does not change that number,

$$a + 0 = a, \qquad a \cdot 1 = a.$$

These laws are the same for various classes of numbers; we may consider here rational numbers, or real numbers, or complex numbers. In general, *systems of objects subject to the same fundamental laws* (or axioms) may be considered as analogous to each other, and this kind of analogy has a completely clear meaning.

(2) The addition of *real* numbers is analogous to the multiplication of *positive* numbers in still another sense. Any real number r is the logarithm of some positive number p,

$$r = \log p.$$

(If we consider ordinary logarithms, $r = -2$ if $p = 0.01$.) By virtue of this relation, to each positive number corresponds a perfectly determined real number, and to each real number a perfectly determined positive number. In this correspondence the addition of real numbers corresponds to the multiplication of positive numbers. If

$$r = \log p, \quad r' = \log p', \quad r'' = \log p'',$$

then any of the following two relations implies the other:

$$r + r' = r'', \qquad pp' = p''.$$

The formula on the left and that on the right tell the same story in two different languages. Let us call one of the coordinated numbers the translation of the other; for example, let us call the real number r (the logarithm of p) the *translation* of p, and p the *original* of r. (We could have interchanged the words "translation" and "original," but we had to choose, and having chosen, we stick to our choice.) In this terminology addition appears as the translation of multiplication, subtraction as the translation of division, 0 as the translation of 1, the commutative law and associative law for the addition of real numbers are conceived as translations of these laws for the multiplication of positive numbers. The translation is, of course, different from the original, but it is a correct translation in the following sense: from any relation between the original elements, we can conclude with certainty the corresponding relation between the corresponding elements of the translation, and *vice versa.* Such a correct translation, that is a *one-to-one correspondence that preserves the laws of certain relations,* is called *isomorphism* in the technical language of the mathematician. Isomorphism is a fully clarified sort of analogy.

(3) A third sort of fully clarified analogy is what the mathematicians call in technical language *homomorphism* (or *merohedral isomorphism*). It would take too much time to discuss an example sufficiently, or to give an exact description, but we may try to understand the following approximate description. Homomorphism is a kind of *systematically abridged translation.* The original is not only translated into another language, but also abridged so that what results finally from translation and abbreviation is uniformly, systematically condensed into one-half or one-third or some other fraction of the original extension. Subtleties may be lost by such abridgement but everything that is in the original is represented by something in the translation, and, on a reduced scale, the relations are preserved.

20. *Quotations.*

"Let us see whether we could, by chance, conceive some other general problem that contains the original problem and is easier to solve. Thus, when we are seeking the tangent at a given point, we conceive that we are just seeking a straight line which intersects the given curve in the given point and in another point that has a given distance from the given point. After having solved this problem, which is always easy to solve by algebra, we find the case of the tangent as a special case, namely, the special case in which the given distance is minimal, reduces to a point, vanishes." (Leibnitz)

"As it often happens, the general problem turns out to be easier than the special problem would be if we had attacked it directly." (P.G. Lejeune-Dirichlet, R. Dedekind)

"[It may be useful] to reduce the genus to its several species, also to a few species. Yet the most useful is to reduce the genus to just one minimal species." (Leibnitz)

"It is proper in philosophy to consider the similar, even in things far distant from each other." (Aristotle)

"Comparisons are of great value in so far as they reduce unknown relations to known relations.

"Proper understanding is, finally, a grasping of relations (un saisir de rapports). But we understand a relation more distinctly and more purely when we recognize it as the same in widely different cases and between completely heterogeneous objects." (Arthur Schopenhauer)

You should not forget, however, that there are two kinds of generalizations. One is cheap and the other is valuable. It is easy to generalize by *diluting*; it is important to generalize by *condensing*. To dilute a little wine with a lot of water is cheap and easy. To prepare a refined and condensed extract from several good ingredients is much more difficult, but valuable. Generalization by condensing compresses into one concept of wide scope several ideas which appeared widely scattered before. Thus, the Theory of Groups reduces to a common expression ideas which were dispersed before in Alegbra, Theory of Numbers, Analysis, Geometry, Crystallography, and other domains. The other sort of generalization is more fashionable nowadays than it was formerly. It dilutes a little idea with a big terminology. The author usually prefers to take even that little idea from somebody else, refrains from adding any original observation, and avoids solving any problem except a few problems arising from the difficulties of his own terminology. It would be very easy to quote examples, but I don't want to antagonize people.[7]

Second part

The examples and comments of this second part are all connected with sect. 6 and each other. Many of them refer directly or indirectly to ex. 21, which should be read first.

21. *The conjecture E.* We regard the equation

$$\sin x = x \left(1 - \frac{x^2}{\pi^2}\right)\left(1 - \frac{x^2}{4\pi^2}\right)\left(1 - \frac{x^2}{9\pi^2}\right)\dots$$

as a conjecture; we call it the "conjecture E." Following Euler, we wish to investigate this conjecture inductively.

Inductive investigation of a conjecture involves confronting its consequences with the facts. We shall often "predict from E and verify." "Predicting from E" means deriving under the assumption that E is true, "verifying" means deriving without this assumption. A fact "agrees with E" if it can be (easily) derived from the assumption that E is true.

In the following we take for granted the elements of the calculus (which; from the formal side, were completely known to Euler at the time of his discovery) including the rigorous concept of limits (about which Euler never attained full clarity). We shall use only limiting processes which can be justified (most of them quite easily) but we shall not enter into detailed justifications.

22. We know that $\sin(-x) = -\sin x$. Does this fact agree with E?

23. Predict from E and verify the value of the infinite product

$$\left(1 - \frac{1}{4}\right)\left(1 - \frac{1}{9}\right)\left(1 - \frac{1}{16}\right)\dots\left(1 - \frac{1}{n^2}\right)\dots \quad .$$

24. Predict from E and verify the value of the infinite product

$$\left(1 - \frac{4}{9}\right)\left(1 - \frac{4}{16}\right)\left(1 - \frac{4}{25}\right)\dots\left(1 - \frac{4}{n^2}\right)\dots \quad .$$

25. Compare ex. 23 and 24, and generalize.

26. Predict from E the value of the infinite product

$$\frac{2\cdot 4}{3\cdot 3}\cdot\frac{4\cdot 6}{5\cdot 5}\cdot\frac{6\cdot 8}{7\cdot 7}\cdot\frac{8\cdot 10}{9\cdot 9}\dots .$$

27. Show that the conjecture E is equivalent to the statement

$$\frac{\sin \pi z}{\pi} = \lim_{n=\infty} \frac{(z+n)\dots(z+1)z(z-1)\dots(z+n)}{(-1)^n(n!)^2} \quad .$$

28. We know that $\sin(x + \pi) = -\sin x$. Does this fact agree with E?

29. The method of sect. 6 (2) leads to the conjecture

$$\cos x = \left(1 - \frac{4x^2}{\pi^2}\right)\left(1 - \frac{4x^2}{9\pi^2}\right)\left(1 - \frac{4x^2}{25\pi^2}\right)\dots \quad .$$

Show that this is not only analogous to, but a consequence of, the conjecture E.

30. We know that

$$\sin x = 2 \sin (x/2) \cos (x/2).$$

Does this fact agree with E?

31. Predict from E and verify the value of the infinite product

$$\left(1 - \frac{4}{1}\right)\left(1 - \frac{4}{9}\right)\left(1 - \frac{4}{25}\right)\left(1 - \frac{4}{49}\right) \cdots .$$

32. Predict from E verify the value of the infinite product

$$\left(1 - \frac{16}{1}\right)\left(1 - \frac{16}{9}\right)\left(1 - \frac{16}{25}\right)\left(1 - \frac{16}{49}\right) \cdots .$$

33. Compare ex. 31 and 32, and generalize.

34. We know that $\cos(-x) = \cos x$. Does this fact agree with E?

35. We know that $\cos(x + \pi) = -\cos x$. Does this fact agree with E?

36. Derive from E the product for $1 - \sin x$ conjectured in sect. 6 (4).

37. Derive from E that

$$\cot x = \cdots + \frac{1}{x + 2\pi} + \frac{1}{x + \pi} + \frac{1}{x} + \frac{1}{x - \pi} + \frac{1}{x - 2\pi} + \cdots .$$

38. Derive from E that

$$\begin{aligned} \cot x = \frac{1}{x} &- \frac{2x}{\pi^2}\left(1 + \frac{1}{4} + \frac{1}{9} + \frac{1}{16} + \frac{1}{25} + \cdots\right) \\ &- \frac{2x^3}{\pi^4}\left(1 + \frac{1}{16} + \frac{1}{81} + \frac{1}{256} + \frac{1}{625} + \cdots\right) \\ &- \frac{2x^5}{\pi^6}\left(1 + \frac{1}{64} + \frac{1}{729} + \cdots\right) \\ &- \cdots \end{aligned}$$

and find the sum of the infinite series appearing as coefficients on the right hand side.

39. Derive from E that

$$\frac{\cos x}{1 - \sin x} = \cot\left(\frac{\pi}{4} - \frac{x}{2}\right)$$

$$= -2\left(\frac{1}{x-\frac{\pi}{2}} - \frac{1}{x+\frac{3\pi}{2}} + \frac{1}{x-\frac{5\pi}{2}} + \frac{1}{x+\frac{7\pi}{2}} + \ldots\right)$$

$$= \frac{4}{\pi}\left(1 - \frac{1}{3} + \frac{1}{5} - \frac{1}{7} + \frac{1}{9} - \ldots\right)$$

$$+ \frac{8x}{\pi^2}\left(1 + \frac{1}{9} + \frac{1}{25} + \frac{1}{49} + \frac{1}{81} \ldots\right)$$

$$+ \frac{16x^2}{\pi^3}\left(1 - \frac{1}{27} + \frac{1}{125} - \frac{1}{343} + \ldots\right)$$

$$+ \frac{32x^3}{\pi^4}\left(1 + \frac{1}{81} + \frac{1}{625} + \ldots\right)$$

$$+ \ldots$$

and find the sum of the infinite series appearing as coefficients in the last expression.

40. Show that

$$1 + \frac{1}{4} + \frac{1}{9} + \frac{1}{16} + \frac{1}{25} + \ldots = \frac{4}{3}\left(1 + \frac{1}{9} + \frac{1}{25} + \frac{1}{49} + \ldots\right)$$

which yields a second derivation for the sum of the series on the left.

41. (continued). Try to find a third derivation, knowing that

$$\arcsin x = x + \frac{1}{2}\frac{x^3}{3} + \frac{1}{2}\frac{3}{4}\frac{x^5}{5} + \frac{1}{2}\frac{3}{4}\frac{5}{6}\frac{x^7}{7} + \ldots$$

and that, for $n = 0, 1, 2, \ldots,$

$$\int_0^1 (1-x^2)^{-1/2}x^{2n+1}\,dx = \int_0^{\pi/2} (\sin t)^{2n+1}\,dt = \frac{2 \cdot 4 \ldots 2n}{3 \cdot 5 \ldots (2n+1)}.$$

42. (continued). Try to find a fourth derivation, knowing that

$$(\arcsin x)^2 = x^2 + \frac{2}{3}\frac{x^4}{2} + \frac{2}{3}\frac{4}{5}\frac{x^6}{3} + \frac{2}{3}\frac{4}{5}\frac{6}{7}\frac{x^8}{4} + \ldots$$

and that, for $n = 0, 1, 2, \ldots$

$$\int_0^1 (1-x^2)^{-1/2}x^{2n}\,dx = \int_0^{\pi/2} (\sin t)^{2n}\,dt = \frac{1}{2}\frac{3}{4}\cdots\frac{2n-1}{2n}\frac{\pi}{2}.$$

43. Euler (*Opera Omnia*, ser. 1, vol. 14, p. 40–41) used the formula

$$1 + \frac{1}{4} + \frac{1}{9} + \frac{1}{16} + \ldots$$

$$= \log x \cdot \log(1-x) + \frac{x + (1-x)}{1} + \frac{x^2 + (1-x)^2}{4}$$

$$+ \frac{x^3 + (1-x)^3}{9} + \ldots,$$

valid for $0 < x < 1$, to compute numerically the sum of the series on the left hand side.

(a) Prove the formula

(b) Which value of x is the most advantageous in computing the sum on the left?

44. *An objection and a first approach to a proof.* There is no reason to admit a priori that $\sin x$ can be decomposed into linear factors corresponding to the roots of the equation

$$\sin x = 0.$$

Yet even if we should admit this, there remains an objection: Euler did *not* prove that

$$0, \quad \pi, \quad -\pi, \quad 2\pi, \quad -2\pi, \quad 3\pi, \quad -3\pi, \quad \ldots$$

are *all* the roots of this equation. We can satisfy ourselves (by discussing the curve $y = \sin x$) that there are no other real roots, yet Euler did by no means exclude the existence of complex roots.

This objection was raised by Daniel Bernoulli (a son of Jean, 1700–1788). Euler answered it by considering

$$\begin{aligned}\sin x &= (e^{ix} - e^{-ix})/(2i)\\ &= \lim_{n\to\infty} P_n(x)\end{aligned}$$

where

$$P_n(x) = \frac{1}{2i}\left[\left(1 + \frac{ix}{n}\right)^n - \left(1 - \frac{ix}{n}\right)^n\right]$$

is a polynomial (of degree n if n is odd).

Show that $P_n(x)$ has no complex roots.

45. *A second approach to a proof.* Assuming that n is odd in ex. 44, factorize $P_n(x)/x$ so that its k-th factor approaches

$$1 - \frac{x^2}{k^2\pi^2}$$

as n tends to ∞, for any fixed k ($k = 1, 2, 3, \ldots$).

46. *Dangers of analogy.* In short, the analogy between the finite and the infinite led Euler to a great discovery. Yet he skirted a fallacy. Here is an example showing the danger on a smaller scale.

The series

$$1 - \frac{1}{2} + \frac{1}{3} - \frac{1}{4} + \frac{1}{5} - \frac{1}{6} + \frac{1}{7} - \frac{1}{8} + \ldots = l$$

converges. Its sum l can be roughly estimated by the first two terms:

$$1/2 < l < 1.$$

Now

$$2l = \frac{2}{1} - \frac{1}{1} + \frac{2}{3} - \frac{1}{2} + \frac{2}{5} - \frac{1}{3} + \frac{2}{7} - \frac{1}{4} + \dots .$$

In this series, there is just one term with a given even denominator (it is negative, but two terms with a given odd denominator (one positive, and the other negative). Let us bring together the terms with the same odd denominator:

$$\begin{aligned} &\frac{2}{1} - \frac{1}{2} - \frac{2}{3} - \frac{1}{4} + \frac{2}{5} - \dots \\ -&\frac{1}{1} \qquad\; - \frac{1}{3} \qquad\; - \frac{1}{5} \\ =\;& 1 - \frac{1}{2} + \frac{1}{3} - \frac{1}{4} + \frac{1}{5} - \dots \\ =\;& l. \end{aligned}$$

Yet $2l \neq l$, since $l \neq 0$. Where is the mistake and how can you protect yourself from repeating it?

NOTES

1. This section reproduces with slight changes a Note of the author in the *American Mathematical Monthly,* v. 55 (1948), p. 241–243.

2. Much later, almost ten years after his first discovery, Euler returned to the subject, answered the objections, completed to some extent his original heuristic approach, and gave a new, essentially different proof. See L. Euler, *Opera Omnia,* ser. 1, vol. 14, p. 73–86, 138–155, 177–186, and also p. 156–176, containing a note by Paul Stäckel on the history of the problem.

3. Under sect. 6 (3), (4), (5). For Euler's own summary see *Opera Omnia,* ser. 1, vol. 14, p. 140.

4. The representation of sin x as an infinite product.

5. Especially the product for $1 - \sin x$.

6. Sir Isaac Newton's *Mathematical Principles of Natural Philosophy and his System of the World.* Translated by Motte, revised by Cajori. Berkeley, 1946; see p. 551.

7. Cf. G. Polya and G. Szego, *Aufgaben und Lehrstaze aus der Analysis,* vol. 1, p. VII.

PART II

Mathematical Practice

Without the myth of foundations to distract it, philosophy can quite naturally turn to a reexamination of mathematical practice. It is the practice of mathematics that gives rise to any philosophical perplexities we might have about mathematics and the practice that holds the key to any solutions we might obtain. The essays in the following section were chosen because they approach the issue of mathematical practice in a fresh way, without allegiance to foundational dogmas. The authors include mathematicians, philosophers, and logicians, as well as a computer scientist or two.

The first set of essays explores some general issues in mathematical practice, starting with the concept of informal proof. Actually, the phrase, 'informal proof' is slightly misleading for in fact it denotes the ordinary proofs of everyday mathematics in all their rigor. When philosophers and philosophically minded mathematicians reflect on ordinary proofs, they realize that such proofs are still far removed from the idealized formal proofs that foundations require. So they coin the term 'informal proofs' for ordinary proofs, reserving "proof" as a philosophical synonym for 'formal proof'. In actual practice it is the other way around: mathematicians have to go out of their way to talk about formal proofs.

It is the ordinary proofs, the informal ones, that are the locus of many familiar aspects of mathematical experience. Such basic concepts as lemma, counterexample, explanation and development have their roots in ordinary proofs and apply only derivatively, if at all, to formal proofs. Of these, the concept of development is especially important and so the second group of essays focuses on the growth of mathematical knowledge. Development or change is an essential aspect of informal proof. Informal proofs are located in a continuous process that begins with plausibility arguments for conjectures, refines these into (informal) proofs, and finally tests these and assimilates them into mathematics. From this perspective, anyone who wants to understand mathematics must come to terms with growth and change in mathematics. (From the foundational point of view, on the other hand, development is noteworthy only because it leads to static, formal proofs which are the proper object of philosophical concern.) The essays in the second section argue that any serious attempt to understand the evolution of mathematics should begin by locating the practicing mathematicians in a socio-historical context and proceed by applying the best available methods of scientific inquiry to this subject.

The final group of essays continues the themes of informal proof and mathematical change with respect to a particular change that mathematics is presently undergoing. Mathematicians are coming to grips with computers. Each of the final essays attempts to draw some general philosophical morals from the interaction of mathematics and computer technology. Not surprisingly, they all agree that the interaction yields evidence for the quasi-empiricist account of mathematics. (Foundationalists, by contrast, must deny that computers can have any significant impact on mathematics. It is as if mathematicians were simply using bigger pencils!)

In summary, the following essays argue the philosophical relevance of mathematical practice. The crucial step in approaching them is our willingness to conceive of mathematics as a rational human activity, that is, as a practice. To some readers, this point will seem obvious. Of course mathematics is a rational activity, not some kooky cult phenomenon. Of course mathematics is a human activity—better it should be seen as the activity of ants or the product of stars in their courses? Such readers should turn to the following essays where they will find much to think about.

However, there are other readers who will find the idea of mixing practice with philosophy of mathematics to be utterly foreign and wrong headed. Some readers of my acquaintance are convinced that this concern is itself an irrational cult phenomenon! The arguments for this position are many, but not all that varied.

For instance, some note that attention to mathematical practice would introduce all sorts of quasi-empirical elements into the philosophy of mathematics, elements such as informal proofs, fallible mathematicians, socio-historical contexts, and even sophisticated technology. From the foundational viewpoint, the philosophy of mathematics must be a priori, not quasi-empirical. Hence philosophy should not concern itself with mathematical practice.

Secondly, it might be argued that the practice of mathematics is essentially the verification of rigorous proofs. Thus, in order to understand the practice, we must first understand rigorous proofs, and this is the business of foundations. So a platonist might explain rigorous proof in terms of classical logic and insight into the universe of sets; a formalist in terms of classical logic and the manipulation of formal systems; an intuitionist in terms of intuitionistic logic and species of mental constructions. Then each would add that actual practice is just this sort of theoretical activity in disguise. First comes the theory, only after it comes the practice.

Finally, it might be argued that mathematics does not turn on the accidents of human evolution. It transcends the human species and is, in fact, the most transcendental of all subjects. There is no room in the philosophy of mathematics for such quasi-empirical topics as discovery and communication, informal proofs, errors, explanations, history or cultures, computers or psychology.

My reply to such arguments is that they are but the vestiges of foundationalism. Apart from the dogmas of foundationalism, the arguments can be refuted by simply exhibiting the specific philosophical insights that follow from a study of mathematical practice. The following essays establish this point in detail. Let me conclude this introduction to the philosophy of mathematical practice by sketching a more general argument.

No one can deny that the philosophy of mathematics must eventually address the issue of actual mathematical practice. No account of mathematics can be satisfactory, no matter how rigorous, formal and elegant it may be, if it leads to the conclusion that no one in the twentieth century knows any real mathematics. Any acceptable account of mathematics must explain the bulk of mathematical practice; otherwise we could not recognize it as an account of *mathematics.* The issue open to debate is not whether, but rather when and to what extent, we should focus on practice in philosophy.

Granted that the philosophy of mathematics must attend to mathematical practice, how should we characterize this practice? One plausible answer, and the answer of quasi-empiricism, is that we ought to look at practice in some detail and let the results of our observations guide our characterization. In order to oppose this answer one would have to appeal to some a priori characterization of mathematical practice. The most obvious characterization is that mathematical practice is essentially the justification of mathematicians' claims to knowledge. In other words, practice matters to philosophy insofar as mathematicians actually prove theorems. On the surface, this characterization would appear to rule out many of the quasi-empirical elements of practice such as discovery, communication, explanation, and pedagogy.

Upon reflection, however, we can see that this is not necessarily the case. Even if the essence of mathematical practice were to prove theorems or to justify claims to knowledge, it might well be that the verification of proofs is a public affair, an elaborate social process that proceeds by the canons and paradigms of a particular community of experts. Several of the following essays argue just this point. In this case the verification of proofs would involve such factors as the dissemination of results through a community, the education of experts, the hierarchies of authority—all of which are quasi-empirical. Indeed the philosophy of science seems to be making progress by attending to just such possibilities, why not the philosophy of mathematics?

Thus, even if mathematical practice could be restricted, a priori, to proving theorems, it would not follow that the details of such practice would be irrelevant to philosophy. To establish the latter claim, we need an additional assumption. We need to begin with an a priori conception of proof as formal deduction or purely demonstrative reasoning, or even, as a kind of mathematical object itself, for example, as a certain set of finite sequences of formulas. Only then could the philosophy of mathematics justifiably restrict itself to explaining that a priori conception of proof, that is, to presenting the one and only foundation of mathematics. On the other hand, if mathematical proofs are ultimately informal proofs, then quasi-empiricism can take hold by insisting that informal proofs must be characterized by their roles in the practice in which they appear.

So one can only reject the thesis that mathematical practice is a viable topic in the philosophy of mathematics by backing oneself into an exceedingly narrow philosophical corner. I can see no reason for doing this other than an antecedent commitment to foundationalism. Without the doctrine of foundationalism, the way is clear to a reexamination of mathematical practice.

What Is Mathematical Practice?

HAO WANG

Theory and Practice in Mathematics

In this essay Hao Wang combines a technical mastery of mathematical logic with a sensitivity to the deepest issues of philosophy. The major part of it was published in 1961 as "Process and Existence in Mathematics."[1] It does not offer a continuous development as much as a tentative sketch of a new landscape, marking out areas for further exploration. The style is reminiscent of Wittgenstein's style of philosophical investigation with a great deal of overlapping and doubling back. However virtually every important point made anywhere in the anthology is discussed by Wang.

He begins his discussion of mathematical activity by considering some simple, familar proofs to isolate the moment of illumination or of grasping a proof. From the perspective of mathematical activity it is not enough that a proof exist in some abstract sense, it must be somehow connected to an actual mathematician in order to enter into mathematical knowledge.

> Even if a miracle reveals that there is a way of seeing the geographical contours of Venus as a proof of Fermat's conjecture, how do we know that we shall ever be able to find suitable perspectives to make such an undigested proof perspicuous?

So Wang is led to the idea that actual proofs (informal proofs, usable proofs) must be 'perspicuous' or 'surveyable' or 'capable of being taken in.' Closely related to the idea of perspicuous proof is that of feasible procedure. The value of the millionth digit in the expansion of pi is decidable in principle, but we don't know it in the absence of a feasible procedure for obtaining it. These two anthropocentric

Reprinted, with permission, from Humanities Press, Inc., Atlantic Highlands, N.J. 07716, and from Routledge & Kegan Paul, PLC, London.

elements of mathematics "combine to account for and give directions to much of our mathematical activity."

Along the way Wang notes the relevance (and irrelevance) of mathematical logic to mathematics. The second section of his essay addresses the question of reducing mathematics to logic (and set theory) directly. It is a marvelous dialectic of pros and cons but the basic conclusion seems a healthy skepticism about the ultimate significance of such a reduction.

> Do we reduce mathematics to abstract set theory or do we get set theory out of mathematics by padding? . . . In this process [adding more and more sets to make the surface appear smooth], we lose sight of the distinctions between interesting and uninteresting sets, useful and useless real numbers. In order to recover the distinctions once more, we have to take off the padding. Could we perhaps describe this reverse process as reducing (e.g., 'Mrs E. is on a diet') abstract set theory to mathematics?

The overall effect of Wang's arguments is to broaden our conception of what is philosophically relevant about mathematics. Of course, if one insists on looking at the world through rose-colored glasses, one sees a rose-colored world. Wang examines a number of 'one-sided views' of mathematics and, like Goodman, objects to them for what they leave out. When it comes his turn to answer the question what is mathematics, however, he passes. The correct answer remains to be given although "righly or wrongly, one wishes for a type of foundational studies which would have deeper and more beneficial effects on pedagogy and research in mathematics and the sciences." Nevertheless, he does offer some important suggestions in this direction. The basic concepts, he suggests, will not be set or structure but the existing body of mathematics. As a first step in characterizing this body, we might construct an abstract history of mathematics "concerned less with historical details than with conceptual landmarks." Wang adumbrates such a history, trying to steer between too much fragmentation on the one hand and too quick generalization on the other.

In the last section of his essay, Wang explores some practical aspects of mathematics using a list of unsolved problems to assess the development of mathematics. He notes some provocative analogies between mathematical views and political views.

Mathematical practice, perspicuity, anthropocentrism, history, now politics—what a different world from the eternal unchanging realm of Platonic entities! No wonder traditional Platonists are annoyed by the idea of mathematical practice. In defense of Wang, we would do well to recall the Aristotelian slogan; "Of course I love Plato, but I love truth more."[2]

NOTES

1. *Essays on the Foundations of Mathematics,* Bar-Hillel et al., eds., North-Holland, Amsterdam (1961), 328–351. See also "Logic, Computation and Philosophy," *L'age de la Science,* 3 (1970), 101–115.

2. See the *Nichomachean Ethics,* Book One, Chapter Six, for the original source of this traditional slogan.

• • • • •

1 ACTIVITY AND FEASIBILITY

In learning elementary geometry, we are asked to prove the equality of the base angles of an isosceles triangle and observe it. The happy idea of constructing a new line from the top vertex to the base enables us to notice relations between the parts of the new diagram, thereby proving the conclusion. Or, alternatively, we can get the conclusion directly by observing the possibility of a rigid motion in space that interchanges the two base vertices.

We are asked to find the sum of the first 10,000 positive integers, and hit on the device of rearranging the numbers to look like:

$$\begin{array}{llll} 1 & 2 & \ldots & 5000 \\ 10000 & 9999 & \ldots & 5001. \end{array}$$

We notice each of the 5000 columns add up to 10001.

When the service of a mathematician is requested by an engineer or a physicist, he reformulates the problem in a more idealized form, striking out all the factual details he judges to be irrelevant. This reformulation may require the joint efforts of a mathematician and a practitioner of the source subject, sometimes combined in one person. The new problem is more abstract and retains only a skeleton of the original problem. It is more perspicuous, at least to the properly trained mind which is often able to juggle it to get a method of solution either by standard techniques or by inventing new mathematics. Sometimes the application of the method to the specific problem may be tedious and, for example, calculating machines may have to be used to supply an actual solution.

In each case, there are interplays of schematic representations (diagrams, graphs, arrays of characters such as numerals, variables, schematic letters, logical and mathematical constants) and mental experimentations. We are interested in schemata or diagrams rather than pictures or portraits, because we are concerned not with all the factual details about them, but rather with their skeletons and structures, the 'formal facts' about them, the forms and patterns revealed by them. They are aids to our imagination in the process of reasoning, and, as such, essential to mathematics. This does not mean that we always have to draw the diagrams on paper or blackboards, nor that mathematics is a manipulation of symbols. It is not the physical production of the diagrams that distinguishes the mathematical activity, but the possibility of using them to assist our mental experimentations in the search for desired necessary connections.

The mind participates actively in seeing, e.g., an array of numbers, as paired off suitably to create a new uniformity. Thus this 'seeing as' enables us to take in at a glance the 5000 pairs of numbers which all have the same sum 10001. In this respect, the dots are not 'mere abbreviations' either, because they, or something else like them, are indispensable for grasping the array of numbers at one go; they embody the formal fact that we see the 5000 pairs as a whole string with a definite beginning, a definite end, and a definite way of continuation. In doing this calculation, one is likely to make (mental) experiments such as trying to look for suggestions from summing up a small number of integers. But calculation is not itself an experiment, since once the path is found, certainty intervenes.

To prove that for every prime p, there is a greater prime, the crucial construction is, of course, the function $p! + 1$. Here it is not natural to describe this function as obtained by the act of 'seeing as.' In general, the types of constructions are varied and heterogenous. Once we have got $p! + 1$, we show that, for all q, $q < p$, q does not divide it by seeing $p!$ as qP, where P is the product of all $m < p$, except $m = q$.

Suppose we are to prove that in a right triangle, $c^2 = a^2 + b^2$, and are given the following diagram:

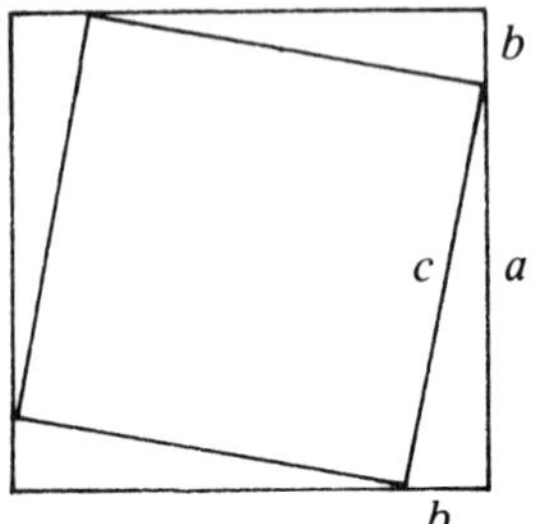

We see that the area of the big square is the same as the sum of the area of the small square and the area of the four right triangles. We write this out: $(a + b)^2 = c^2 + 4\ (\frac{1}{2}ab)$. Then, lo and behold, we get $c^2 = a^2 + b^2$. Here, we would say that for the purpose of proving the desired theorem, finding the above diagram is a much bigger step than the rest.

Or, to prove the same theorem, we may easily think of drawing a square on each side of the right triangle. Then we may get the vague idea that if we draw any three 'similar' figures on the sides, the situation would be the same. In particular, we may choose three right triangles which are reflections of ACD, BCD, ABC and see that since $ABC = BCD + ACD$, the area of the one on c is obviously the sum of the areas of the triangles on a and b.

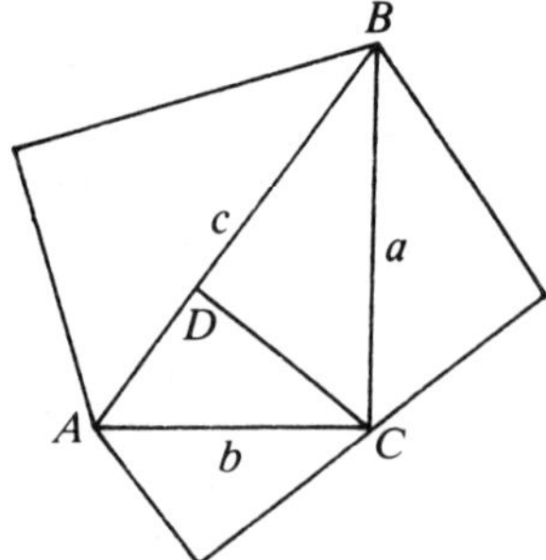

Hence, the same relation holds among the three squares, and $c^2 = a^2 + b^2$. Many people would find the proof not sufficiently conclusive as it stands, but it can be expanded into a more convincing form.

In searching for a solution, the activity is directed to a definite goal. One is easily led to ask how the mental experiments are chained together. The technical problem about methods of discovering solutions ('how to solve it') is not one for the philosophy of mathematics, although it is of pedagogic interest and central for the mechanical simulation of the mathematical activity. The nature of inferring and the compulsion of the logical 'must,' once the inference is made, is indeed the concern of philosophers. We accept, as a matter of fact, a sequence of symbols as an application of a certain rule, e.g. the modus ponens. Here we may easily get into the slippery ground of truth by convention, synthetic a priori, self-evidence. But an underlying foundation is the sociological fact that it is so accepted. And this sociological fact involves a variety of different factors: among them, the biological and the physiological, which are likely to be the ultimately decisive elements.

That Beethoven continued to compose good music after he had gone deaf is important for the study of the activity of composing music. Similarly, blind mathematicians are a phenomenon which should shed some light on the nature of the mathematical activity. It is very striking that most of us would find it difficult, if not impossible, to multiply three 7-digit numbers in our head. For one thing it is not easy to retain the question without the assistance of paper and pencil. If a child asks his blind father to help him do such a sum, he would probably ask the child to serve as his pencil and paper to record the question and the intermediate results. If such assistance is denied a blind mathematician who wishes to do complicated numerical calculations, he would have to train himself to be a calculating prodigy.

That pencil and paper are indispensable to complicated calculations is certainly an important fact about the calculating activity. Most of us do not memorize a large number of telephone numbers but we remember, or rather know, different methods of finding them out. We do not learn the multiplication table to 100 times 100 but only to 9 times 9, or 12 times 12. In more advanced mathematical activities, most of the things which a mathematician knows have not come to him through a deliberate effort to memorize. Interconnections not only increase the number of things remembered but also their duration and their quality. Certain things are kept simultaneously in the head, and these enable one to spin out a great many things in sequence. The spinning power of a head with structured memories and dispositions determines the power to experiment mentally and the ability to do mathematics. When one says that mathematics is an activity of the pure intellect, it cannot be to deny that sense perceptions and memory form an integral part of it, but rather than an excellent eyesight or a good memory is not a distinguishing characteristic of better mathematical capabilities.

Some problem-solving is prompted by practical needs, others by analogy with existing problems. Not all mathematical activity is problem-solving. Esthetic needs and the desire to systematize and smooth out things lead to the development and improvement of mathematical theories. It is among such results that the thesis of the reducibility of mathematics to logic comes in. And it is along such a path that one is led to what might be called the librarian's definition of pure mathematics as the class of all conditional propositions in which all constants are logical constants.

'All *A* are *B*, all *B* are *C*; therefore, all *A* are *C*' is a diagram and traditional logic is a sort of mathematics, as ticktacktoe is a sort of board game. One many feel that, being so crude and inefficient, it hardly deserves the fair name of mathematics. However, family resemblance with mathematical logic seems to lend some color to it. Traditional logic is more a hindrance than a help to right reasoning that is quite adequately taken care of by our natural power. This is seen from the fact that the more purely rational an activity is, the less it is needed. Mathematics is least in need of it while election politics, judging from Susan Stebbing's studies, needs it most.

Mathematical logic has to a considerable extent suffered the same kind of misfortune. Logic is primarily interested in the analysis of a proof into as many distinct steps as possible, and not, like mathematics, in efficient methods of reasoning which can produce remote consequences in one swoop or unravel an involved entanglement. When, e.g., an elementary branch of it gets practical applications in making machines, it does this only, so to say, accidentally and against its own will. It is by leaving behind the basic concerns of logic and pursuing the subject as a simple sort of mathematics that the application is made.

The breaking up of a proof into a large number of small steps is desirable in so far as the set of all possible different small steps is in general less complex than the set of a smaller number of different bigger steps. This seems obvious, since the union of all small steps which make up one big step is simpler than the big step which contains the simple steps (possibly with some repetitions) plus a special mode of combination, and some small steps generally occur in a number of different big steps. There is, however, no equally obvious reason why such simplification should be desirable for the mathematical activity. In fact, since we are quite at home with the bigger steps, one is inclined to think that by mutliplying the pieces in each proof, the breaking up only serves to slow us down and make it harder for us to take a proof in.

Few mathematicians have taken the trouble to learn the theory of quantifiers and they are none the worse for their ignorance. It sounds idle to rejoice over the accomlishment that when a logician has analyzed and reformulated a proof, even a machine can check it for correctness. Nobody, not even a logician, checks an elaborate mathematical proof in this manner, and so far machines have not been used to check proofs.

Thirty years ago it must have appeared that if man finds such a way of checking proofs tedious, machines would not do it any better either in speed or in accuracy. The appearance of large machines and the rapidity with which their speed and reliability have been improved, is one of the unexpected occurrences in history which yield consequences which are hard to predict.

There is, however, a distinct possibility that in this connection a basic application of logic will be found that is based on the essence rather than the accidents of logic: viz. to handle inferences as efficiently as calculations. For example, some preliminary work has already enabled a common machine to prove all theorems in *Principia* of quantification theory with equality in a few minutes.

Grammar is of little help in learning one's native language or cultivating elegant writing. And we do not worry about the theory of sound waves when learning to speak. Phonetics is a little more relevant, although few can afford tuition from Professor Higgins. If mathematical logic were a little less pure, perhaps it could assist a mathematician to learn some alien branch of mathematics. In its present aloof form, however, a training in mathematical logic is neither necessary nor likely to speed up the pursuit of other branches of mathematics.

On the other hand, if a machine is to do mathematics, it is necessary that methods of logic be explicitly included. This provides incentive for doing more detailed work on the decision problem and proof procedures for logic.

Moreover, considerations about the practical feasibility of alternative procedures are pushed to the forefront. This supplements the basic concern that a mathematical argument should be perspicuous, surveyable, or capable of being taken in. These two aspects of the problem of efficiency are not identical. For example, a less efficient proof procedure is generally easier to describe, and the argument for proving its adequacy is generally easier to grasp. On the other hand, the two aspects combine to account for and give direction to much of our mathematical activity. To stress the requirements that procedures be feasible and that proofs be surveyable, one might coin the label 'praximism.'

In a different direction, the project of mechanical mathematics calls our attention to the problem of formalizing methods of finding proofs. Theoretically dispensible methods and strategies will be included to speed up the search for proofs. Here we have another hitherto largely neglected domain which is susceptible of a treatment by methods similar to those used in the more elementary parts of mathematical logic. Such problems are on a different level from the study of the psychology of mathematical invention. We may be able to simulate the external circumstances of preparation under which Poincaré's exceptional subconscious functions. But it seems preposterous to suppose we are capable of endowing a machine with a subconscious, much less with one comparable to Poincaré's.

If a machine produces a proof of Fermat's conjecture with one million lines, we still have the somewhat easier task of making the proof perspicuous. This would be a situation where we could say, in a clear sense, that a proof exists but nobody has understood it. Somebody would undoubtedly prefer to say that there is no proof yet, just as he would say that a machine cannot calculate, cannot prove, because there must be a final contact which lights up the whole thing and only a man can establish this contact by taking in the whole process that makes up the calculation or the proof.

When interesting mathematical questions can be settled by machines, our chief concern will be shifted to the methods of proof and their coding. And we do not expect to have 10^6 lines of coding. We synthesize and abbreviate as we make progress, in order to press more and more into the brain as a bounded finite machine. With the increasing power of mechanized methods, an economy in storage is achieved by substituting general methods for particular arguments. Instead of a single proof requiring 10^6 lines, it should be possible to organize all our mathematical knowledge and have it contained in so many lines.

Definitions generally reveal new aspects and thereby help to direct the course of our thinking into certain channels. Consider, for example, the development of arithmetic within the framework of set theory. Through the linking definitions, the theorems of set theory can be divided into two classes: those which correspond to theorems of arithmetic and those which do not. Theorems of both classes are, one is inclined to think, in the system all along; the linking definitions do not change their meaning but merely provide a different way of looking at those in the first class. Most of us have seen pictures which appear to be a mess at first, but reveal, e.g., a human face upon closer scrutiny. The physical object that is the picture is not affected by the different impressions which we get from it. The picture, however, means different things before and after we discern a face. This, one feels, is also the situation when linking definitions enable us to see certain sentences of set theory as disguised arithmetic sentences. If one is afraid that next time he will forget how he can discern a face, he may, as a reminder, trace certain parts of the picture by a red pencil. As a result, everybody can immediately see a face, although the configurations in the picture remain the same. Does it make an essential difference whether the stress is made by a red pencil or just seen in our mind's eye?

Does a proof change the meaning of a hitherto unproved mathematical proposition? Does a new proof of a methematical theorem change its meaning? The answer is undoubtedly: sometimes it does, usually it does not. The point of the question is probably not to suggest the instability of mathematical concepts but rather to point to an abstractly human element in the meaning of mathematical concepts. Think of the proposition as a station in a formal system. The country is there, but we do not know whether there is any road which leads to the station. Presently we find one road, then we find another. But the country is the same, the station is the same. Both of us understand the proposition that there are infinitely many prime numbers. You know a proof of it but I do not. Does it have the same meaning for both of us? It is not yet known whether there are infinitely many pairs of primes n and $n + 2$ ('twin primes'). Will a proof of the proposition change its meaning? The proof will reveal new connections and provide reminders which enable every member of the mathematical community to see the proposition as true. Does the increase of knowledge affect the meaning of a proposition or is the relation between knowledge and meaning only an external one resembling the relation between the weight of an elephant and our knowledge of it?

Elephants exist independently of our knowledge, but in what sense does a proof exist independently of all knowledge? Once a proof is found, it can be codified and put at its proper place within a textbook, but where did it reside previously? More, to call several pages of printed marks a proof presupposes a good deal of the sociological circumstances which make them a proof. For instance, they are sufficient to recreate in a few people the gradual process which culminates finally in seeing that the concluding proposition of the several pages must be true. We are reluctant to deny that every possible proof in a formal system exists even before we have singled it out and digested it by constructions, mental or with red pencils. Under suitable conditions of size and endurance, a machine can eventually grind it out. In this sense, the undigested proof has existed all along, even though the digested proof has to be invented. Is, however, an undigested proof a proof?

To say that it is a proof because it is, though undigested, digestable, leads to the question of distinguishing digestable in principle from digestable as a matter of fact. Even if a miracle reveals that there is a way of seeing the geographical contours of Venus as a proof of Fermat's conjecture, how do we know we shall ever be able to find suitable perspectives to make such an undigested 'proof' perspicuous? It seems like a dogma to say that every undigested proof will eventually be digested. If one does not wish to assert so much, then it is hard to provide, without circularity, a sense of 'digestable' according to which every undigested proof is digestable.

I think I know how to add and multiply. But it would be easy to find complicated problems which I cannot do within two hours. For instance, multiplying 78 by 78, 78 times. With some effort, we can also find computation problems which I cannot do, at any rate by the ordinary technique, within a month, or within my lifetime. In what sense do I know how to add and multiply? Not just in the sense that I can handle small numbers, because I feel I can deal with large numbers too. Or perhaps, if I live long enough, say by keeping my self fit like a great athlete, I shall be able to complete even the most complicated additions and multiplications? But then surely I cannot do them with the ordinary technique for there would be neither enough chalk, nor sufficiently large blackboards.

These considerations strike one as utterly irrelevant. When I say I can do addition and multiplication, I do not mean to preclude the possibility that practical difficulties may prevent me from carrying out certain complicated calculations. I feel I can do them, shall we say, in principle. One is generally not expected to do artifically elaborate calculations. If it were the case that nobody was interested in multiplications of less than 300 numbers each with more than 10 digits, then one might say that nobody could multiply unless he was assisted by a machine.

In this connection, it may be instructive to consider the following inductive argument: 1 is small; if n is small, $n + 1$ is small; therefore, every number is small.

The words 'can,' 'decidable,' etc. mean different things in pure mathematics and applied mathematics, in actual mathematical activities and in the discussions of mathematical logicians. A man says that the further expansion of π is a further expansion of mathematics and that the question changes its status when it becomes decidable. Since what the millionth place of the decimal expansion of π is, is a theoretically decidable question, the man seems to be inconsistent in saying that a ground for the decision has yet to be invented. This is so only if we think of decidable in the logician's sense. In the sense of actually doing mathematics, the question is not yet decidable because it is to be expected that some ingenious general argument is required to supply the required digit and prove to the satisfaction of mathematicians that it is indeed the desired one. And it strikes one as dogmatism to assert categorically that such an argument will be found. It is true that finitists and intuitionists do not worry about such questions because once a problem is decidable in theory, they lose all interest in it. This, however, does not mean one cannot interest oneself in feasibility as a concept worthy of philosophical considerations.

Confusions arise when two men each choose one of the two different senses and refuse to recognize that there is also the other sense. Perhaps a phenomenologist is one who permits both senses and distinguishes them from each other. At any rate, it seems convenient to make use of both senses, at least until we have more successfully unified them.

There is a great gap between what can be done in principle and what can be done in practice. Often we are interested in broadening the range of the latter. That is why such techniques as the use of the Arabic notation, logarithmic tables, and computing machines are important. (The second and the third differ from the first in that we are not aware of the steps in the calculation.) Are they only of practical importance or are they also of theoretical interest? Shall we say that theoretical and practical significances merge in such fundamental improvements in the technology of mathematics?

It is not always easy to draw the line between theoretical and practical. Numbers of the form $2^{(2^n)} + 1$ are called Fermat's numbers because Fermat conjectured that all such numbers are prime. It has been proved since Fermat's time that, for $n = 5, 6, 7, 8$, all Fermat's numbers are composite. A proof for each case was a nontrivial piece of mathematics, even though, with patience, these questions could be settled simply by the ordinary methods of calculation. One might say that the proofs provide us with new techniques for deciding problems which could otherwise be solved by uninspired laborious computation.

In mathematics the introduction of new techniques is important and definitions do serve to introduce new techniques. It is therefore misleading to speak of them as 'mere abbreviations.' Even if, after a proof of a theorem in number theory has been discovered, it is possible to eliminate defined terms and translate the proof into the primitive notation of set theory, the translated proof would not have been discovered by one who worked exclusively with the primitive notation of set theory. Nor could the translated proof in practice be understood correctly even if one was aware of the definitions.

2 REDUCING MATHEMATICS TO LOGIC

The more sensational reduction of mathematics to logic is the thesis that definitions of mathematical concepts can be found in logic such that mathematical theorems can be transformed unconditionally into theorems in logic. This is plausible only if 'logic' is understood in a very broad sense to include set theory as a part.

The term 'set theory' is less familiar than the term 'logic,' but then, at the same time, more unambiguous too. Since set theory is itself a branch of mathematics, the question is that of reducing other branches of mathematics to this particular one. In this sense, the matter is initially a domestic affair of mathematics. The concern of philosophers has come about partly as a result of the historical accident that Frege and Russell, rightly or wrongly, connected it with philosophy, and that at least one of them is such a good propagandist. Nonetheless, the persistence of such interest surely cannot be discarded simply by deploring the poverty of philosophy. After all, even if set theory is but another branch of mathematics, the claim that all other branches are reducible to it makes it a proper concern of philosophers.

The most interesting case is number theory. If we are concerned only with numerical formulas containing addition and multiplication, it appears possible to find theorems of logic which correspond to them rather naturally. On the other hand, if we are concerned with general laws of arithmetic as well, the reduction is only possible when we take set theory rather than logic proper.

It is puzzling that Kant called '7 + 5 = 12' synthetic a priori and that Frege believed himself to have refuted this by his reduction of arithmetic to logic. One way to make the two viewpoints plausible seems to be the following. In order that an equation be analytic, the two sides must have the same sense, not just the same denotation. One is tempted to say that '7 + 5' and '12' have different senses, although they have the same denotation. Hence, '7 + 5 = 12' is synthetic and a priori, its necessity not being questioned here. But there is a natural way of reducing '7 + 5 = 12' to a theorem of logic. Suppose we use the abbreviations:

$$(E!_1x)Gx \quad \text{for} \quad \exists x_1 \forall y\, [Gx_1 \wedge (Gy \supset y = x_1)]$$

$$(E!_2x)\,Gx \quad \text{for}$$

$$\exists x_1 \exists x_2 \forall y [x_1 \neq x_2 \wedge Gx_1 \wedge Gx_2 \wedge (Gy \supset (y = x_1 \vee y = x_2))]$$

Then the corresponding theorem of logic is:

(*) $\qquad (E!_7x)\,Gx \wedge (E!_5x)\mathrm{H}x \wedge \forall \mathrm{u}\ \neg(Gu \wedge Hu) \supset (E!_{12}x)(Gx \vee Hx)$

Since it is natural to regard all theorems of logic, i.e. the theory of quantifiers with equality, as analytic, Frege seems to have shown that '7 + 5 = 12' is analytic.

There are a number of difficulties in this explanation. The negation of something like (*) does not give us what we want if we are interested in proving, e.g., '7 + 6 ≠ 12.' The obstacle arises because the letters *G, H* serve as free variables so that we have to quantify them to get the correct negation. We certainly do not wish to say that '7 + 5 = 12' is analytic but '7 + 6 ≠ 12' is synthetic a priori. Moreover, there is no way to get around the need for existence assumptions in one form or another. If there are not enough entities in the universe of discourse, the antecedent of (*), for instance, would be always false, and we can derive, e.g., 12 = 13. In fact both objections can be combined and met by assuming that there are infinite sets or that all finite sets exist. We are led back to the reduction of arithmetic to set theory, and there is an obvious choice between saying that arithmetic has been shown to be analytic (Frege) and saying that logic (more correctly, set theory) has been shown to by synthetic (Russell at one time).

Although the numerals, 5, 7, 12 occur in (*) as subscripts, there is no direct circularity in the reduction, because we can expand (*) and avoid the use of numerals by employing sufficiently many distinct variables. A striking feature of the reduction is that short propositions are reduced to long ones. As a result, it would be very clumsy if one were to do arithmetic in such a notation, and we are quickly forced to introduce abbreviations. This is rightly considered an inessential complication for the simple reason that the reduction is not meant to introduce a new technique of calculation. It only yields an informal result about calculations as a byproduct: that one could do arithmetic in the complicated symbolism too. This depends on the reduction plus the information that one can do arithmetic in the customary notation.

A more basic difficulty of the reduction is the accompanying increase in conceptual complexity. If we attempt to give a proof of (*) in the expanded form, we find ourselves counting the distinct variables, and going through, in addition to operations with logic, exactly the same kind of moves as in elementary calculations. We are able to see that (*) is a theorem of logic only because we are able to see that a corresponding arithmetic proposition is true, not the other way round. By tacking 'frills' on an arithmetic proof of '7 + 5 = 12', we get a proof of (*) in logic. 'A definition of christening in a particular church is no longer a definition of christening.'

There are different ways of defining arithmetic concepts in set theory. If we imagine a determinate situation with one specific formal system of set theory, one of arithmetic, and one specific set of linking definitions, then there is a theorem in the primitive notation of set theory that corresponds to the arithmetic theorem '1000 + 2000 = 3000'. The formula would be forbiddingly long. Does it mean the same thing as the original formula of arithmetic? When one who is not aware of the definitions is faced with the long formula, he might be at a loss to see any clear connections between the two formulas. He may be sufficiently familiar with set theory to understand the long formula and still not recognize its relation to the short one. Or even if he knows the definitions and is asked to simplify the long formula according to them, chances are he will make errors and arrive at some incorrect result. We are inclined to think that such considerations are irrelevant as far as the intended meaning of the formulas is concerned. But if a man fails to see the equivalence of the two formulas even after hours of hard labor, can we still say that the two formulas mean the same thing to him?

This is an artificial question because nobody is expected to write out or work with the long formula in order to do arithmetic calculations. We have a short argument to show that there must be such a formula, and that nearly exhausts the meaning of the hypothetical assertion that we could work directly with it too. When it is a matter of doing mathematics, we naturally fall back on the best available technique we have. If we had only the long version at first, then we would as a matter of fact not be able to do much calculating until we hit on some systematic way of changing it into a short version. We may spend many hours to read a long formal proof, but when we understand it, we do not give each line the same status, but work out an easily memorizable structure which may include known theorems, lemmas, subcases, reminders that certain successions of steps are of certain familiar forms. We do not have to keep all details of the structure in mind at the same time. The proof may be a mile long, but we can still plant posts as we go along and not worry about parts changing when we are not looking at them. As soon as we are convinced that some parts do give us a subtheorem which is the only contribution those parts can make toward proving the final theorem, we need retain only the subtheorem in our head.

If set theory alone is given but the linking definitions with arithmetic are still missing, then we do not yet have arithmetic in full force because we would not and could not, as a matter of fact, do the arithmetic proofs and calculations in set theory. If both set theory and the linking definitions are given, we continue to do arithmetic as before only with the awareness that there is a sense in which our proofs and calculations could be translated into set theory. But doing arithmetic is still different from doing set theory. We do not change our manner of doing arithmetic. That is the sense in which arithmetic has not been reduced to set theory, and, indeed, is not reducible to set theory.

Do we reduce mathematics to abstract set theory or do we get set theory out of mathematics by padding? In analysis, we find certain real numbers such as π and e of special significance. Somehow we are led to the search for a general theory of real numbers. Since we want the theory to be general, we postulate many more real numbers in order to make the surface smooth. When we find that real numbers, natural numbers and many other things can all be treated as sets, we are induced to search for a general theory of sets. Then we add many more other sets in order to make the surface appear smooth. 'If tables, chairs, cupboards, etc., are swathed in enough paper, certainly they will look spherical in the end.' In this process, we lose sight of the distinctions between interesting and uninteresting sets, useful and useless real numbers. In order to recover the distinctions once more, we have to take off the padding. Could we perhaps describe this reverse process as reducing (e.g. 'Mrs. E is on a diet') abstract set theory to mathematics?

If we think in terms of true propositions about natural numbers, then set theory is also reducible to arithmetic at least in the sense that, given any consistent formal system for set theory, a translation can be found such that all theorems turn into true arithmetic propositions. The same is true of any other branch of mathematics on account of the possibility of an arithmetic representation of formal systems. Hence, we can also say that all mathematics is reducible to arithmetic, but in a sense quite different from, for instance, what was known as the arithmetization of analysis. Arithmetization of logic involves a change of subject from talk about sets, etc., to talk about how we talk.

When we ask, 'what is a number,' 'what is the number one,' we seem to be after an answer as to what numbers *really* are. If numbers are neither subjective nor outside of us in space, what could they be? And then it is gratifying to get the answer that they are really certain classes. One is relieved to have thus unmasked numbers. What does the unmasking accomplish? Frege's definition of number seems to resemble rather closely our unanalyzed concept of number so that we are sometimes inclined to take it as providing a true analysis of our intentions. But what more?

Apparently there is the belief that the reduction puts mathematics on a more trustworthy basis. Otherwise, the paradoxes about sets would not have induced Frege to say that the foundation of arithmetic wobbles. This is, as we now know, unjustified. We understand arithmetic better than set theory, as evidenced by the highly informative consistency proofs for arithmetic. The foundation of arithmetic is more trustworthy than that of set theory—what would be of greater interest is rather to found set theory on arithmetic, or on an extension of arithmetic to infinite ordinals.

There are different ways of defining numbers in terms of classes. Each of them leads to and from the undefined concept of number, and they are seen to be equivalent not through the interconnection between themselves but by way of the channels connecting them to the naked concept of number. Perhaps this indicates a certain priority of numbers to their corresponding classes?

Identifying numbers with suitable classes is said to be 'recommended by the fact that it leaves no doubt as to the existence-theorem.' 'Postulating' a limit to fill the gap for each Dedekind cut is said to have advantages which are the same as those 'of theft over honest toil,' while the course of honest toil is to identify the limit with the class of ratios in the lower section of the cut. It is in a sense true that the latter course 'requires no new assumptions, but enables us to proceed deductively from the original apparatus of logic.' This is so, however, only because in the original apparatus of logic we have already made assumptions of the same kind. If the existence of the postulated limit is called into question, the existence of its corresponding class is equally doubtful. There is no reason to suppose that numbers evaporate but classes are rocks.

The reduction to set theory gives 'the precise statement of what philosophers meant in asserting that mathematics is a priori.' This is neither an informative statement nor a true one.

It is said that the axioms of arithmetic admit diverse interpretations while the reduction eliminates such ambiguities. True, the concept of set is involved in the axiom of induction and the intended interpretation of the concept of set assures the intended interpretation of the axioms of arithmetic. But arithmetic presupposes only inductive sets which are a particular type of set. Moreover, we should not confuse the possibility of incorrect interpretations with the impossibility of correct interpretations. It is possible both to interpret the axioms of arithmetic correctly and to interpret the axioms of set theory incorrectly. Moreover, interpreting the axioms of set theory involves greater conceptual difficulties.

Surely one cannot deny that Frege's definition has the great virtue of taking care of applications? This is undoubtedly the case if we perform a multiplication just in accordance with the rules of calculation or argue formally by observing the rules of logic. But the application of number to empirical material forms no part of either logic or set theory or arithmetic. There may be some doubt if we consider the proposition 'Paris has 4 million inhabitants' as an application of the number 4 million, and the proposition 'two rabbits plus two rabbits yield four rabbits' as an application of the mathematical proposition '$2 + 2 = 4$.'

Such applications can appear neither in arithmetic nor in set theory for the simple reason that words such as 'Paris,' 'rabbits,' 'inhabitants' do not occur in the vocabularies of these theories, and the set-theoretical definition of numbers offers no help. If it is meant that the definition enables us to apply numbers within the framework of a wider language, then it is not clear why the same does not apply without the definition. Suppose we are to infer the proposition 'she has two virtues' from the proposition 'her only virtues are beauty and wit.' It is apparently thought that the inference can only be made by using Frege's definition of the number 2, because otherwise the class of her virtues cannot be shown to have the number 2. If, however, the full richness of ordinary discourse is permitted, we can surely make the inference without appeal to Frege's definition.

In any case, why should such applications be taken as the proper business of set theory or of arithmetic? Mathematics and its applications are two things which can conveniently be studied separately. If the desire is to have a general language which includes both mathematics and other things, the link between numbers can just as well be provided by axioms which assert, for example, that a class has $n + 1$ members if and only if it is gotten from a class with n members by adding a new member. In other words, if we adopt the course of taking numbers as undefined, we can still, if we wish, add axioms to do the job of Frege's definitions. The effects are the same except that mathematics and its application are divided at a more natural boundary.

3 WHAT IS MATHEMATICS?

The most impressive features of mathematics are its certainty, its abstractness and precision, its broad range of applications, and its dry beauty. The precision and certainty are to a large extent due to the abstractness which also in part explains the wide applicability. But the close connection to the physical world is an essential feature which separates mathematics from mere games with symbols. Mathematics coincides with all that is the exact in science.

According to Kant, mathematics is determined by the form of our pure intuition so that it is impossible to imagine anything violating mathematics. If we agree that the physical world, including our brains, is a brute fact, this view can be said to imply that the external world, including the physiological structure of our mind, determines mathematics. The discovery of non-Euclidean geometries need not be regarded as refuting Kant's doctrine, since we can construe them as superstructures on the Euclidean, or an even weaker, geometry. A more serious objection is that Kant's theory does not provide enough elucidation of the principles by which these and other superstructures are to be set up.

As we all know, Shaw was accustomed to exaggerate. He defended himself by arguing that shock value is the best way to call attention to new ideas. In a similar spirit, we may hope to clarify our vague thoughts by examining a few one-sided views of mathematics.

3.1 Mathematics is the class of (logically) valid or necessary propositions 'p implies q.' Thus, given any theorem q, we can write the conjunction of the axioms employed in its proof as p, and 'p implies q' is a theorem in elementary logic. In this somewhat trivial sense, all mathematics is reducible to elementary logic. This really says nothing about mathematics proper, since one would like to assert p and q unconditionally. This evades the whole question why certain p, e.g. mathematical induction, is accepted as a mathematical truth. Moreover, the concepts of validity and necessity (or possibility) are to be explained by the concept of set or perhaps by concepts like law and disposition. A related view is to construe logic more broadly so as to include propositions such as 'For all x and y, if x and y have no common members, x has 7 members, y has 5 members, then $x \cup y$ has 12 members.' then one has to define numbers in logic, and so on. Such a view is akin to the next one.

3.2 Mathematics is axiomatic set theory. In a definite sense, all mathematics can be derived from axiomatic set theory. To be definite, we can adhere to a standard system commonly referred to as *ZF*. This is the counterpart of Frege's and Russell's reduction of mathematics to logic and paradoxically also of Poincaré's 1900 remark about the arithmetization of mathematics ('numbers and their sets'). This is what most impressed the logical positivists, leading to, among other things, an emphasis on axiomatization and formalization. There are several objections to this identification. As we know, there are many difficulties in the foundations of set theory. This view leaves unexplained why, of all possible consequences of set theory, we select only those which happen to be our mathematics today, and why certain mathematical concepts and results are more interesting than others. It does not help to give us an intuitive grasp of mathematics such as that possessed by a powerful mathematician. By burying, e.g., the individuality of natural numbers, it seeks to explain the more basic and the clearer by the more obscure. There is the side issue of logicism which continues to be upheld in some quarters despite definitive evidence against it. In at least one important case, this mysterious state of affairs is based on a mistaken identification of Frege's logical theory of sets (extensions of predicates) with Cantor's mathematical theory of sets. The argument goes like this. Frege's theory looks like logic and mathematics can be reduced to Cantor's theory; therefore, by the identification, mathematics is reducible to logic.

In an autobiography, Einstein gave as his reason for choosing physics over mathematics the lack of unity in mathematics. We may wonder whether set theory might not give a unity to mathematics. The formal system *ZF* is, of course, neither complete nor categorical. Moreover, it cannot even decide familiar mathematical propositions such as the continuum hypothesis. Hence, as a comprehensive system, it is conceptually unsatisfactory. If now we leave aside higher infinities and confine ourselves to more applicable mathematics such as classical analysis, number theory, and abstract algebra, it seems reasonable to agree that almost all familiar theorems have counterparts in *ZF*. Could we claim that *ZF*, together with the derivation of different branches of mathematics from *ZF*, provides a rough indication of the sort of unity we look for?

One objection is that the representation is not faithful enough. In particular, it tends to miss the more abstract aspect of mathematics. Certainly the postulates of a group or a field are satisfied by various and diverse models. Even the theorems of classical analysis can be proved in axiom systems of very different strength. This suggests the possibility of a web of axiom systems such that each system determines an abstract structure, viz. the class of all possible models of the system. Something like *ZF* or a more adequate enlargement yet to be contrived encloses all these systems in the sense that none postulates the existence of any object not envisaged by it.

From this approach one might even prove metatheorems about all models of a system without circularity, because they can also be proved in some fairly weak system which admits of both very big models and rather small ones. If we devised such a web of perhaps no more than ten systems, we would get a sort of skeleton, which could only be made into a living form by the addition of facts about the present state, a guess at future trends, and the historical highlights of mathematics.

3.3 Mathematics is the study of abstract structures. This appears to be the view of Bourbaki. An influential sequence of books has been written to substantiate this view. They make a conscious attempt to divorce mathematics from applications which is not altogether healthy. The inadequacy of this outlook is revealed not only by the omission of various central results of a more combinatorial sort, but especially by the lack of intrinsic justification of the selection of structures which happen to be important for reasons quite external to this approach. The constructive content of mathematical results is not brought out. There is also a basic inconsistency insofar as lip service is paid to an axiomatic set theory as the foundation, while serious foundational researches are frowned upon. It would conform more to the general spirit if number, set, and function were treated in a more intuitive manner. That would at least be more faithful to the actual practice of working mathematicians today.

3.4 Mathematics is to speed up calculations. Here calculations are not confined to numerical ones. Algebraic manipulations and juggling with logical expressions (e.g. in switching theory) are also included. A somewhat broader view would be to say that every serious piece of mathematics must have some algorithmic content. A different, though related, position would be to say that all mathematics is to assist science, to assist us to understand and control nature. These views seem to make it impossible to explain, e.g., why we often prefer more elegant proofs with higher bounds and why we take great delight in impossibility results. One could argue that there is in addition the human element in mathematical activites so that it is essential, even for applications, that the situation should be perspicuous. Thus, we can better grasp an elegant proof and, indirectly, are enabled thereby to look for more efficient algorithms; and impossibility results tell us the limitations of given methods, helping the search for positive results in the long run. This kind of argument is, however, typical of philosophers stretching a position to try to fit in unwanted facts.

So much for oversimplifications.

If we review quickly the history of mathematics, we find quite a few surprises. What appears particularly attractive is that there is room for a serious and fruitful synthesis of mathematics and work in the philosophy of mathematics which would help the progress of mathematics itself by making the subject more appealing and by fighting against excessive specialization.

Foundational studies in this century have been very fruitful in several ways. The possibilities and limitations of formalization have been much clarified. There is a better understanding of constructive methods. And the explication of mechanical procedures has yielded many fundamental results, especially negative ones, on decidability and solvability. On the whole, there remains, however, the impression that foundational problems are somewhat divorced from the main stream of mathematics and the natural sciences. Whether this is as it should be seems a highly debatable point.

The principal source of the detachment of mathematics from mathematical logic is that logic jumps more quickly to the more general situation. This implies a neglect of mathematics as a human activity, in particular, of the importance of notation and symbolism, and of the more detailed relations of mathematics to applications. It is philosophically attractive to study in one sweep all sets, but in mathematics we are primarily interested in only a very small range of sets. In a deeper sense, what is more basic is not the concept of set but rather the existing body of mathematics. For example, the distinction between linear and nonlinear problems, the invention of logarithms, the different ways of enumerating finite sequences, the nature of complex numbers and their functions, or the manipulation with infinities by physicists (such as Dirac's delta function and the intrustion of infinities in quantum electromagnetic theory) all seem to fall outside the range of problems which interest specialists in foundational studies. Rightly or wrongly, one wishes for a type of foundational studies which would have deeper and more beneficial effects on pedagogy and research in mathematics and the sciences.

As a first step, one might envisage an 'abstract history' of mathematics that is concerned less with historical details than with conceptual landmarks. This might lead to a resolution of the dilemma between too much fragmentation and too quick a transfer to the most general.

3.5.1 Concrete arithmetic began with practical problems. The idealization of the indefinite expandability of the sequence of numbers and the shift from individual numbers to general theorems about all numbers gave rise to the theory of numbers. Only around 1888 was Dedekind able to formulate the so-called Peano axioms by analyzing the very concept of number.

3.5.2 The solution of equations together with the use of literal symbols such as letters for unknowns marked the beginning of algebra ('transposition and removal'). Only in 1591 (F. Viéta) were letters used for known quantities as well (variables and parameters).

3.5.3 Geometry deals with spatial forms and geometrical quantities such as length and volume. The number of a set is an abstraction from that which is invariant under any changes whatsoever in the properties and mutual relations of the objects in the set (e.g. color, weight, size, distance), provided only the identity of each object is not disturbed (by splitting or merging). Similarly a geometrical figure or body is an abstraction of an actual body viewed purely with regard to its spatial form, leaving out all its other properties. Rather suprisingly, such an abstract study led not only to pure geometry but also to the first extensive example of the deductive method and axiomatic systems. There was even a geometrical algebra in Greece.

3.5.4 Measurement of length and volume is a union of arithmetic and geometry, applying units to calculate a number. This, just as the solution of equations, is a natural way of leading to fractions and even irrational numbers. The desire to have an an absolutely accurate, or rather indefinitely improvable, measurement leads to the general concept of 'real number'. Algebra led to negative numbers and complex numbers. But a better understanding of complex numbers was only reached through their geometrical representations.

3.5.5 By the way, in terms of speeding up computations, the invention of logarithms (Napier, 1614) was a great advance.

3.5.6 In an indeterminate equation, say $3y - 2x = 1$, we may view x and y not only as unknowns but as variables so that the given equation expresses the interdependence of these two variables. The general concept of function or interdependence is the subject matter of analysis. Using the Cartesian coordinates, we get a connection between algebra and geometry, with function playing the central role. In this sense, analytic geometry may be said to be the simplest branch of analysis. It is implicitly assumed that we deal with at least all real numbers.

3.5.7 If we add in addition the concept of change or motion, and study a broader class of functions, we arrive at the calculus. The original source was geometry and mechanics (tangent and velocity, area and distance). Theories of differential and integral equations search for functions rather than numbers as solutions. Such theories develop naturally both from applications and from an intrinsic combination of the calculus with the algebraic problem of solving equations. In the same spirit, functional analysis is not unlike the change from algebra to analysis, the interest being no longer confined to finding individual functions but rather to studying the general interdependence of functions.

3.5.8 It is not easy to understand why functions of complex variables turned out to be so elegant and useful. But it certainly was a gratifying phenomenon that an extension served to clarify many facts in the original domain. Incidentally, if we require the axioms of fields be satisfied, extensions of complex numbers are not possible, e.g., for quaternions multiplicaiton is not commutative.

3.5.9 The lively development of the theory of probability has been connected with statistical mechanics, and its foundations are a fascinating but elusive subject.

3.5.10 In algebra, Galois theory not only gives a conclusive treatment of the solution of equations but opens up a more abstract study of abstract structures dealing with operations on arbitrary elements rather than just numbers.

3.5.11 The greatest changes in geometry have been the discovery of non-Euclidean geometries and Riemann's general ideas about the possibility of many different 'spaces' and their geometries. Figures are generalized to arbitrary sets of points.

3.5.12 The development in functions of a real variable touches on various conceptual problems such as the definition of real number, and the meaning of 'measure.'

In this century, the development of logic, the emergence of computing machinery, and the prospect of new applications in the biological sciences and in linguistics all tend to emphasize what might be called 'discrete mathematics,' even though continuous mathematics is well entrenched and as lively as ever.

One of the very basic problems is that we still do not have any definitive theory of what a real number or what a set of integers is. Perhaps we can never have a definitive theory. It seems quite unknown how this fundamental unclarity affects the rest of mathematics and the novel applications of mathematics in physics.

Relative to different concepts of set and proof, one could reconstrue most of mathematics in several different ways. Are these different formulations just essentially equivalent manners of describing the same grand structure or does there exist a natural framework in which everything becomes more transparent?

4 PRACTICAL ASPECTS OF MATHEMATICS

We have mentioned the anthropocentric elements of surveyability of proofs and feasibility of calculations. There are also ethical, political, and sociological aspects of mathematics. We may ask for practical justifications for developing a particular branch of mathematics or proving a particular theorem. We may reflect on how the general line of development of mathematics is determined and, in particular, how fashions, personalities, applications, intrinsic merits, and other factors interact. It is remarkable that mathematics is harder to popularize than other sciences. This is in part caused by the fact that mathematics has more than other sciences a special language of its own.

There is a familiar aphorism that mathematics is a language. In one sense, the concepts of mathematics are more independent of language, tying up with 'pure intuition.' At the same time, mathematics is perhaps the most efficient language (for those who understand it), as, e.g. exemplified by Littlewood's inferences from a diagram on the table of an unfamiliar room.[1] Mathematics is much more than a language insofar as it is much more than just a means of communication. It has its own language, but that is very different from saying that it is a language.

In 1900, Hilbert proposed a very influential list of twenty-three mathematical problems. H. Weyl once suggested the idea of using this list as a basis to review the overall progress of mathematics during several decades. J. von Neumann was asked to offer a modern list in 1954 but pleaded inability to cover wide areas of mathematics. It seems likely that nobody today is in a position to make up a list comparable to Hilbert's relative to his time.

If a sufficiently representative group of people put together a list of twenty or thirty central problems today, one could use this problem list as a basis to

1 picture the present state of mathematics and its relations to other sciences; 2 review the history; 3 predict future trends; 4 discern some sort of conceptual unity of the whole of mathematics; 5 discuss some of the perennial epistemological questions.

By the way, a comprehensive list of general problems would include (a) certainty and necessity (synthetic a priori or not); (b) mathematical existence (and methods of construction); (c) the driving force in mathematics (utility, esthetic appeal and art for art's sake, fashions and their cause, curiosity); (d) the mathematical activity (notation and abbreviations, heuristics, the phenomenon of physically blind mathematicians); (e) the nature of mathematical proofs (formalization and intuitive evidence); (f) exposition, teaching, and mechanization of mathematics (problems of communication contrasted with the obtaining of new pieces of mathematics, the possibility of mathematical criticism as an analog of literary criticism); (g) pure versus applied mathematics (criterion for judging the value of mathematical models of empirical situations, distance from applications); (h) mathematics as a 'language.'

It is neither necessary nor sufficient that the problems be famous ones. For example, Fermat's and Goldbach's conjectures and the four-color problem should probably not be included unless somebody has some promising idea of attack which, even if it fails, would yield a rich harvest of byproducts. On the other hand, since a number of serious mathematicians are thinking about the Riemann hypothesis, this may be worth including, providing one places it in an informative context.

It is in general not easy to find problems which are both sharp and of central interest. Usually, the sharp problems are not obviously fundamental, while the fundamental problems tend to be nebulous, waiting for the extraction of more specific questions. We may illustrate this situation by describing a few problems (or vague areas of research) suggested by mathematical logic, which is a highly nonrepresentative branch of mathematics.

1. *A more adequate axiom system of set theory.* A central question is to codify somehow the notion of an arbitrary subset of a given set, in particular, of the set of positive integers, and the idea of possible levels of iterating the power set operation. In a certain sense, we can never get a formal system which is completely adequate. But it might be possible to obtain a natural formal system in which, for example, the continuum hypothesis is decidable. Moreover, it is desirable to think of exact ways of relaxing the concept of formal systems to permit, say, a 'semiformal' system that would codify adequately the power set of the set of positive integers. A sharp formulation of the quest for new axioms is the study of axioms for large cardinals. There is also considerable interest in trying to relate such axioms to various restricted forms of the axiom of determinateness (on infinite games).

2. *Consistency of impredicative definitions.* Often this is expressed as the question of establishing the consistency of classical analysis. The commonly accepted axiom systems for classical analysis are, besides being inadequate (not providing enough real numbers), lacking in transparency on account of the acceptance of sets introduced by impredicative definitions. It

is desirable to find more articulate reasons for believing that they lead to no contradictions.

3. *Solvable and unsolvable problems.* Theoretical work on algorithms has made it possible to prove general impossibility results. It is natural to attempt to get such results in older mathematical disciplines. There have been successes with the word problem for groups and Hilbert's tenth problem (on the integer solutions of Diophantine equations). There are attempts to settle Burnside's problem in group theory and the equivalence problem of three-dimensional topological manifolds. It is also likely that one could get significant unsolvability results on the solution of differential equations, the quadratic programming problem, and so on. Two specific problems which are expected to get positive solutions are the concatenation analog of Hilbert's tenth problem and the Gödel case of logical sentences with equality included.[2-3]

4. *The mechanization of mathematical arguments.* The attempt to use computers as an aid to mathematical research would seem to lead to radically new types of problem such as the efficiency of decision procedures, the reorganization of our knowledge in a branch of mathematics, say number theory, with emphasis on sharp classifications of data, and formalization of heuristics.

5. *Feasible decidability.* There is a good deal of interest in the complexity of calculations. One looks for a natural and stable concept of feasible calculability according to which, for example, the traveling salesman problem is undecidable. An exact definition of computational complexity should also make it possible to give a sharp sense in which, for example, multiplication is more complex than addition.

It is undeniable that fashions and strong personalities have their influences in mathematics, as elsewhere. For example, many people feel unhappy over the proliferation of the designing and building of mathematical structures and blame this in part on fashions. One feels that in the long run the general line of development is determined by more objective factors such as fundamental applications and intrinsic conceptual interest.

The position of constructivists provides a concrete and sharp example. The constructivists believe that they have the true or correct view of mathematics. In addition, they sometimes predict that their position will triumph. Here we find a close analogy with political views: we ought to strive for the correct ideal and, in addition, the correct ideal will win out in the long run anyhow.

On February 9, 1918, G. Polya and H. Weyl made a wager in Zurich with twelve other mathematicians as witnesses.[4] Since the wager is formulated in a particularly interesting way, we quote it at length.

> Concerning both the following theorems of contemporary mathematics:
> (1) Every bounded set of numbers has a least upper bound,
> (2) Every infinite set of numbers has a countable subset,
> Weyl prophesies:
> A. Within 20 years (that is, by the end of 1937), Polya himself, or a majority of the leading mathematicians, will admit that the concepts of number, set,

and countability, which are involved in these theorems and upon which we today commonly depend, are completely vague; and that there is no more use in asking after the truth or falsity of these theorems in their currently accepted sense than there is in considering the truth of the main assertions of Hegel's physics.
B. It will be recognized by Polya himself, or by a majority of the leading mathematicians, that, in any wording, theorems (1) and (2) are false, according to any rationally possible clear interpretation (either distinct such interpretations will be under discussion, or agreement will already have been reached); or that if it comes to pass within the allotted time that a clear intepretation of these theorems is found such that at least one of them is true, then there will have been a creative achievement through which the foundation of mathematics will have taken a new and original turn, and the concepts of number and set will have acquired meanings which we today cannot imagine. Weyl wins if the prophecy is fulfilled; otherwise, Polya wins.

Polya relates that when the bet was called, in 1940, everybody, with one exception (K. Gödel), said he (Polya) had won.

More recently, E. Bishop made a similar prophecy.[5]

> This book is a piece of constructivist propaganda, designed to show that there does exist a satisfactory alternative. To this end we develop a large portion of abstract analysis within a constructive framework. . . . These immediate ends tend to an ultimate goal—to hasten the inevitable day when constructive mathematics will be the accepted norm.

There is a disagreement over the issue whether constructivism is 'realist' or 'idealist.' On the one hand, classicists may be thought to be realists because they seem to be more willing to envisage abstract entities. On the other hand, Bishop prefers to call the classicists idealists since they tend to forget the true (i.e. numerical) content of mathematical statements. Another disagreement is whether classicial or constructive analysis is more appropriate to applications in physics.

In many cases, doing a piece of mathematics is justified by appealing to its intrinsic interest or its relevance to other interesting mathematics. This can be contrasted with justifications in terms of the welfare or interest of society and mankind. If satisfying the rational interest of mankind is to constitute justification, we have to admit that there are different views of what this rational interest consists in. It is easy to accept the justification that knowledge is power or that knowledge makes man master and governor of nature. In such terms, mathematics is to be justified by its physical applications, actual and potential, and perhaps less directly by its disciplinary role in scientific thinking. There is also the tradition of allowing practical justifications broader than the utilitarian one: knowledge as the actualization of human reason, as a cultural value, as art, and so on.

Kant offers an interesting contrast between practical and pathological interests:[6]

> The dependence of the power of appetition on sensations is called an inclination, and thus an inclination always indicates a *need.* The dependence of a contingently determinable will on principles of reason is called an *interest.*

> Hence an interest is found only where there is a dependent will which in itself is not always in accord with reason: to a divine will we cannot ascribe any interest. But even the human will can *take an interest* in something without therefore *acting from interest.* The first expression signifies *practical* interest in the action; the second *pathological* interest in the object of the action. The first indicates only dependence of the will on principles of reason by itself; the second its dependence on principles of reason at the service of inclination—that is to say, where reason merely supplies a practical rule for meeting the need of inclination.

Even though there is social support for mathematics in many societies, this fact alone does not yield a practical justification. With regard to some branches of mathematics, it may have been a mistaken belief in their practical value which has led to the support. Or a bad government could encourage mathematics with a view to keeping a group of people out of mischief which would be, in the objective sense, valuable to social progress. In fact, many contemporary intellectuals have discovered an eternal contradiction between the universal knowledge they search for and the special way of thinking they have acquired from the particular environments in which they have been brought up. Hence, for each individual mathematician, the problem of practical justification is of a higher order of difficulty than that for a particular area of mathematics.

NOTES

1. J.E. Littlewood, *A mathematician's miscellany,* 1953, p. 50.
2. See H. Löb, *J. symbolic logic,* vol. 21, 1956, p. 66; and K. Gödel, *Monatsh. Math. Physik,* vol. 40, 1933.
3. The Gödel case of identity has been shown unsolvable by Werren Goldfarb, *J. symbolic logic*, vol. 49, 1984, p. 1237.
4. A report on this wager is scheduled for publication in *Math. Zeitschrift.*
5. Errett Bishop, *Foundations of constructive analysis,* 1967, pp. ix–x.
6. Kant, *Groundwork of the metaphysics of morals,* B38. (English translation by H.J. Paton, p. 81).

IMRE LAKATOS

What Does a Mathematical Proof Prove?[1]

Lakatos's brief essay develops some of the topics introduced by Wang, informal proofs and the role of history in the philosophy of mathematics. Like Wang, Lakatos gives examples of informal proofs which 'intuitively' show their conclusions without explicit postulates or well-defined logical rules. Such proofs are common in mathematical practice and they work. They are not generally infallible, Lakatos observes, for they are occasionally refuted by some "hitherto unthought-of possibility." So he calls this common method of establishing mathematical facts 'thought experiments', a term that goes well with quasi-empiricism.

One of Lakatos's primary concerns is to relate informal proofs to formal proofs. A standard assumption, which he wishes to argue against, is that informal proofs have been superseded by formal proofs. Informal proofs, on this assumption, are relics of less critical days, 'mere persuasive arguments', or abbreviated formal proofs. Lakatos's argument has two parts. On the one hand he stresses the limited ways in which formal proofs supersede informal proofs. In particular, formal proofs do not eliminate the possibilities of doubt or error, but at best isolate them on the assumptions of the formal consistency of the background theory and its material adequacy.

Secondly he argues that, in any case, formal proofs can be superseded by informal proofs. On the basis of formal results, we can give informal proofs not formalizable in the original theory. Lakatos calls these post-formal proofs. For example, a formal proof that Fermat's conjecture was undecidable could be used in an informal proof that the conjecture is true. Lakatos's argument at this point is somewhat sketchy, but the following seems to be what he had in mind. If Fermat's conjecture is formally undecidable, then there aren't any natural numbers x, y, z, n with $n > 2$ and $x^n + y^n = z^n$. For if there were, the calculations of x^n, y^n, z^n, and $x^n + y^n$ would yield a formal proof that the conjecture is false,

Reprinted from the MATHEMATICS, SCIENCE AND EPISTEMOLOGY, by Imre Lakatos by permission of Cambridge University Press. September 1979, pp. 540–551.

contrary to hypothesis. Thus Fermat's conjecture is, if formally undecidable, both true and informally provable! (That it is undecidable is explained by the presence of nonstandard models of arithmetic in which the theorem is false. Its undecidability implies that we could consistently add as a new axiom that $(Ex)(Ey)(Ez)(En > 2)\ (x^n + y^n = z^n)$, but that no standard numbers satisfy this formula.)

Lakatos begins his paper by raising the question of historicism. His explanation of the relation between informal and formal proofs presupposes a general pattern of evolutionary or historical development of proof through pre-formal, formal and post-formal stages. He confronts the prevalent objection of his day in the question "Does this inject a disastrous historicism into sound philosophy of mathematics?" Lakatos pleads guilty to historicism but not to any disastrous effects. "I am quite convinced that even the poverty of historicism is better than the complete absence."

It is important to be clear on what historicism means in this context. It does not mean the mere collection of historical facts nor the claim that such facts wear their philosophical significance on their sleeves. It is a more abstract history that is at issue here, like Wang's organization of conceptual landmarks. In this abstract sense of history it is difficult to do much philosophy of mathematics without injecting some historicism. Even the formalist uses some history to explain how formal proofs are to be seen as an improvement over informal proofs. Lakatos' point is that by ignoring history we are condemned to a naive historicism, and with a little consideration of historical issues, we could do much better.

• • • • •

On the fact of it there should be no disagreement about mathematical proof. Everybody looks enviously at the alleged unanimity of mathematicians; but in fact there is a considerable amount of controversy in mathematics. Pure mathematicians disown the proofs of applied mathematicians, while logicians in turn disavow those of pure mathematicians. Logicists disdain the proofs of formalists and some intuitionists dismiss with contempt the proofs of logicists and formalists.

I shall begin with a rough classification of mathematical proofs; I classify all proofs accepted as such by working mathematicians or logicians under three heads:

(1) pre-formal proofs
(2) formal proofs
(3) post-formal proofs.

Of these (1) and (3) are kinds of informal proofs.

I am afraid that some ardent Popperite may already be rejecting all that I am about to say on account of my classification. He will say that these misnomers clearly prove that I really think that mathematics has some necessary, or at least standard, pattern of historical development—pre-formal, formal- and post-formal stages, and that I am already showing my hand—that I want to inject a disastrous historicism into sound mathematical philosophy.

It will turn out in the course of my paper that this, in fact, is just what I should like to do: I am quite convinced that even the poverty of historicism is better than the complete absence of it—always providing of course that it is handled with the care necessary in dealing with any explosives.

As a consequence of the unhistorical conception of 'formal theory' there has been a lot of discussion as to what constitutes a respectable formal system out of the immense multitude of capriciously proposed consistent formal systems which are mostly uninteresting games. Formalists had to disentangle themselves from these difficulties. They could of course have done this by dropping their basic outlook, but they have tended to prefer complicated *ad hoc* corrections. They look for criteria distinguishing those formal systems which are *'interesting'* or *'acceptable'* and so on, thus betraying their bad consciences in accepting the pure formalist conception according to which mathematics is the set of *all consistent* formal systems. For instance, Kneale says that a mathematical system should be 'interesting.' His definition runs as follows: 'A possible—[possible means complying with some usual concept of modern rigour—i.e. consistent] system is interesting mathematically if it is rich in theorems and has many connections with other parts of mathematics, and in particular with the arithmetic of natural numbers.[2] Curry, who is a most extreme representative of formalism, introduces the notion of 'acceptability'. He says: 'The primary criterion of acceptability is empirical; and the most important considerations are adequacy and simplicity.[3] I fear there is a point on which I slightly disagree with their approach: they select from a previously given set of formal systems those which are interesting or acceptable. I should like to reverse the order: we should speak of formal systems only if they are formalizations of established informal mathematical theories. No further criteria are needed. There is indeed no respectable formal theory which does not have in some way or another a respectable informal ancestor.

Now I come back to our original subject: proofs. Most of the students of the modern philosophy of mathematics will instinctively define proof according to their narrow formalist conception of mathematics. That is, they will say that a proof is a finite sequence of formulae of some given system, where each formula of the sequence is either an axiom of the system or a formula derived by a rule of the system from some of the preceding formulae. 'Pure' formalism admits any formal system, so we must always specify in which system *S* we operate; then we speak only about an *S*-proof. Logicism admits essentially only one large distinguished system, and so essentially admits a single concept of proof.

One of the most outstanding features of such a formal proof is that we can mechanically decide of any given alleged proof if it really was a proof or not.

But what about an *in*formal proof? Recently there have been some attempts by logicians to analyse features of proofs in informal theories. Thus a well known modern text-book of logic says that an 'informal proof' is a formal proof which suppresses mention of the logical rules of inference and logical axioms, and indicates only every use of the specific postulates.[4]

Now this so-called 'informal proof' is nothing other than a proof in an axiomatized mathematical theory which has already taken the shape of a hypothetico-deductive system, but which leaves its underlying logic unspecified. At the present stage of development in mathematical logic a competent logician can grasp in a very short time what the necessary underlying logic of a theory is, and can formalize any such proof without too much brain-racking.

But to call this sort of proof an informal proof is a misnomer and a misleading one. It may perhaps be called a quasi-formal proof or a 'formal proof with gaps' but to suggest that an informal proof is just an incomplete formal proof seems to me to be to make the same mistake as early educationalists did, when, assuming that a child was merely miniature grown-up, they neglected the direct study of child behaviour in favour of theorizing based on simple analogy with adult behaviour.

But now I should like to exhibit some truly informal, or, to be more precise, pre-formal proofs.

My first example will be a proof of Euler's well-known theorem on simple polyhedra.[5] The theorem is this: Let V denote the number of vertices, E the number of edges and F the number of faces of a simple polyhedron; then invariably

$$V - E + F = 2.$$

By a polyhedron is meant a solid whose surface consists of a number of polygonal faces, and a simple polyhedron is one without 'holes', so that its surface can be deformed continuously into the surface of a sphere. The proof of this theorem runs as follows:

Let us imagine a simple polyhedron to be hollow, with a surface made of thin rubber (see Figure 1 (*a*)). Then if we cut out one of the faces of the hollow polyhedron, we can deform the remaining surface until it stretches out flat on a plane (see Figure 1 (*b*)). Of course, the areas of the faces and the angles between the edges of the polyhedron will have changed in this process. But the network of vertices and edges in the plane will contain the same number of vertices and edges as did the original polyhedron, while the number of polygons will be one less than in the original polyhedron, since one face was removed. We shall now show that for the plane network, $V - E + F = 1$, so that, if the removed face is counted, the result is $V - E + F = 2$ for the original polyhedron.

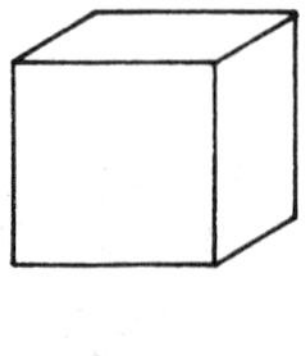

(*a*)

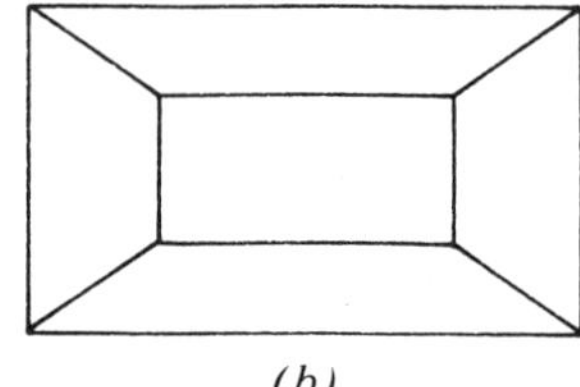

(*b*)

FIG. 1

We 'triangulate' the plane network in the following way: in some polygon of the network which is not already a triangle we draw a diagonal. The effect of this is to increase both E and F by 1 thus preserving the value of $V - E + F$. We continue drawing diagonals joining pairs of points until the figure consists entirely of triangles, as it must eventually (see Figure 2(*a*)). In the triangulated network, $V - E + F$ has the value that it had before the division into triangles, since the drawing of diagonals has not changed it. Some of the triangles have edges on the boundary of the plane network. Of these some, such as ABC, have only one edge on the boundary, while other triangles may have two edges on the boundary. We take any boundary triangle and remove that part of it which does not also belong to some other triangle. Thus, from ABC we remove the edge AC and the face, leaving the vertices A, B, C, and the two edges AB and BC [see Figure 2(*a*)]; while from DEF we remove the face, the two edges DF and FE, and the vertex F [see Figure 2(*b*)]. The removal of a triangle of type ABC decreases E and F by 1, while V is unaffected, so that $V - E + F$ remains the same. The removal of a triangle of type DEF decreases V by 1, E by 2 and F by 1, so that $V - E + F$ again remains the same. By a properly chosen sequence of these operations we can remove triangles with edges on the boundary (which changes with each removal) until finally only one triangle remains, with its three edges, three vertices and one face. For this simple network $V - E + F = 3 - 3 + 1 = 1$. But we have seen that by constantly erasing triangles $V - E + F$ was not altered. Therefore in the original plane network $V - E + F$ must equal 1 also, and thus equals 1 for the polyhedron with one face missing. We conclude that $V - E + F = 2$ for the complete polyhedron.

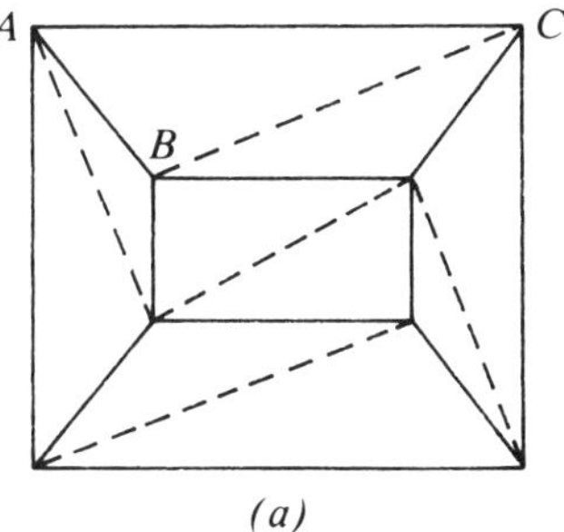

(*a*)

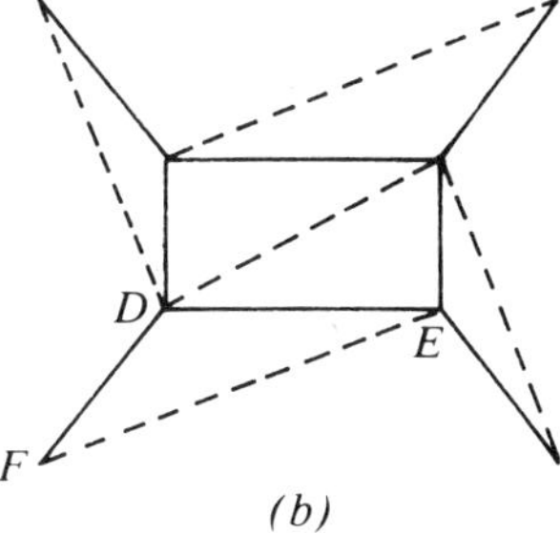

(*b*)

FIG. 2

I think that mathematicians would accept this as a proof, and some of them will even say that it is a beautiful one. It is certainly sweepingly convincing. But we did not *prove* anything in any however liberally interpreted logical sense. There are no postulates, no well-defined underlying logic, there does not seem to be any feasible way to formalize this reasoning. What we were doing was *intuitively showing that the theorem was true. This is a very common way of establishing mathematical facts*, as mathematicians now say. The Greeks called this proces *deikmyne* and I shall call it *thought experiment*.

Now is this a proof? Can we give a definition of proof which would allow us to decide at least *practically*, in most cases, if our proof is really a proof or not? I am afraid the answer is 'no'. In a genuine low-level pre-formal theory proof cannot be defined; theorem cannot be defined. There is no method of verification. As a strict logician like Dr. Nidditch would surely say, it is—I quote—'*mere* persuasive argumentation, rhetorical appeal, reliance on intuitive insight or worse'.[6]

But if there is no method of verification, there is certainly a method of falsification. We can point out some hitherto unthought of possibilities. For instance assume that we had omitted to stipulate that the polyhedron be simple. We may not have thought of the possibility of the polyhedron having a hole in it (in which case the theorem would be subject to many counterexamples).[7] Actually Cauchy made this 'mistake'.[8] This is the frequently occurring phenomenon of mathematical theorems being 'stated in a false generality'.

For the sake of a better and simpler illustration let me quote another famous thought experiment with a celebrated falsification. The problem is to find the two points P and Q that are as far apart as possible on the surface or boundary of any triangle. The answer is easy to guess; P and Q are the ends of the longest side. This can easily be proved by the sort of thought experiment which we just used; no axioms, no rules, but convincing force. Let us see:

If one of the points, say P, lies on the *inside* of the triangle, then PQ obviously does not have its maximum length. For on the extension of the line PQ there is obviously a point P' that is further from Q than P is, and that is still inside the triangle. If both P and Q lie on the *boundary* of the triangle, but one of them, say P, is not a vertex, then we can obviously find a nearby point P' on the boundary that is further from Q than the distance PQ. Therefore PQ can be a maximum only if both P and Q are vertices; otherwise it certainly is not. Thus PQ is a side of the triangle and must obviously be the longest side.

It is obvious that the same thought experiment can be accomplished for polygons to 'prove' the following theorem: in order that two points on the surface of a polygon be farthest apart, they must be two of the vertices that are farthest apart.

I think this should be quite convincing. Nevertheless there is an unthought-of possibility which may spoil our pleasure. Apply the same thought-experimental procedure to this figure:

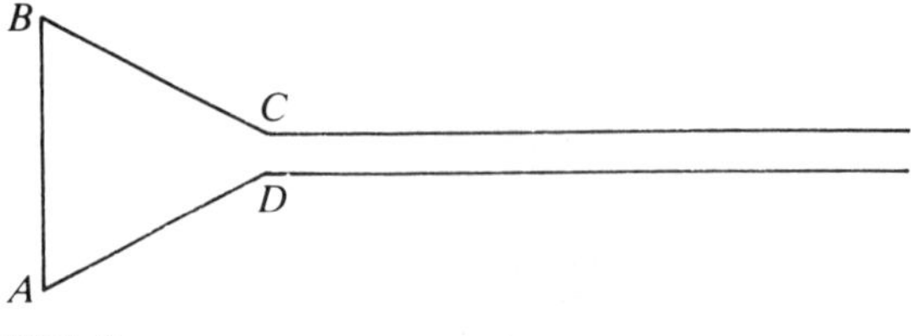

FIG. 3

Suppose P and Q lie anywhere inside the figure or on the boundary, even including the possibility that they may be at any of the four vertices A, B, C, D. [Unless PQ is exactly the side AB, a nearby point P' can be found within the figure such that the distance $P'Q$ is greater than the distance PQ.] Just as in the earlier cases, for each pair of points P, Q we can find a nearby pair that are further apart in every case except when the pair is A, B. No pair other than *A, B* can give a maximum. If we now follow the previous argument strictly, we must conclude that *AB* is the maximum.

The falsification of our argument ran along the same lines as in the case of Euler's theorem for *all* polyhedra. We thought we showed more than we actually did. In our second case, we showed only that the maximum must be such and such *if the maximum exists at all.* In the case of Eurler's theorem we only showed the truth of the theorem for the case where our rubber sheet could really be stretched out to the plane without any holes in it.

I should like to emphasize that the correction of such mistakes can be accomplished on the level of the pre-formal theory, by a new pre-formal theory.

The thought experiments I have just presented constitute only one type of pre-formal proof. There are others, basically different; ones for instance with the rather exciting property that in a certain sense we may say that contrary to the thought experiments we have just considered, they may be verified but not falsified. They give quite an insight into the nature of rules in a pre-formal theory and in pre-formal rigour.[9]

But now let us turn to axiomatized theories. Up to now no informal mathematical theory could escape being axiomatized. We mentioned that when a theory has been axiomatized, then any competent logician can formalize it. But this means that proofs in axiomatized theories can be submitted to a preemptory verification procedure, and this can be done in a foolproof, mechanical way. Does this mean that for instance if we prove Euler's theorem in Steenrod's and Eilenberg's fully formalized postulate system[10] it is impossible to have any counterexample? Well, it is certain that we won't have any counterexample formalizable in the system [assuming the system is consistent]; but we have no guarantee at all that our formal system contains the full empirical or quasi-empirical stuff in which we are really interested and with which we dealt in the informal theory. There is no formal criterion as to the correctness of formalization.

Well-known examples of 'falsified' formalizations are (1) the formalization of the theory of manifolds by Riemann, where there is no account of Möbius-strips; (2) the Kolmogorov-axiomatization of probability theory, in which you cannot formalize such intuitive statements as 'every number turns up in the set of natural numbers with the same probability'.[11] As a final but most interesting example I should mention (3) Gödel's opinion that the Zermelo-Fraenkel and kindred systems of formalized set theory are not correct formalizations of pre-formal set theory as one cannot disprove in them Cantor's continuum-hypothesis.[12]

I will show with a trivial example how little formalization may add to the demonstrative or convincing force of informal thought experiments. You remember the proof of Euler's theorem? A formalist will certainly reject it. But it won't be easy for him to reject the following 'proof': set up a formal system, with one axiom: *A*; no rules [except that all axioms are theorems!]. The interpretation of *A* is Euler's theorem. This system I think complies with the strictest demands of formalism.

Does all this mean that proof in a formalized theory does not add anything to the certainty of the theorem involved? Not at all. [In the informal proof it may turn out that we failed to make some assumption explicit which results in there being a counterexample to the theorem. But, on the other hand, if we manage to *formalize* a proof of our theorem within a formal system, we know that there will never be a counterexample to it which could itself be formalized within the system, as long as that system is consistent.] For instance, if we had a formal proof of Fermat's last theorem, then if our formalized number theory is consistent it would be impossible for there to be a counterexample to the theorem formalizable within the system.

Now we see that if formalization (we shall use this term from now on as essentially having the same meaning as axiomatization) conforms with some informal requirements, such as enough intuitive counterexamples being formalized in it and so on, we gain quite a lot in the value of proofs. But if we try to formalize a pre-formal theory too early, there can be unfortunate results. I wonder that would have happened if probability theory had been axiomatized just in order to supply 'foundations' for probability theory, before the discovery of Lebesgue-measure. Or, to take another example, it is clear that it would have been wasted time and effort to formalize metamathematics at the time of finitary illusionism, because later it turned out that the only useful methods must reach not only just beyond finitary tools but even beyond the object-theory in question. In an immaturely axiomatized algebra—axiomatized so as not to allow for complex numbers, say—we could never prove for instance that an equation of nth degree cannot have more than n real roots. Sometimes a well-formed formula of a theory T may be undecidable in the theory, but it may well be decided if suitably interpreted in a different theory, which may not even be an extension of the original theory. It is very difficult to decide in which theory a mathematical statement is really provable: for instance just take some theorems formalizable in the theory of real functions but provable only in the theory of complex functions, or theorems formalizable in measure theory, but provable only in the theory of distributions and so on. Even after a theory has been fruitfully axiomatized, there may arise issues which can bring about a change in axiomatization. This is now going on in probability theory. Axiomatization is a big turning point in the life of a theory, and its importance surpasses its impact on proofs; but its impact on proofs is immense in itself. While in an informal theory there really are unlimited possibilities for introducing more and more terms, more and more hitherto hidden axioms, more and more hitherto hidden rules in the form of new so-called 'obvious' insights, in a formalized theory imagination is tied down to a poor recursive set of axioms and some scanty rules.

Let me finally turn to the third part of my classification: to *post*-formal proofs. Here I shall just make a few programmatic remarks.

Two types of post-formal proofs are well-known. The first type is represented by the Duality Principle in Projective Geometry which says that any properly-worded valid statement concerning incidences of points and lines on a projective plane gives rise to a second valid statement when the words 'point' and 'line' are interchanged. For instance if the statement 'Any two distinct lines in the same plane determine a unique point' is valid, then so is the statement 'Any two distinct points in the same plane determine a unique line'. But then in proving the second statement we use a theorem of the system and another theorem, a meta-theorem, which we cannot specify, and still less prove, without specifying the concepts of provability in the system, theorem in the system and so on. This meta-theorem which we use like a lemma in our proof of an informal mathematical theory is not just about lines or points but about lines, points, provability, theoremhood and so on. Although projective geometry is a fully axiomatized system, we cannot specify the axioms and rules used to prove the Principle of Duality, as the meta-theory involved is informal.

The second class of post-formal proofs I should mention is the class of proofs of undecidability. As students of mathematical logic know, in the last few years it has turned out that formal proofs really prove much more than we want them to prove. Namely, to put it very roughly indeed, axioms in the most important mathematical theories implicitly define not just one, but quite a family of structures. For instance, Peano's axioms may be satisfied not only by our familiar natural numbers, but by some quite queer structures, Skølem's functions, which are far from being isomorphic with the set of natural numbers. Thus it turns out that when we fight hard to prove an arithmetical theorem, we prove at the same time some theorem in this other absolutely unintended structure. Now there are always statements, which are true in one structure but false in the other. Such statements are undecidable in the common formal structure. Are we helpless in such a situation? To see the point better, let us take a concrete, though hypothetical example. If we could prove that Fermat's theory is undecidable, then are we forever helpless to say anything about the truth of Fermat's theorem? Not at all. We may again call informal reasoning to our help, and try to operate informally *only* in the intended model. A concrete example of this is Gödel's proof [that his undecidable sentences are *true* (i.e. true in the standard model)]. But such post-formal proofs are certainly informal and so they are subject to falsification by the later discovery of some not-thought-of possibility.

Now at the present stage of our mathematical knowledge undecidable sentences occur only in rather artificial examples and do not affect the bulk of mathematics. But this situation may turn out similar to the case of transcendental numbers, which occurred first rather as exceptions and later turned out to be the more general case. So post-formal methods may gain in importance as undecidability encroaches more and more on mathematics.[13]

And now a brief summary. We saw that mathematical proofs are essentially of three different types: pre-formal; formal; post-formal. Roughly the first and third prove something about that sometimes clear and empirical, sometimes vague and 'quasi-empirical' stuff, which is the real though rather evasive subject of mathematics. This sort of proof is always liable to some uncertainty on account of hitherto unthought-of possibilities. The second sort of mathematical proof is absolutely reliable; it is a pity that it is not quite certain—although it is approximately certain—what it is reliable about.

NOTES

1. This paper seems to have been written some time between 1959 and 1961 for Dr. T.J. Smiley's seminar at Cambridge. Lakatos's own copy contains several hand-written corrections; some by himself and some by Dr. Smiley. We have incorporated them into the text. There is no indication that Lakatos ever returned to this paper after 1961. He subsequently changed his mind on some of the points made in the paper and had no plans to publish it himself (*eds.*, Worrall and Curne).

2. Kneale [1955], p. 106.

3. Curry [1958], p. 62.

4. Suppes [1957], p. 128.

5. For a full discussion of the history of this theorem, see Lakatos [1976*c*].

6. Nidditch [1957], p. 5.

7. One such counterexample is the 'picture frame' (Lakatos [1976*c*], p. 19) (*eds.*).

8. Cauchy [1813].

9. We have been unable to find out what Lakatos had in mind here (*eds.*).

10. Eilenberg and Steenrod [1952].

11. See Renyi [1955] (*eds.*).

12. For more detail on this point and references to Gödel's opinions, see Lakatos' earlier paper in this volume.

13. This has begun to happen, notably with the Paris–Harrington results. See their paper "A mathematical incompleteness in Peano Arithmetic" in J. Barwise, ed., *Handbook of Mathematical Logic* (Amsterdam: North-Holland, 1977).

PHILIP J. DAVIS

Fidelity in Mathematical Discourse: Is One and One Really Two?

The discovery of mathematical logic convinced many mathematicians and philosophers that this was the royal road to foundations. Thus convinced, they were anxious to rid philosophy of mathematics of all empirical considerations. None was more adamant than Gottlob Frege who in his masterpiece *The Foundations of Arithmetic* not only sketched the logical deduction of arithmetic but inveighed against psychologism and historicism in philosophy. Frege remarked in passing

> A delightful example of the way in which even mathematicians can confuse the grounds of proof with the mental or physical conditions to be satisfied if the proof is to be given is to be found in E. Schroder. Under the heading 'Special Axiom' he produces the following: "The principle I have in mind might well be called the Axiom of Symbolic Stability. It guarantees us that throughout all our arguments and deductions the symbols remain constant in our memory—or preferably on paper" and so on.[1]

Frege's repudiation of 'psychologism' has been so influential that it is with some surprise we find Davis, nearly a century after Frege, considering a principle very similar to Schroder's Special Axiom.

> Distinct Symbols can be Created. Instances of a given symbol can be created. Symbols can be processed and reproduced and concatenated with absolute fidelity. Symbols can be recognized as distinct or identical as the case warrants.

More surprising is Davis's view that it is the Fregean Platonist who must make this assumption! Most surprising, and a sign of the radical new directions in philosophy of mathematics, is Davis' contention that this principle is false!

Of course Davis is aware that an orthodox foundationalist would deny the relevance of symbolic stabilty insofar as mathematics is conceived to exist without physical carriers such as flesh and blood mathematicians. However our only entrance into such pure mathematics is through the practice of the mathematicians

Reprinted, with permission, from AMERICAN MATHEMATICAL MONTHLY, Vol. 79, No. 3, March 1972, pp. 252–263.

who deliver it for philosophical inspection in the first place. Even the Platonist must relate his or her abstraction to the practice from which it is derived: we must not saw off the branch on which we are sitting. Nor will it suffice, as Frege thought, to attempt to distinguish between the grounds of a proof and the mental or physical conditions to be satisfied if the proof is to be given. For as Frege constantly stressed, the grounds of a proof are revealed only by *following* through the proof step by step in completely rigorous fashion. It is just those operations which are necessary to follow a proof that are the concern of Davis. Contrary to Frege, he suggests with considerable plausibility that such operations are never absolutely certain, but performable only with a certain probability of success. There is no perfect fidelity in mathematics, only sufficiently good approximations.

The upshot of this is that Davis discovers a new question in philosophy of mathematics—"what is the mathematics of error?" Frege himself tried to outlaw this question. Committed to the view that mathematical knowledge was a priori, he could announce that the very idea of mathematical (i.e., a priori) error is "as complete a nonsense as, say, a blue concept." Frege's position is reminiscent of the neo-scholastic distinction between the Church Visible and the Church Invisible. The Church Visible is what the layperson sees, a human institution subject to the vicissitudes of human error. The Church Invisible is the real church whose purity is guaranteed by God. The possibility of an error in the workings of the Church Invisible is as complete a nonsense as, say, a blue angel. Whatever its merits in theology, this attitude distorts our perception of mathematics. It forces us to ignore those many components of mathematical practice that serve to *minimize* error as outside real 'mathematics'.

Perhaps the major consequence of admitting mathematical errors into philosophy is the different conception of proof it suggests. In the presence of potential error the authenticity of a mathematical proof itself ceases to be absolute and becomes only probabilistic. Davis offers a suggestive analogy with regard to computer proofs.

> A parallel with relativity theory can be made here. Newtonian mechanics grew up in a regime of low velocities and hence no relativity correction $(1 - (v/v_c)^2)^{1/2}$ is necessary. Conventional (precomputer) mathematics grew up in a regime in which proof lengths were sufficiently low so that fidelity could be considered absolute and the laws of information theory are irrelevant. It is also possible that mathematics might move into a period and into a corpus of material where the proof aspect ceases to have classical significance and where one can live intimately with less than perfect fidelity.

Computer proofs are discussed elsewhere in this anthology, but as Davis points out, they are not the only source of possible error in mathematics. The informal proofs considered by Wang and Lakatos are not only subject to some unthought-of possibility for counterexample, but, in many respects, are much better adapted to survive small errors than formal proofs in which each step is on a par. The outline of the informal proof offers us a scaffolding from which we can patch up details, but a formal proof, a line by line deduction, consists only of details. There remains much to be said about probabilistic proofs and errors in mathematics, but Davis provides us with a stimulating beginning.

NOTE

1. *The Foundations of Arithmetic*, Basil Blackwell, Oxford (1968), viii–ix.

• • • • •

> "I wanted certainty in the kind of way in which people want religious faith. I thought that certainty is more likely to be found in mathematics than elsewhere. But I discovered that many mathematical demonstrations, which my teachers expected me to accept, were full of fallacies, and that, if certainty were indeed discoverable in mathematics, it would be in a new field of mathematics, with more solid foundations than those that had hitherto been thought secure. But as the work proceeded, I was continually reminded of the fable about the elephant and the tortoise. Having constructed an elephant upon which the mathematical world could rest, I found the elephant tottering, and proceeded to construct a tortoise to keep the elephant from falling. But the tortoise was no more secure than the elephant, and after some twenty years of very arduous toil, I came to the conclusion that there was nothing more that I could do in the way of making mathematical knowledge indubitable."
>
> BERTRAND RUSSELL,
> *Portraits from Memory*

1 PLATONIC MATHEMATICS

The twentieth century has not yet delineated definitively the working principles and the broad articles of faith of what has come to be called "Platonic mathematics". Among these principles might be listed:

1. *The belief in the existence of certain ideal mathematical entities such as the real number system.*
2. *The belief in certain modes of deduction.*
3. *The belief that if a mathematical statement make sense, then it can be proven true or false.*
4. *The belief that fundamentally, mathematics exists apart from the human beings that do mathematics. Pi is in the sky.*

These beliefs have been questioned; and in the last century a number of distinguished mathematicians have raised their voices against one or more of them. These mathematicians include Kronecker, Borel, Brouwer, Gödel, Weyl, and in more recent times, E. Bishop. One objection raised by some materialists is that the physical world may be completely finite, and this is hard to accommodate to an infinity of integers. Other objections have to do with the axiom of choice, the axiom of the excluded middle, etc.

As far as No. 3 is concerned, the work of Gödel and the Logical School has put the *coup de grâce* on this principle; yet–and by no means strangely–it persists as a psychological prop in one's daily work. I once asked a very distinguished number theoretician whether he thought that Fermat's Last Theorem was one of the unprovable statements in the sense of Gödel. His answer was quick and definite: "It is not. We are just too dumb to find the proof." The truth of the matter is that if mathematics were ever to enter into a region where it is frustrated by too many interesting but unprovable statements, then this would cast a blight on the methodology and ritual surrounding the notion of proof.

The questioning of Platonic mathematics has led to other types of mathematics variously called intuitionistic mathematics, constructivistic mathematics, recursive mathematics, and other names. Some of these are subsets of the usual mathematics. The computing machine has undoubtedly reopened and reinforced some of the arguments. The reception given to non-Platonic mathematics ranges all the way from coolness to indifference. One recalls the story of Kronecker in the 1880s. Someone came to him and told him that Lindemann had just proved that pi was a transcendental number. "Very interesting," said Kronecker, "but pi doesn't exist." This skepticism was largely ignored. At a series of recent lectures on non-Platonic mathematics, a typical comment was "Well presented, but irrelevant. Let's get back to our (Platonic) drawing boards." Undoubtedly in 1971, one can earn a living with Platonic mathematics, and if mathematician A spouts some Platonism to mathematician B and the latter responds in kind, then there is at least human significance in the act. The emperor may be walking around in his underwear, but if the court is also, they can make a life together.

It is the object of this essay to present additional aspects of the non-Platonicity of mathematics.

Several years ago I did some experiments using the computer to prove and derive theorems in elementary analytic geometry.[2] These experiments inevitably led to speculation on the difference in the level of credibility of a theorem which has been proved or derived by machine as opposed to one which has been "hand crafted" in the traditional fashion. This essay is an outcome of this experience. The particular arguments made here have not been put forth elsewhere at any length, and lead to the conclusion that mathematics, in some of its aspects, takes on the nature of an experimental science.

2 SYMBOLS

It is commonplace that mathematics is done with symbols. Figures, words, graphs, special symbols of all sorts litter the mathematical page. The most common mode of operation is from the sheet of paper, the blackboard, the sandpit in the case of Archimedes, the TV computer screen in the case of a latter day Archimedes, into the brain through the eye and the optic nerve. Presumably, when this symbolic information enters the brain, it leaves a physical trace there. The symbols are then processed by the brain and hard copy output may be made via hand or mouth. If there were never any oral or written or action output (such as with the educated horse who when cued stamps with his foreleg in answer to arithmetic problems) then mathematics might exist, but not in the manner in which we know it.

The principal symbol of mathematics, then, is the graphical symbol, perceived by the eye. There are blind mathematicians of first rank (such as L. Pontryagin) and it would be interesting to hear what he has to say about his manner of symbol formulation, manipulation, and space percepton. I am not aware of any mathematicians who are blind and deaf mutes, but I presume that Helen Keller who graduated from Radcliffe could do sums.

If one believes in Platonic mathematics, then it is possible to free mathematics from the symbols that carry it. After all, the spoken word "two" and the Arabic symbol "2", the Braille symbol for two, have a common interpretation. Hence, there must be, so the argument goes, a concept of twoness which is symbol-free. As Plato put it, mathematical objects are perceived by the soul. Be this as it may, I cannot give a simple instance of symbolless, soul mathematics. Even if I knew one, how could I communicate it, short of telepathy?

3 PROOF

One of our most precious inheritances from Greek mathematics is the notion of proof. Certain statements are derivable from other statements by means of "pure reason", and a corpus of connected material can be built up in which all statements are derived from a few fundamental statements known as axioms. This is the program set forth in Euclid, and this, after 2300 years, remains the beau ideal of mathematical exposition. In fact, some authorities believe that this is the hallmark of mathematics. Now, what is the purpose of a proof and how is a proof carried out? If you read Plato (Meno, 87) you find Socrates going through a derivation with a slave boy. Using the famous Socratic method, he leads the boy by the nose, so to speak, to the result that in a 45°, 45°, 90° triangle, the area of the square on the hypothenuse has double the area of the square on the short side. This dialogue creates the impression first of all of the derivation of new knowledge *ex nihilo* (or ex very little), and secondly of establishing firmly on the basis of a few easily accepted premises a statement which is far less transparent. To prove is to establish beyond the question of doubt, and mathematics has been thought capable of just such a thing. History does not prove, sociology does not prove, physics does not prove, philosophy does not prove, religion (if we can forget the church's unrequited seven hundred year love affair with Aristotelianism) does not prove. Mathematics alone proves, and its proofs are held to be of universal and absolute validity, independent of position, temperature or pressure. You may be a Communist or a Whig or a lapsed Muggletonian, but if you are also a mathematician, you will recognize a correct proof when you see one.

These two aspects of Socrates' teaching: proof as a program of certification—let's not call it establishing truth—and proof as a program of discovery and of new mathematics formation are present in today's mathematics. The most charming instance of success of the first part of Euclid's program is undoubtedly contained in John Aubrey's brief life of the philosopher Thomas Hobbes:

> He (Thomas Hobbes) was 40 years old before he looked on Geometry; which happened accidentally. Being in a Gentleman's Library, Euclid's *Elements* lay open, and 'twas the 47 El. libri I. He read the Proposition. By G . . . , sayd he (he would now and then sweare an emphatical Oath by way of emphasis) this is impossible! So he reads the Demonstration of it, which referred him back to a Proposition, which Proposition he read. That referred him back to another, which he also read. *Et sic deinceps* [and so on] that at last he was demonstratively convinced of that trueth. This made him in love with Geometry.

But the facts of the matter are somewhat different. If you think you could talk to your favorite bartender and lead him by the nose á la Socrates and have him arrive at the Stone-Weierstrass theorem, think again. The path would turn him off the way I am turned off by Spinoza's proofs in ethics. As Poincaré observed, the ability to follow a mathematical argument is spread unevenly through the populace. For the professional mathematician, proof may be less a matter of convincing oneself psychologically of the truth of a statement than of merely assigning the tags 'true' or 'false' to the statement. But a balance must be struck. For as N. Bourbaki has written,

> "Indeed, every mathematician knows that a proof has not been 'understood' if one has done nothing more than verify step by step the correctness of the deductions of which it is composed and has not tried to gain a clear insight into the ideas which have led to the construction of this particular chain of deductions in preference to every other one."

Secondly, mathematics can and has been done in a "proofless" atmosphere. The Egyptians and Babylonians had piled up a considerable body of mathematics before even the Greeks came along with their proofs. If one reads Ptolemy one sees how proofless material can exist side by side with the mathematics of proof. In today's world, the physicist and engineer often work in absence of proof, it being sufficient to work formally and symbolically and have the work backed by a physical intuition or by an experimental confirmation.

Despite these two mathematical worlds, which have for a long time existed side by side, mathematicians, and in particular mathematical logicians have over the past century systematized and made precise the notion of a proof. Without attempting the technicalities, the matter seems to come down to this. The axioms, i.e., the primitive statements or assumptions are representable as certain strings of atomic symbols. The theorems are representable as certain other strings of atomic symbols. Proving is the process of passing form an axiom string to a theorem string by a finite sequence of allowable elementary transformations. To verify that the next man's putative theorem is, in fact, the theorem he claims it to be, is merely to verify that the sequence of string transformations are in order. The whole thing is in principle perfectly mechanizable and is work for a slave boy or our modern equivalent, the computer. From this point of view to verify an advanced statement is similar to establishing the arithmetic theorem $123 + 456 = 579$. We merely process the data. Proof is at once the glory of mathematics and its least human aspect.

A proof can be compared with a program. The axioms are analogous to the input. The theorem is analogous to the output while the proof is the program. To find a proof consists of finding a program. To verify a given proof we need only rerun the program.

4 FIDELITY

I come now to the nub of my argument. Mathematics, as we have seen, proceeds through symbols and symbol manipulation. It therefore assumes that we can create distinct symbols, recognize strings of symbols, reproduce symbols, concatenate symbols. A symbol has a physical trace. It is a blob of ink or a vibration in the air, etc. If I mark down two 1's these 1's may be identical on the macroscopic level, but not at the microscopic. It is impossible to create identical symbols. Like snowflakes, they are all different. If they are "nearly" identical, they may be perceived variously. The eye may be dim, the ear heavy, the brain fatigued. The computer may slip a pulse, its voltages may drop, it may be communicated with over a noisy channel.

As part of the assumptions of Platonic mathematics we should therefore list:

FIG. 1. Are all the symbols above instances of the same symbol? As of 1971, high fidelity recognition by machine of hand written characters has proved to be difficult.

0. *Distinct Symbols can be Created. Instances of a given symbol can be created. Symbols can be processed and reproduced and concatenated with absolute fidelity. Symbols can be recognized as distinct or identical as the case warrants.*

An orthodox Platonist might say the above is unnecessary insofar as mathematics exists without physical carriers. A non-Platonist, particularly one who has been exposed to communication theory, will say this is nonsense. We can do these things only with a certain probability of success. The probability maybe very high indeed, but there may be occasional failure. What is the mathematics of failure? Without making too many distinctions, let us agree indifferently to call an act of recognizing, reproducing, or processing one symbol 'an operation.' Let the probability of carrying out an operation with perfect fidelity be p. The number p satisfies the inequality

$$0 < p < 1$$

and we shall think of p as being very close to 1. A realistic value of p depends upon who or what is doing the symbol processing and under what circumstances. I know that in doing sums or in typing up an IBM card my personal probability may be around

$$p \approx 1 - 10^{-2}.$$

I have heard figures around

$$p \approx 1 - 10^{-9} \text{ to } p \approx 1 - 10^{-12}$$

quoted for computing machines. Now if the probability of success in one elementary operation is p, then, assuming independence, which may or may not be true, the probability of success in a sequence of n operations is p^n. Thus if n is very large, this probability goes down considerably. Now what probability of failure will you tolerate? One in a thousand? Then you want

$$p^n \geq 1 - 10^{-3} \text{ or } n \log p \geq \log (1 - 10^{-3}).$$

If now $p = 1 - \frac{1}{m}$,

then we want

$$n \leq \frac{\log\left(1 - \frac{1}{1000}\right)}{\log\left(1 - \frac{1}{m}\right)}.$$

Since $\log(1 - h) \approx -h$ for small h, we need

$$n \leq \frac{m}{1000}.$$

In other words, to keep within the required confidence limits, we should not carry out more than $m/1000$ operations. Now the number of operations which go on inside a computer are enormous, so that the chance of failure is not infinitesimal in terms of lifetime probabilities. (In "Computer Programming for Accuracy," Proceeding of the 1968 Army Numerical Analysis Conference, U.S. Army Research Office, Durham, North Carolina, J.M. Yohe lists 38 types of errors that may occur in carrying out a computer computation. These are grouped under seven major categories as follows: Errors due to hardware limitations, errors due to software limitations, errors due to hardware failure, errors due to software failure, errors due to program failure, errors due to faulty operation, errors due to inadequate planning. A similar list for mathematics produced in the conventional handcrafted fashion would surely be interesting.)

Repeating a computation by way of check helps, of course. If a complicated computation is carried out with a probability of success of $1 - 1/r$ $(r > 1)$, and is performed independently ν times, then the probability of at least one success in the ν blocks of computation is $1 - (1/r)^\nu$. Thus, the level of confidence is raised.

Consider then simple addition of numbers carried out in the usual way. If there are too many digits in the numbers, then the probability of a computation being accurate (or of discovering which of a block of independently arrived at answers is the correct one) might be small. The reader need only insert his favorite probabilities for himself and for his machine in the above formulas. Perhaps we need to take a number of over a million digits or over a billion digits to make success unlikely. No matter. Platonic mathematics guarantees an unlimited number of integers and each integer has a decimal representation.

Ordinary arithmetic is one of the most elementary of the mathematical disciplines. Among the theorems of arithmetic are the various sums. Here is a theorem in arithmetic: $12345 + 54321 = 66666$. If this theorem does not excite you particularly, this is your value judgment and is extraneous to the mathematical structure. It might excite a Kabalist or an income tax consultant. Now, as we have observed, the arithmetic of excessively large numbers can be carried out only with diminishing fidelity. As we get away from trivial sums, arithmetic operations are enveloped in a smog of uncertainty. The sum 12345 + 54321 is not 66666. It is not a number. It is a probability distribution of possible answers in which 66666 is the odds-on favorite. (A somewhat less transparent example is this. Consider the popular solitaire game called "Canfield". If the rules are fixed, and the line of play specified unambiguously, then the expected value of Canfield constitutes a mathematical theorem which is of considerable interest in some quarters. As far as I am aware, because of the complexity of Canfield, no one has been able to use the elementary textbook theorems on combinatorial probability to arrive at the expected value. Yet, all we have to do in principle is to examine each of the 52! games that are possible and average their values.)

There is a parallel with the limitations of physical measurement. There is wisdom in the primitive counting system one, two, three, many, myriads.

PROBLEM: Given

A = 117777777111717171717771711717111111177717177711771177171717171777171777171717
171777111717111111717777111717171111717177171

B = 777771711711111777777711111111117717171711177777171777711171711111717117171777
11111117171777777777111717177771111777117177771

Find $A + B$.

The numbers A and B cannot be reproduced with perfect fidelity, let alone added.

5 FIDELITY IN PROOFS

The authenticity of a mathematical proof is established by verifying that a sequence of transformations of atomic symbol strings is legitimate. In point of fact, proofs are not written in terms of atomic strings. They are written in a mixture of common discourse and mathematical symbols. *Definitions* are made to serve as abbreviations for longer combinations of words and symbols. *Lemmas* are introduced as temporary platforms and scaffoldings from which one can argue with less fatigue and hence greater security. *Corollaries* are introduced for the psychological lift of obtaining deep theorems cheaply.

Splicing two theorems is standard practice. In the course of a proof, one cites Euler's Theorem, say, by way of authority. The onus is now on the reader to supply the particular theorem of Euler that the author is talking about and to verify that all the conditions (in their most modern formulation) which are necessary for the applicability of the theorem are, in fact, present.

If splicing is common to lend authority, then *skipping* is even more common. By skipping, I mean the failure to supply an important argument. Skipping occurs because it is necessary to keep down the length of a proof, because of boredom (you cannot really expect me to go through every single step, can you?), superiority (the fellows in my club all can follow me) or out of inadvertence. Thus, far from being an exercise in reason, a convincing certification of truth, or a device for enhancing the understanding, a proof in a textbook on advanced topics is often a stylized minuet which the author dances with his readers to achieve certain social ends. What begins as reason soon becomes aesthetics and winds up as anaesthetics.

To go from the foundations of mathematics to any of the advanced topics on the frontier can be done in about 5 or 6 books. Perhaps 1500 pages of proof text of current style. This is humanely broken into smaller bits. The lengths of these smaller bits vary from discipline to discipline. Perhaps number theory has the longest individual proofs. I know one proof in Landau which is over a hundred pages long. I have before me a book on advanced topics in analysis just off the press. The average length of the proofs seems to be about 10 lines. This mirrors the *sitzfleisch* of the contemporary reader.

I do not know many people who would volunteer to check a fifty page proof. Value judgments would enter; it would depend on what is at stake. A purported proof of the Riemann Hypothesis might attract more checkers than the sum of two excessively long integers. But one doesn't have to deal with fifty page proofs: most proofs in research papers are unchecked other than by the author. But then, most theorems are without issue: the last of a line of noble thought. They remain unchecked in the light of usage. They are loaded with errors.

If computing machines are employed either to check manipulation worked out by hand, or as has been done in some instances, to develop new theorems, the same remarks apply, but the probabilities may be altered. An interesting aspect of the problem of fidelity arises in programming. There are programs which are hundreds of thousands of words and instructions long. Such programs are frequently written by batteries of programmers and the parts are spliced together. Now the problem is this: what in fact does the program do? Well, ask the programmers what it does. "My part works," says the first programmer over the phone from a laboratory 2000 miles away where he has just taken a new job. "So does mine," says the second programmer who is still around but whose program is loaded with bugs that have not yet emerged. The third programmer: alas for flesh and blood, he died several months ago.

The program itself is the only complete description of what the program will do. This assumes that you know how the machine itself interprets a program—and this is not always the case. There may be no absolutely complete description of what the machine will do in a given instance. And all of this assumes that the machine treats its electronic symbols with perfect fidelity. (To add to the indeterminacy, in a poorly designed computational system, the way the computer processes, my input may depend upon what my colleague down the hall is doing on his terminal. Of the concepts of fuzzy languages, algorithms, and environments, see, e.g., Zadeh.[3]) This leads one to the pragmatic solution: run the program and you will see. You may learn that the performance is acceptable. In other cases you may not even be able to judge the quality of the output rationally. It may be a matter of faith.

Extremely long programs represent theorems of a kind. They may be far less trivial than some current frontier mathematics of conventional sort in terms of their distance from atomic symbolisms. But the problem is that we do not know and cannot know what the theorem says.

The upshot of this discussion is that the authenticity of a mathematical proof is not absolute, but only probabilistic. Proofs have attached to themselves lists of discoverers, sponsors, users, checkers, authenticators, rearrangers, generalizers, simplifiers, rediscoverers, swamis, communicants, and historians. These lists are all incorporated into the scholarly apparatus of publication and in the constant exposure that goes on the blackboard.

Proofs cannot be too long, else their probabilities go down and they baffle the checking process. To put it in another way: all really deep theorems are false (or at best unproved or unprovable). All true theorems are trivial.

A parallel with relativity theory can be made here. Newtonian mechanics grew up in a regime of low velocities and hence no relativity correction $(1 - (v/v_c)^2)^{1/2}$ is necessary. Conventional (precomputer) mathematics grew up in a regime in which proof lengths were sufficiently low so that the fidelity could be considered absolute and the laws of information theory are irrelevant. It is also possible that mathematics might move into a period and into a corpus of material where the proof aspect ceases to have the classical significance and where one can live intimately with less than perfect fidelity.

6 ON THE OBSERVED INCIDENCE OF ERROR

What I have to say here is largely a collection of gossip. Since the subject is touchy, I shall begin at home.

FIG. 2. A digitalized Santa is a mathematical object and its transformations are analogous to theorems. The aesthetic appeal of such theorems may have a different basis than that of classical mathematics. Less than perfect fidelity in processing is probably not very damaging.

The original printing of Davis, *Interpolation and Approximation*, contained at least 4 typewritten pages of errata. These range all the way from minor typos to errors of more mathematical substance. There is at least one bad proof and one theorem erroneously worded which if taken literally, is false. Davis and Rabinowitz, *Numerical Integration*, a smaller book whose galleys were proofread by both authors, has about a typewritten page of errors. One formula is just plain wrong. It was copied, without checking from the original author who worked it out wrong. Other errors are less easily alibied.

The original printing of *A Handbook of Mathematical Functions*, a thousand page compendium of formulas and tables which was put out by the National Bureau of Standards and which has sold more than 100,000 copies to date, contained more than several hundred errors. In the old days, when table making was a handcraft, some table makers felt that every entry in a table was a theorem (and so it is) and must be correct. Others took a relaxed, quality control attitude. One famous table maker used to put in errors deliberately so that he would be able to spot his work when others reproduced it without his permission.

I have before me a highly important book on advanced topics on analysis published about 15 years ago. After the book appeared, the author circulated to his friends an errata sheet of about 10 pages.

I have before me also the mimeographed 1925 notes of E.H. Moore of the University of Chicago on Hermitian matrices. One hundred eighty pages of notes are followed by 26 pages of errata.

There is a story to the effect that when B.O. Peirce's popular *A Table of Integrals* had just appeared, Professor Peirce offered a dollar to any student who discovered an error in it. Allowing an inflation rate of 3 or 4 to 1, I doubt whether any prudent author today would make a similar offer for his book. (D.E. Knuth has an open offer of this sort for his series of books on the art of computer programming.)

A recent issue of the *Notices* of the American Mathematical Society ran abstracts of about 130 papers: Five papers were listed as "Withdrawn." Presumably some of them had mistakes.

The *Mathematical Reviews* of December 1970, reports a paper entitled "The Decline and Fall of a Theorem of Zarankiewicz."

A past editor of the *Mathetical Reviews* once told me—somewhat in jest—that 50% of all mathematics papers printed are flawed.

A colleague reports refereeing a paper whose main theorem was invalid because the author spliced onto an erroneously stated theorem in a major reference book in topology. The words 'closed' and 'open' had inadvertently been interchanged in the reference.

There is a book entitled *Erreurs de Mathématiciens* by Maurice Lecat, published in 1935 in Brussels. This book contains more than 130 pages of errors committed by mathematicians of the first and second rank from antiquity to about 1900. There are parallel columns listing the mathematician, the place where his error occurs, the man who discovers the error and the place where the error is dicussed. For example, J.J. Sylvester committed an error in "On the Relation between the Minor Determinant of Lineraly Equivalent Quadratic Factors," Philos. Mag., (1851) pp. 295–305. This error was corrected by H.E. Baker in the *Collected Papers of Sylvester*, Vol. I, pp. 647–650.

In 1917 H.W. Turnbull calculated a system of 125 invariants of two quaternary quadratic forms. In 1929 Williamson found that three were reducible. In 1946, Turnbull himself found that five more were reducible, while in 1947, J.A. Todd found a further reducible one. Does it matter?

A mathematical error of international significance may occur every twenty years or so. By this I mean the conjunction of a mathematician of great reputation and a problem of great notoriety. Such a conjunction occurred around 1945 when H. Rademacher thought he had solved the Riemann Hypothesis. There was a report in *Time* magazine. Another instance was around 1860 when Kummer, following in the erroneous footsteps of Cauchy and Lamé, thought he had solved the Fermat Last Theorem.

7 CONCLUSIONS

Symbols and operations do not have a precise meaning, but only a probabilistic meaning.

A derivation of a theorem or a verification of a proof has only probabilistic validity. It makes no difference whether the instrument of derivation or verification is man or a machine. The probabilities may vary, but are roughly of the same order of magnitude when compared with cosmic probabilities.

E. Borel once suggested that the following chances constitute an unobservable event:

On the human scale:	1 chance in 10^6
On the terrestrial scale:	1 chance in 10^{15}
On the cosmic scale:	1 chance in 10^{50}
Absolute zero:	1 chance in 10^{500}

Mathematics has some of the aspects of an experimental science. We are saved from chaos by the stability of the universe which implies the repeatability of experiments and the self-correcting features of usage.

Mathematics has been Platonic for years. Does this rob it of a certain freedom and vitality which might be obtained by openly recognizing its probabilistic nature?

It is possible that a new type of mathematics might develop in which the "Derivations" or the "processes" are so enormously long that the probabilistic nature of the result will be an integral feature of the subject.

REFERENCES

[1] N. Bourbaki, The architecture of mathematics, this MONTHLY, 57 (1950) 221–232.

[2] E. Cerutti and P.J. Davis, FORMAC meets PAPPUS: Some observations on elementary analytic geometry by computer, this MONTHLY, 76 (1969) 895–905.

[3] L.A. Zadeh, Fuzzy algorithms, Information and Control, 12 (1963) 94–102.

PHILIP J. DAVIS AND REUBEN HERSH

The Ideal Mathematician

We conclude the general introduction to mathematical practice with a delightful account of how it sometimes appears 'from the inside', as it were. Many mathematicians will recognize their colleagues in the picture, and perhaps even themselves. The rest of us will recognize many of the theoretical issues discussed in this section presented in a very immediate way. The presentation is lighthearted, but the questions that it raises are often very sobering. I am reminded of an example of Wittgenstein's concerning a tribe of people who taught their children how to count up to a certain number explicitly, by rote. When they had learned to do this the children were then encouraged to 'go on' to count even higher by a suggestive sign. Most of the children did catch on and learned to count this way but, Wittgenstein ominously adds, "If a child does not respond to the suggestive gesture, it is separated from the others and treated as a lunatic".[1]

Many people are put off by the bleakness of Wittgenstein's vision. Matters can not be so accidental or arbitrary, they want to say. Surely there is a more solid grounding to mathematics than the ability to 'catch on' to suggestive gestures and the threat of ostracism.[2] But listen carefully to the ideal mathematician. To be sure, he does not dismiss people as 'lunatics', but he does dismiss them as 'mathematically untalented', with the simple justification that he is best qualified to judge. "If not me", he says, "who?" This excerpt is taken from the authors' *The Mathematical Experience*.

NOTES

1. *The Blue and Brown Books*, Basil Blackwell, Oxford (1960), 93.
2. Could Wittgenstein, for all his bleakness, be correct? For a detailed consideration of this point, see S. Kripke's *Wittgenstein on Rules and Private Language*, Harvard University Press, Cambridge (1982).

• • • • •

We will construct a portrait of the "ideal mathematician." By this we do not mean the perfect mathematician, the mathematician without defect or limitation. Rather, we mean to describe the most mathematician-like mathematician, as one might describe the ideal thoroughbred greyhound, or the ideal thirteenth-century monk. We will try to construct an impossibly pure specimen, in order to exhibit the paradoxical and problematical aspects of the mathematician's role. In particular, we want to display clearly the discrepancy between the actual work and activity of the mathematician and his own perception of his work and activity.

The ideal mathematician's work is intelligible only to a small group of specialists, numbering a few dozen or at most a few hundred. This group has existed only for a few decades, and there is every possibility that it may become extinct in another few decades. However, the mathematician regards his work as part of the very structure of the world, containing truths which are valid forever, from the beginning of time, even in the most remote corner of the universe.

He rests his faith on rigorous proof; he believes that the difference between a correct proof and an incorrect one is an unmistakable and decisive difference. He can think of no condemnation more damning than to say of a student, "He doesn't even know what a proof is." Yet he is able to give no coherent explanation of what is meant by rigor, or what is required to make a proof rigorous. In his own work, the line between complete and incomplete proof is always somewhat fuzzy, and often controversial.

To talk about the ideal mathematician at all, we must have a name for his "field," his subject. Let's call it, for instance, "non-Riemannian hypersquares."

He is labeled by his field, by how much he publishes, and especially by whose work he uses, and by whose taste he follows in this choice of problems.

He studies objects whose existence is unsuspected by all except a handful of his fellows. Indeed, if one who is not an initiate asks him what he studies, he is incapable of showing or telling what it is. It is necessary to go through an arduous apprenticeship of several years to understand the theory to which he is devoted. Only then would one's mind be prepared to receive his explanation of what he is studying. Short of that, one could be given a "definition," which would be so recondite as to defeat all attempts at comprehension.

The objects which our mathematician studies were unknown before the twentieth century; most likely, they were unknown even thirty years ago. Today they are the chief interest in life for a few dozen (at most, a few hundred) of his comrades. He and his comrades do not doubt, however, that non-Riemannian hypersquares have a real existence as definite and objective as that of the Rock of Gibraltar or Halley's comet. In fact, the proof of the existence of non-Riemannian hypersquares is one of their main achievements, whereas the existence of the Rock of Gibraltar is very probable, but not rigorously proved.

It has never occurred to him to question what the word "exist" means here. One could try to discover its meaning by watching him at work and observing what the word "exist" signifies operationally.

In any case, for him the non-Riemannian hypersquare exists, and he pursues it with passionate devotion. He spends all his days in contemplating it. His life is successful to the extent that he can discover new facts about it.

He finds it difficult to establish meaningful conversation with that large portion of humanity that has never heard of a non-Riemannian hypersquare. This creates grave difficulties for him; there are two colleagues in his department who know something about non-Riemannian hypersquares, but one of them is on sabbatical, and the other is much more interested in non-Eulerian semirings. He goes to conferences, and on summer visits to colleagues, to meet people who talk his language, who can appreciate his work and whose recognition, approval, and admiration are the only meaningful rewards he can ever hope for.

At the conferences, the principal topic is usually "the decision problem" (or perhaps "the construction problem" or "the classification problem") for non-Riemannian hypersquares. This problem was first stated by Professor Nameless, the founder of the theory of non-Riemannian hypersquares. It is important because Professor Nameless stated it and gave a partial solution which, unfortunately, no one but Professor Nameless was ever able to understand. Since Professor Nameless' day, all the best non-Riemannian hypersquarers have worked on the problem, obtaining many partial results. Thus the problem has acquired great prestige.

Our hero often dreams he has solved it. He has twice convinced himself during waking hours that he had solved it but, both times, a gap in his reasoning was discovered by other non-Riemannian devotees, and the problem remains open. In the meantime, he continues to discover new and interesting facts about the non-Riemannian hypersquares. To his fellow experts, he communicates these results in a casual shorthand. "If you apply a tangential mollifier to the left quasi-martingale, you can get an estimate better than quadratic, so the convergence in the Bergstein theorem turns out to be of the same order as the degree of approximation in the Steinberg theorem."

This breezy style is not to be found in his published writings. There he piles up formalism on top of formalism. Three pages of definitions are followed by seven lemmas and, finally, a theorem whose hypotheses take half a page to state, while its proof reduces essentially to "Apply Lemmas 1–7 to definitions A–H."

His writing follows an unbreakable convention: to conceal any sign that the author or the intended reader is a human being. It gives the impression that, from the stated definitions, the desired results follow infallibly by a purely mechanical procedure. In fact, no computing machine has ever been built that could accept his definitions as inputs. To read his proofs, one must be privy to a whole subculture of motivations, standard arguments and examples, habits of thought and agreed-upon modes of reasoning. The intended readers (all twelve of them) can decode the formal presentation, detect the new idea hidden in lemma 4, ignore the routine and uninteresting calculations of lemmas 1, 2, 3, 5, 6, 7, and see what the author is doing and why he does it. But for the noninitiate, this is a cipher that will never yield its secret. If (heaven forbid) the fraternity of non-Riemannian hypersquares should ever die out, our hero's writings would become less translatable than those of the Maya.

The difficulties of communication emerged vividly when the ideal mathematician [IM] received a visit from a public information officer [PIO] of the University.

PIO: I appreciate your taking time to talk to me. Mathematics was always my worst subject.

IM: That's O.K. You've got your job to do.

PIO: I was given the assignment of writing a press release about the renewal of your grant. The usual thing would be a one-sentence item, "Professor X received a grant of *Y* dollars to continue his research on the decision problem for non-Riemannian hypersquares." But I thought it would be a good challenge for me to try and give people a better idea about what your work really involves. First of all, what is a hypersquare?

IM: I hate to say this, but the truth is, if I told you what it is, you would think I was trying to put you down and make you feel stupid. The definition is really somewhat technical, and it just wouldn't mean anything at all to most people.

PIO: Would it be something engineers or physicists would know about?

IM: No. Well, maybe a few theoretical physicists. Very few.

PIO: Even if you can't give me the real definition, can't you give me some idea of the general nature and purpose of your work?

IM: All right, I'll try. Consider a smooth function $\int$ on a measure space Ω taking its value in a sheaf of germs equipped with a convergence structure of saturated type. In the simplest case . . .

PIO: Perhaps I'm asking the wrong questions. Can you tell me something about the applications of your research?

IM: Applications?

PIO: Yes, applications.

IM: I've been told that some attempts have been made to use non-Riemannian hypersquares as models for elementary particles in nuclear physics. I don't know if any progress was made.

PIO: Have there been any major breakthroughs recently in your area? Any exciting new results that people are talking about?

IM: Sure, there's the Steinberg-Bergstein paper. That's the biggest advance in at least five years.

PIO: What did they do?

IM: I can't tell you.

PIO: I see. Do you feel there is adequate support in research in your field?

IM: Adequate? It's hardly lip service. Some of the best young people in the field are being denied research support. I have no doubt that with extra support we could be making much more rapid progress on the decision problem.

PIO: Do you see any way that the work in your area could lead to anything that would be understandable to the ordinary citizen of this country?

IM: No.

PIO: How about engineers or scientists?

IM: I doubt it very much.

PIO: Among pure mathematicians, would the majority be interested in or acquainted with your work?

IM: No, it would be a small minority.
PIO: Is there anything at all that you would like to say about your work?
IM: Just the usual one sentence will be fine.
PIO: Don't you want the public to sympathize with your work and support it?
IM: Sure, but not if it means debasing myself.
PIO: Debasing yourself?
IM: Getting involved in public relations gimmicks, that sort of thing.
PIO: I see. Well, thanks again for your time.
IM: That's O.K. You've got a job to do.

Well, a public relations officer. What can one expect? Let's see how our ideal mathematician made out with a student [S] who came to him with a strange question.

S: Sir, what is a mathematical proof?
IM: You don't know *that*? What year are you in?
S: Third-year graduate.
IM: Incredible! A proof is what you've been watching me do at the board three times a week for three years! That's what a proof is.
S: Sorry, sir, I should have explained. I'm in philosophy, not math. I've never taken your course.
IM: Oh! Well, in that case—you have taken *some* math, haven't you? You know the proof of the fundamental theorem of calculus—or the fundamental theorem of algebra?
S: I've seen arguments in geometry and algebra and calculus that were called proofs. What I'm asking you for isn't *examples* of proof, it's a definition of proof. Otherwise, how can I tell what examples are correct?
IM: Well, this whole thing was cleared up by the logician Tarski, I guess, and some others, maybe Russell or Peano. Anyhow, what you do is, you write down the axioms of your theory in a formal language with a given list of symbols or alphabet. Then you write down the hypothesis of your theorem in the same symbolism. Then you show that you can transform the hypothesis step by step, using the rules of logic, till you get the conclusion. That's a proof.
S: Really? That's amazing! I've taken elementary and advanced calculus, basic algebra, and topology, and I've never seen that done.
IM: Oh, of course no one every really *does* it. It would take forever! You just show that you could do it, that's sufficient.
S: But even that doesn't sound like what was done in my courses and textbooks. So mathematicians don't really do proofs, after all.
IM: Of course we do! If a theorem isn't proved, it's nothing.
S: Then what is a proof? If it's this thing with a formal language and transforming formulas, nobody ever proves anything. Do you have to know all about formal languages and formal logic before you can do a mathematical proof?
IM: Of course not! The less you know, the better. That stuff is all abstract nonsense anyway.

S: Then really what *is* a proof?

IM: Well, it's an argument that convinces someone who knows the subject.

S: Someone who knows the subject? Then the definition of proof is subjective; it depends on particular persons. Before I can decide if something is a proof, I have to decide who the experts are. What does that have to do with proving things?

IM: No, no. There's nothing subjective about it! Everybody knows what a proof is. Just read some books, take courses from a competent mathematician, and you'll catch on.

S: Are you sure?

IM: Well—it is possible that you won't, if you don't have any aptitude for it. That can happen, too.

S: Then *you* decide what a proof is, and if I don't learn to decide in the same way, you decide I don't have any aptitude.

IM: If not me, then who?

Then the ideal mathematician met a positivist philosopher [PP].

PP: This Platonism of yours is rather incredible. The silliest undergraduate knows enough not to multiply entities, and here you've got not just a handful, you've got them in uncountable infinites! And nobody knows about them but you and your pals! Who do you think you're kidding?

IM: I'm not interested in philosophy, I'm a mathematician.

PP: You're as bad as that character in Molière who didn't know he was talking prose. You've been committing philosophical nonsense with your "rigorous proofs of existence." Don't you know that what exists has to be observed, or at least observable?

IM: Look, I don't have time to get into philosophical controversies. Frankly, I doubt that you people know what you're talking about; otherwise you could state it in a precise form so that I could understand it and check your argument. As far as my being a Platonist, that's just a handy figure of speech. I never thought hypersquares existed. When I say they do, all I mean is that the axioms for a hypersquare possess a model. In other words, no formal contradiction can be deduced from them, and so, in the normal mathematical fashion, we are free to postulate their existence. The whole thing doesn't really mean anything, it's just a game, like chess, that we play with axioms and rules of inference.

PP: Well, I didn't mean to be too hard on you. I'm sure it helps you in your research to imagine you're talking about something real.

IM: I'm not a philosopher, philosophy bores me. You argue, argue and never get anywhere. My job is to prove theorems, not to worry about what they mean.

The ideal mathematician feels prepared, if the occasion should arise, to meet an extragalactic intelligence. His first effort to communicate would be to write down (or otherwise transmit) the first few hundred digits in the binary expansion of pi. He regards it as obvious that any intelligence capable of intergalactic communication would be mathematical and that it makes sense to talk about mathematical intelligence apart from the thoughts and actions of human beings. Moreover, he regards it as obvious that binary representation and the real number pi are both part of the intrinsic order of the universe.

He will admit that neither of them is a natural object, but he will insist that they are discovered, not invented. Their discovery, in something like the form in which we know them, is inevitable if one rises far enough above the primordial slime to communicate with other galaxies (or even with other solar systems).

The following dialogue once took place between the ideal mathematician and a skeptical classicist [SC].

SC: You believe in your numbers and curves just as Christian missionaries believed in their crucifixes. If a missionary had gone to the moon in 1500, he would have been waving his crucifix to show the moon-men that he was a Christian, and expecting them to have their own symbol to wave back.[1] You're even more arrogant about your expansion of pi.

IM: Arrogant? It's been checked and rechecked, to 100,000 places!

SC: I've seen how little you have to say even to an American mathematician who doesn't know your game with hypersquares. You don't get to first base trying to communicate with a theoretical physicist; you can't read his papers any more than he can read yours. The research papers in your own field written before 1910 are as dead to you as Tutankhamen's will. What reason in the world is there to think that you could communicate with an extragalactic intelligence?

IM: If not me, then who else?

SC: Anybody else! Wouldn't life and death, love and hate, joy and despair be messages more likely to be universal than a dry pedantic formula that nobody but you and a few hundred of your type will know from a hen-scratch in a farmyard?

IM: The reason that my formulas are appropriate for intergalactic communication is the same reason they are not very suitable for terrestrial communication. Their content is not earthbound. It is free of the specifically human.

SC: I don't suppose the missionary would have said quite that about his crucifix, but probably something rather close, and certainly no less absurd and pretentious.

The foregoing sketches are not meant to be malicious; indeed, they would apply to the present authors. But it is a too obvious and therefore easily forgotten fact that mathematical work, which, no doubt as a result of long familiarity, the mathematician takes for granted, is a mysterious, almost inexplicable phenomenon from the point of view of the outsider. In this case, the outsider could be a layman, a fellow academic, or even a scientist who uses mathematics in his own work.

The mathematician usually assumes that his own view of himself is the only one that need be considered. Would we allow the same claim to any other esoteric fraternity? Or would a dispassionate description of its activities by an observant, informed outsider be more reliable than that of a participant who may be incapable of noticing, not to say questioning, the beliefs of his coterie?

Mathematicians know that they are studying an objective reality. To an outsider, they seem to be engaged in an esoteric communion with themselves and a small clique of friends. How could we as mathematicians prove to a skeptical outsider that our theorems have meaning in the world outside our own fraternity?

If such a person accepts our discipline, and goes through two or three years of graduate study in mathematics, he absorbs our way of thinking, and is no longer the critical outsider he once was. In the same way, a critic of Scientology who underwent several years of "study" under "recognized authorities" in Scientology might well emerge a believer instead of a critic.

If the student is unable to absorb our way of thinking, we flunk him out, of course. If he gets through our obstacle course and then decides that our arguments are unclear or incorrect, we dismiss him as a crank, crackpot, or misfit.

Of course, none of this proves that we are not correct in our self-perception that we have a reliable method for discovering objective truths. But we must pause to realize that, outside our coterie, much of what we do is incomprehensible. There is no way we could convince a self-confident skeptic that the things we are talking about make sense, let alone "exist."

NOTE

1. Cf. the description of Coronado's expedition to Cibola, in 1540: " . . . there were about eighty horsemen in the vanguard besides twenty-five or thirty foot and a large number of Indian allies. In the party went all the priests, since none of them wished to remain behind with the army. It was their part to deal with the friendly Indians whom they might encounter, and they especially were bearers of the Cross, a symbol which . . . had already come to exert an influence over the natives on the way" (H.E. Bolton, *Coronado*, University of New Mexico Press, 1949).

The Evolution of Mathematical Practice

RAYMOND WILDER

The Cultural Basis of Mathematics

Raymond Wilder, an accomplished mathematician, was one of the first people to appreciate how attention to mathematical practice could further our understanding of mathematics. For over three decades, he has been working to describe mathematics as an evolving cultural system. His work had been largely ignored by most philosophers who, after all, were committed to some form of foundationalism. It was only after they began to question foundations and to move towards quasi-empiricism that philosophers could appreciate the philosophical significance of Wilder's ideas. Once we attend to mathematical practice, we can recognize that like any other sophisticated human activity it is a cultural product. Mathematical practice, subject to internal pressures and to external pressures, is constantly evolving. Some of our philosophical perplexities can be answered, Wilder realized, by learning how mathematics changes; how it came to be what it is today, *given* what it was in the past.

Such an approach to philosophical understanding is sometimes called evolutionary epistemology. A central project of evolutionary epistemology is to understand how mathematical knowledge *improves* or grows. This view stands in sharp contrast to foundationalism whose central epistemological project is to justify mathematical knowledge once and for all, starting from scratch. A foundationalist is forced to divide mathematical development into two basic periods; that preceding and that following the discovery of foundations. During the pre-foundational period, mathematicians work gropingly towards the truth with questionable methods. After the discovery of foundations, mathematics develops more or less automatically, by accumulating rigorously proved theorems. There is no room for *interesting* evolution in mathematics.

In "The Cultural Basis of Mathematics," Wilder develops the idea that mathematics is, in part, a cultural product. He tries to apply to it the methods of the social sciences, especially anthropology, sociology and history. Mathematical knowledge comes to be seen as a collective possession, that is, as essentially public knowledge. It is the development and communication of this public

Reprinted from Vol. I, PROCEEDINGS OF THE INTERNATIONAL CONGRESS OF MATHEMATICIANS, 1950, pp. 258–271.

knowledge that is the focus of Wilder's cultural approach. The history of mathematics comes to the foreground as a topic of interest. To repeat a point made by Wang, however, it is not history as a record of particular episodes but as a more conceptual record of landmarks that is relevant.

In later works Wilder has developed detailed suggestions for characterizing the conceptual evolution of mathematics. In this early essay (published first in 1950), he is concerned to portray mathematics as subject to the general principles of cultural evolution. The essay stresses the more general kinds of influence that its cultural setting can have on mathematics. It does not address the internal factors that we find at work in mathematical evolution. Other essays in this section take up the slack, as does Wilder himself in his excellent monograph, *Mathematics As a Cultural System.*[1]

NOTE

1. *Mathematics as a Cultural System*, Pergamon Press, Oxford (1981).

• • • • •

I presume that it is not inappropriate, on the occasion of an International Mathematical Congress which comes at the half-century mark, to devote a little time to a consideration of mathematics as a whole. The addresses and papers to be given in the various conferences and sectional meetings will in general be concerned with special fields or branches of mathematics. It is the aim of the present remarks to get outside mathematics, as it were, in the hope of attaining a new perspective. Mathematics has been studied extensively from the abstract philosophical viewpoint, and some benefits have accrued to mathematics from such studies—although generally the working mathematician is inclined to look upon philosophical speculation with suspicion. A growing number of mathematicians have been devoting thought to the Foundations of Mathematics, many of them men whose contributions to mathematics have won them respect. The varying degrees of dogmatism with which some of these have come to regard their theories, as well as the sometimes acrimonious debates which have occurred between holders of conflicting theories, makes one wonder if there is not some vantage point from which one can view such matters more dispassionately.

It has become commonplace today to say that mankind is in its present "deplorable" state because it has devoted so much of its energy to technical skills and so little to the study of man itself. Early in his civilized career, man studied astronomy and the other physical sciences, along with the mathematics these subjects suggested; but in regard to such subjects as anatomy, for example, it was not easy for him to be objective. Man himself, it seemed, should be considered untouchable so far as his private person was concerned. It is virtually only within our own era that the study of the even more personal subjects, such as psychology, has become moderately respectable! But in the study of the behavior of man *en masse*, we have made little progress. This is evidently due to a variety of reasons such as (1) inability to distinguish between group behavior and individual behavior, and (2) the fact that although the average person may grudgingly give in to being cut open by a surgeon, or analyzed by a psychiatrist, those group institutions which determine his system of values, such as nation, church, clubs, etc., are still considered untouchable.

Fortunately, just as the body of the executed criminal ultimately became available to the anatomist, so the "primitive" tribes of Australia, the Pacific Islands, Africa, and the United States, became available to the anthropologist. Using methods that have now become so impersonal and objective as to merit its being classed among the natural sciences rather than with such social studies as history, anthropology has made great advances within the past 50 years in the study of the group behavior of mankind. Its development of the culture concept and investigation of cultural forces will, perhaps, rank among the greatest achievements of the human mind, and despite opposition, application of the concept has made strides in recent years. Not only are psychologists, psychiatrists, and sociologists applying it, but governments that seek to extend their control over alien peoples have recognized it. Manifold human suffering has resulted from ignorance of the concept, both in the treatment of colonial peoples, and in the handling of the American Indian, for example.

Now I am not going to offer the culture concept as an antidote for all the ills that beset mathematics. But I do believe that only by recognition of the cultural basis of mathematics will a better understanding of its nature be achieved; moreover, light can be thrown on various problems, particularly those of the Foundations of Mathematics. I don't mean that it can solve these problems, but that it can point the *way* to solutions as well as show the *kinds* of solutions that may be expected. In addition, many things that we have believed, and attributed to some kind of vague "intuition," acquire a real validity on the cultural basis.

For the sake of completeness, I shall begin with a rough explanation of the concept. (For a more adequate exposition, see [10; Chap. 7] and [18].* Obviously it has nothing to do with culture spelled with a "K", or with degrees from the best universities or inclusion in the "best" social circles. A culture is the collection of customs, rituals, beliefs, tools, mores, etc., which we may call *cultural elements*, possessed by a group of people, such as a primitive tribe or the people of North America. Generally it is not a fixed thing but changing with the course of time, forming what can be called a "culture stream." It is handed down from one generation to another, constituting a seemingly living body of tradition often more dictatorial in its hold than Hitler was over Nazi Germany; in some primitive tribes virtually every act, even such ordinary ones as eating and dressing, are governed by ritual. Many anthropologists have thought of a culture as a super-organic entity, having laws of development all its own, and most anthropologists seem in practice to treat a culture as a thing in itself, without necessarily referring (except for certain purposes) to the group or individuals possessing it.

We "civilized" people rarely think of how much we are dominated by our cultures—we take so much of our behavior as "natural." But if you were to propose to the average American male that he should wear earrings, you

*References in brackets are to the bibliography at the end of the paper. The first number in a bracket refers to the corresponding number in the bibliography, the second number to pages, chapter, or volume of the work indicated.

might, as you picked yourself off the ground, reflect on the reason for the blow that you have just sustained. Was it because he decided at some previous date that every time someone suggested wearing earrings to him he would respond with a punch to the nose? Of course not. It was decided for him and imposed on him by the American culture, so that what he did was, he would say, the "natural thing to do." However, there are societies such as Navajo, Pueblo, and certain Amazon tribes, for instance, in which the wearing of earrings by the males is the "natural thing to do." What we call "human nature" is virtually nothing but a collection of such culture traits. What is "human nature" for a Navajo is distinctly different from what is "human nature" for a Hottentot.

As mathematicians, we share a certain portion of our cultures which is called "mathematical." We are influenced by it, and in turn we influence it. As individuals we assimilate parts of it, our contacts with it being through teachers, journals, books, meetings such as this, and our colleagues. We contribute to its growth the results of our individual syntheses of the portions that we have assimilated.

Now to look at mathematics as a cultural element is not new. Anthropologists have done so, but as their knowledge of mathematics is generally very limited, their reactions have ordinarily consisted of scattered remarks concerning the types of arithmetic found in primitive cultures. An exception is an article [17] which appeared about three years ago, by the anthropologist L.A. White, entitled *The locus of mathematical reality*, which was inspired by the seemingly conflicting notions of the nature of mathematics as expressed by various mathematicians and philosophers. Thus, there is the belief expressed by G.H. Hardy [8; pp. 63–64] that "mathematical reality lies outside us, and that our function is to discover or *observe* it, and that the theorems which we prove, and which we describe grandiloquently as our 'creations' are simply our notes of our observations." On the other hand there is the point of view expressed by P.W. Bridgman [3; p. 60] that "it is the merest truism, evident at once to unsophisticated observation, that mathematics is a human invention." Although these statements seem irreconcilable, such is not the case when they are suitably interpreted. For insofar as our mathematics is a part of our culture, it is, as Hardy says, "outside us." And insofar as a culture cannot exist except as the product of human minds, mathematics is, as Bridgman states, a "human invention."

As a body of knowledge, mathematics is not something I know, you know, or any individual knows: It is a part of our culture, our *collective* possession. We may even forget, with the passing of time, some of our own individual contributions to it, but these may remain, despite our forgetfulness, in the culture stream. As in the case of many other cultural elements, we are taught mathematics from the time when we are able to speak, and from the first we are impressed with what we call its "absolute truth." It comes to have the same significance and type of reality, perhaps, as their system of gods and rituals has for a primitive people. Such would seem to be the case of Hermite, for example, who according to Hadamard [7; p. xii] said, "We are rather servants than masters in Mathematics;" and who said [6; p. 449] in a letter to Königsberger, "—these notions of analysis have their existence apart from us—they constitute a whole of which only a part is revealed to us, incontestably although mysteriously associated with that other totality of things which we perceive by way of the senses." Evidently Hermite sensed the impelling influence of the culture stream to which he contributed so much!

In his famous work *Der Untergang des Abendlandes* [15], O. Spengler discussed at considerable length the nature of mathematics and its importance in his organic theory of cultures. And under the influence of this work, C.J. Keyser published [9] some views concerning *Mathematics as a Culture Clue*, constituting an exposition and defense of the thesis that "The type of mathematics found in any major Culture is a clue, or key, to the distinctive character of the Culture taken as a whole." Insofar as mathematics is a part of and is influenced by the culture in which it is found, one may expect to find some sort of relationship between the two. As to how good a "key" it furnishes to a culture, however, I shall express no opinion; this is really a question for an anthropologist to answer. Since the culture dominates its elements, and in particular its mathematics, it would appear that for mathematicians it would be more fruitful to study the relationship from this point of view.

Let us look for a few minutes at the history of mathematics. I confess I know very little about it, since I am not a historian. I should think, however, that in writing a history of mathematics the historian would be constantly faced with the question of *what sort of material to include*. In order to make a clearer case, let us suppose that a hypothetical person, A, sets out to write a *complete* history, desiring to include all available material on the "history of mathematics." Obviously, he will have to accept some material and reject other material. It seems clear that his criterion for choice must be based on knowledge of what constitutes mathematics! If by this we mean a *definition* of mathematics, of course his task is hopeless. Many definitions have been given, but none has been chosen; judging by their number, it used to be expected of every self-respecting mathematician that he would leave a definition of mathematics to posterity! Consequently our hypothetical mathematician A will be guided, I imagine, by what is *called* "mathematics" in his culture, both in existing (previously written) histories and in works *called* "mathematical," as well as by what sort of thing people who are *called* "mathematicians" publish. He will, then, recognize what we have already stated, that mathematics is a certain part of his culture, and will be guided thereby.

For example, suppose A were a Chinese historian living about the year 1200 (500 or 1500 would do as well). He would include a great deal about computing with numbers and solving equations; but there wouldn't be any geometry as the Greek understood it in his history, simply because it had never been integrated with the mathematics of his culture. On the other hand, if A were a Greek of 200 A.D., his history of mathematics would be replete with geometry, but there would be little of algebra or even of computing with numbers as the Chinese practiced it. But if A were one of our contemporaries, he would include both geometry and algebra because both are part of what we call mathematics. I wonder what he would do about logic, however?

Here is a subject which, despite the dependence of the Greeks on logical deduction, and despite the fact that mathematicians, such as Leibnitz and Pascal, have devoted considerable time to it on its own merits, has been given very little space in histories of mathematics. As an experiment, I looked in two histories that have been popular in this country; Ball's [1] and Cajori's [5], both written shortly before 1900. In the index of Ball's first edition (1888) there is no mention of "logic;" but in the fourth edition (1908) "symbolic and mathematical logic" is mentioned with a single citation, which proved to be a reference to an incidental remark about George Boole to the effect that he "was one of the creators of symbolic or mathematical logic." Thus symbolic logic barely squeezed under the line because Boole was a mathematician! The index of Cajori's first edition (1893) contains four citations under "logic", all referring to incidental remarks in the text. None of these citations is repeated in the second edition. (1919), whose index has only three citations under "logic" (two of which also constitute the sole citations under "symbolic logic"), again referring only to brief remarks in the text. Inspection of the text, however, reveals nearly four pages (407–410) of material under the title "Mathematical logic," although there is no citation to this subject in the index nor is it cited under "logic" or "symbolic logic." (It is as though the subject had, by 1919, achieved enough importance for inclusion as textual material in a history of mathematics although not for citation in the index!)

I doubt if a like situation could prevail in a history of mathematics which covers the past 50 years! The only such history that covers this period, that I am acquainted with, is Bell's *Development of Mathematics* [2]. Turning to the index of this book, I found so many citations to "logic" that I did not care to count them. In particular, Bell devotes at least 25 pages to the development of what he calls "mathematical logic." Can there be any possible doubt that this subject, not considered part of mathematics in our culture in 1900, despite the pioneering work of Peano and his colleagues, is now in such "good standing" that any impartial definition of mathematics must be broad enough to include it?

Despite the tendency to approach the history of mathematics from the biographical standpoint, there has usually existed some awareness of the impact of cultural forces. For example, in commencing his chapter on Renaissance mathematics, Ball points out the influence of the introduction of the printing press. In the latest histories, namely the work of Bell already cited, and Struik's excellent little two volume work [16], the evidence is especially strong. For example, in his introduction, Struik expresses regret that space limitations prevented sufficient "reference to the general cultural and sociological atmosphere in which the mathematics of a period matured —or was stifled." And he goes on to say "Mathematics has been influenced by agriculture, commerce and manufacture, by warfare, engineering and philosophy, by physics and by astronomy. The influence of hydrodynamics on function theory, of Kantianism and of surveying on geometry, of electromagnetism on differential equations, of Cartesianism on mechanics, and of scholasticism on the calculus could only be indicated [in his book];—yet an understanding of the course and content of mathematics can be reached only if all these determining factors are taken into consideration." In his third chapter Struik gives a revealing account of the rise of Hellenistic mathematics, relating it to the cultural conditions then prevailing. I hope that future histories of mathematics will similarly give more attention to mathematics as a cultural element, placing greater emphasis on its relations to the cultures in which it is imbedded.

In discussing the general culture concept, I did not mention the two major processes of cultural change, *evolution* and *diffusion*. By diffusion is meant the transmission of a cultural trait from one culture to another, as a result of some kind of contact between groups of people; for example, the diffusion of French language and customs into the Anglo-Saxon culture following the Norman conquest. As to how much of what we call cultural progress is due to evolution and how much to diffusion, or to a combination of both, is usually difficult to determine, since the two processes tend so much to merge. Consider, for example, the counting process. This is what the anthropologist calls a universal trait—what I would prefer to call, in talking to mathematicians, a cultural invariant—it is found in every culture in at least a rudimentary form. The "base" may be 10, 12, 20, 25, 60—all of these are common, and are evidently determined by other (variable) culture elements—but the counting process in its essence, as the Intuitionist speaks of it, is invariant. If we consider more advanced cultures, the notion of a zero element sometimes appears. As pointed out by the anthropologist A.L. Kroeber, who in his *Anthropology* calls it a "milestone of civilization," a symbol for zero evolved in the cultures of at least three peoples; the Neo-Babylonian (who used a sexagesimal system), the Mayan (who used a vigesimal system), and the Hindu (from whom our decimal system is derived) [10; pp. 468–472]. Attempts by the extreme "diffusionists" to relate these have not yet been successful, and until they are, we can surmise that the concept of zero might ultimately evolve in any culture.

The Chinese-Japanese mathematics is of interest here. Evidently, as pointed out by Mikami [13] and others, the Chinese borrowed the zero concept from the Hindus, with whom they established contact at least as early as the first century, A.D. Here we have an example of its introduction by diffusion, but without such contacts, the zero would probably have evolved in Chinese mathematics, especially since calculators of the rod type were employed. The Chinese mathematics is also interesting from another standpoint in that its development seems to have been so much due to evolution within its own culture and so little affected by diffusion. Through the centuries it developed along slender arithmetic and algebraic lines, with no hint of geometry as the Greeks developed it. Those who feel that without the benefit of diffusion a culture will eventually stagnate find some evidence perhaps in the delight with which Japanese mathematicians of the 17th and 18th centuries, to whom the Chinese mathematics had come by the diffusion process, solved equations of degrees as high as 3000 or 4000. One is tempted to speculate what might have happened if the Babylonian zero and method of position had been integrated with the *Greek* mathematics—would it have meant that Greek mathematics might have taken an algebraic turn? Its introduction into the Chinese mathematics certainly was not productive, other than in the slight impetus it gave an already computational tendency.

That the Greek mathematics was a natural concomitant of the other elements in Greek culture, as well as a natural result of the evolution and diffusion processes that had produced this culture in the Asia Minor area, has been generally recognized. Not only was the Greek culture conducive to the type of mathematics that evolved in Greece, but it is probable that it resisted integration with the Babylonian method of enumeration. For if the latter became known to certain Greek scholars, as some seem to think, its value could not have been apparent to the Greeks.

We are familiar with the manner in which the Hindu-Arabic mathematical cultures diffused via Africa to Spain and then into the Western European cultures. What had become stagnant came to life—analytic geometry appeared, calculus—and the flood was on. The mathematical cultural development of these times would be a fascinating study, and awaits the cultural historian who will undertake it. The easy explanation that a number of "supermen" suddenly appeared on the scene has been abandoned by virtually all anthropologists. A *necessary* condition for the emergence of the "great man" is the presence of suitable cultural environment, including opportunity, incentive, and materials. Who can doubt that potentially great algebraists lived in Greece? But in Greece, although the opportunity and incentive may have been present, the cultural materials did not contain the proper symbolic apparatus. The anthropologist Ralph Linton remarked [12; p. 319] "The mathematical genius can only carry on from the point which mathematical knowledge within his culture has already reached. Thus if Einstein had been born into a primitive tribe which was unable to count beyond three, life-long application to mathematics probably would not have carried him beyond the development of a decimal system based on fingers and toes." Furthermore, the evidence points strongly to the *sufficiency* of the conditions stated: That is, suitable cultural environment is sufficient for the emergence of the great man. If your philosophy depends on the assumption of free will, you can probably adjust to this. For certainly your will is no freer than the opportunity to express it; you may will a trip to the moon this evening, but you won't make it. There may be potentially great blancophrenologists sitting right in this room; but if so they are destined to go unnoticed and undeveloped because blancophrenology is not yet one of our cultural elements.

Spengler states it this way [15tr; vol. II, p. 507]: "We have not the freedom to reach to this or to that, but the freedom to do the necessary or to do nothing. And a task that historic necessity has set *will* be accomplished with the individual or against him." As a matter of fact, when a culture or cultural element has developed to the point where it is ready for an important innovation, the latter is likely to emerge in more than one spot. A classical example is that of the theory of biological evolution, which had been anticipated by Spencer and, had it not been announced by Darwin, was ready to be announced by Wallace and soon thereafter by others. And as in this case, so in most other cases,—and you can recall many such in mathematics—one can after the fact usually go back and map out the evolution of the theory by its traces in the writings of men in the field.

Why are so many giving their lives to mathematics today; why have the past 50 years been so productive mathematically? The mathematical groundwork laid by our predecessors, the universities, societies, foundations, libraries, etc., have furnished unusual opportunity, incentive, and cultural material. In addition, the processes of evolution and diffusion have greatly accelerated. Of the two, the latter seems to have played the greater role in the recent activity. For during the past 50 years there has been an exceptional amount of fusion of different branches of mathematics, as you well know. A most unusual cultural factor affecting the development of mathematics has been the emigration of eminent mathematicians from Germany, Poland, and other countries to the United States during the past 30 years. Men whose interests had been in different branches of mathematics were thrown together and discovered how to merge these branches to their mutual benefit, and frequently new branches grew out of such meetings. The cultural history of mathematics during the past 50 years, taken in conjunction with that of mathematics in ancient Greece, China, and Western Europe, furnishes convincing evidence that *no branch of mathematics can pursue its course in isolation indefinitely, without ultimately reaching a static condition.*

Of the *instruments* for diffusion in mathematics, none is more important, probably, than the journals. Without sufficient outlet for the results of research, and proper distribution of the same, the progress of mathematics will be severely hampered. And any move that retards international contacts through the medium of journals, such as restriction to languages not widely read, is distinctly an anti-mathematical act. For it has become a truism that today mathematics is international.

This brings us to a consideration of symbols. For the so-called "International character" of mathematics is due in large measure to the standardization of symbols that it has achieved, thereby stimulating diffusion. Without a symbolic apparatus to convey our ideas to one another, and to pass on our results to future generations, there wouldn't be any such thing as mathematics—indeed, there would be essentially no culture at all, since, with the possible exception of a few simple tools, culture is based on the use of symbols. A good case can be made for the thesis that man is to be distinguished from other animals by the way in which he uses symbols [18; II]. Man possesses what we might call *symbolic initiative*; that is, he assigns symbols to stand for objects or ideas, sets up relationships between them, and operates with them as though they were physical objects. So far as we can tell, no other animal has this faculty, although many animals do exhibit what we might call *symbolic reflex* behavior. Thus, a dog can be taught to lie down at the command "Lie down," and of course to Pavlov's dogs, the bells signified food. In a recent issue of a certain popular magazine a psychologist is portrayed teaching pigeons to procure food by pressing certain combinations of colored buttons. All of these are examples of symbolic reflex behavior—the animals do not create the symbols.

As an aspect of our culture that depends so exclusively on symbols, as well as the investigation of certain relationships between them, mathematics is probably the furthest from comprehension by the non-human animal. However, much of our mathematical behavior that was originally of the *symbolic initiative* type drops to the *symbolic reflex* level. This is apparently a kind of labor-saving device set up by our neural systems. It is largely due to this, I believe, that a considerable amount of what passes for "good" teaching in mathematics is of the symbolic reflex type, involving no use of symbolic initiative. I refer of course to the drill type of teaching which may enable stupid John to get a required credit in mathematics but bores the creative minded William to the extent that he comes to loathe the subject! What essential difference is there between teaching a human animal to take the square root of 2 and teaching a pigeon to punch certain combinations of colored buttons? Undoubtedly the symbolic reflex type of teaching is justified when the pupil is very young—closer to the so-called "animal" stage of his development, as we say. But as he approaches maturity, more emphasis should be placed on his symbolic initiative. I am reminded here of a certain mathematician who seems to have an uncanny skill for discovering mathematical talent among the undergraduates at his university. But there is nothing mysterious about this; he simply encourages them to use their symbolic initiative. Let me recall parenthetically here what I said about the perennial presence of potential "great men;" there is no reason to believe that this teacher's success is due to a preference for his university by the possessors of mathematical talent, for they usually have no intention of becoming mathematicians when they matriculate. It moves one to wonder how many potentially great mathematicians are being constantly lost to mathematics because of "symbolic reflex" types of teaching.

I want to come now to a consideration of the Foundations of Mathematics. We have witnessed, during the past 50 years, what we might call the most thorough soul-searching in the history of mathematics. By 1900, the Burali-Forti contradiction had been found and the Russell and other antinomies were soon to appear. The sequel is well known: Best known are the attempt of Russell and Whitehead in their monumental *Principia Mathematica* to show that mathematics can be founded, in a manner free of contradiction, on the symbolically expressed principles and methods of what were at the time considered universally valid logical concepts; the formulation, chiefly at the hands of Brouwer and his collaborators, of the tenets of Intuitionism, which although furnishing a theory evidently free of contradiction, introduces a highly complicated set theory and a mathematics radically restricted as compared with the mathematics developed during the 19th century; and the formalization of mathematics by Hilbert and his collaborators, together with the development of a metamathematical proof theory which it was hoped would lead to proofs of freedom from contradiction for a satisfactory portion, at least, of the classical mathematics. None of these "foundations" has met with complete success. Russell and Whitehead's theory of types had to be bolstered with an axiom which they had to admit, in the second edition of *Principia Mathematica*, has only pragmatic justification, and subsequent attempts by Chwistek, Wittgenstein, and Ramsey to eliminate or modify the use of this axiom generally led to new objections. The restricted mathematics known as Intuitionism has won only a small following, although some of its methods, such as those of a finite constructive character, seem to parallel the methods underlying the treatment of formal systems in symbolic logic, and some of its tenets, especially regarding constructive existence proofs, have found considerable favor. The possibility of carrying out the Hilbert program seems highly doubtful, in view of the investigations of Gödel and others.

Now the cultural point of view is not advanced as a substitute for such theories. In my title I have used the word "basis" instead of "foundations" in order to emphasize this point. But it seems probable that the recognition of the cultural basis of mathematics would clear the air in Foundation theories of most of the mystical and vague philosophical arguments which are offered in their defense, as well as furnish a guide and motive for further research. The points of view underlying various attempts at Foundations of Mathematics are often hard to comprehend. In most cases it would seem that the proponents have decided in their own minds just what mathematics is, and that all they have to do is formulate it accordingly—overlooking entirely the fact that because of its cultural basis, mathematics as they know it may be not at all what it will be a century hence. If the thought underlying their endeavors is that they will succeed in trapping the elusive beast and confining it within bounds which it will never break, they are exceedingly optimistic. If the culture concept tells us anything, it should teach us that the first rule for setting up any Foundation theory is that it should only attempt to encompass specific portions of the field as it is known in our culture. At most, a Foundation theory should be considered as a kind of constitution with provision for future amendments. And in view of the situation as regards such principles as the choice axiom, for instance, it looks at present as though no such constitution could be adopted by a unanimous vote!

I mentioned "mysticism and vague philosophical arguments" and their elimination on the cultural basis. Consider, for example, the insistence of Intuitionism that all mathematics should be founded on the natural numbers or the counting process, and that the latter are "intuitively given." There are plausible arguments to support the thesis that the natural numbers should form the starting point for mathematics, but it is hard to understand just what "intuitively given" means, or why the classical conception of the continuum, which the Intuitionist refuses to accept, should not be considered as "intuitively given." It makes one feel that the Intuitionist has taken Kronecker's much-quoted dictum that "The integers were made by God, but all else is the work of man" and substituted "Intuition" for "God." However, if he would substitute for this vague psychological notion of "intuition" the viewpoint that inasmuch as the counting process is a cultural invariant, it follows that the natural numbers form for every culture the most basic part of what has been universally called "mathematics," and should therefore serve as the starting point for every Foundations theory; then I think he would have a much sounder argument. I confess that I have not studied the question as to whether he can find further cultural support to meet all the objections of opponents of Intuitionism. It would seem, however, that he would have to drop his insistence that in construction of sets (to quote Brouwer [4; p. 86]) "neither ordinary language nor any symbolic language can have any other role than that of serving as a non-mathematical auxiliary," since no cultural trait on the abstract level of mathematics can be constructed other than by the use of symbols. Furthermore, and this is a serious objection, it appears to ignore *the influence that our language habits have on our modes of thought.*

Or consider the thesis that all mathematics is derivable from what some seem to regard as primitive or universal logical principles and methods. Whence comes this "primitive" or "universal" character? If by these terms it is meant to imply that these principles have a culturally invariant basis like that of the counting process, then it should be pointed out that cultures exist in which they do not have any validity, even in their qualitative non-symbolic form. For example, in cultures which contain magical elements (and such elements form an extremely important part of some primitive cultures), the law of contradiction usually fails. Moreover, the belief that our forms of thought are culturally invariant is no longer held. As eminent a philosopher as John Stuart Mill stated, [14; p. 11], "The principles and rules of grammar are the means by which the forms of language are made to correspond with the universal forms of thought." If Mill had been acquainted with other than the Indo-European language group, he could not have made such an error. The Trobriand Islanders, for example, lack a cause-and-effect pattern of thought; their language embodies no mechanism for expressing a relationship between events. As Malinowski pointed out [11; p. 360], these people have no conception of one event leading up to another, and chronological sequence is unimportant. (Followers of Kant should note that they can count, however.) But I hardly need to belabor the point. As Lukasciewicz and others have observed, not even Aristotle gave to the law of the excluded middle the homage that later logicians paid it! All I want to do in this connection is to indicate that on the cultural basis we find affirmation of what is already finding universal acceptance among mathematical logicians, I believe; namely, that the significance and validity of such material as that in *Principia Mathematica* is only the same as that of other purely formal systems.

It is probably fair to say that the Foundations of Mathematics as conceived and currently investigated by the mathematical logicians finds greatest support on the cultural basis. For inasmuch as there can exist, and have existed, different cultures, different forms of thought, and hence different mathematics, it seems impossible to consider mathematics, as I have already indicated, other than man-made and having no more of the character of necessity or truth than other cultural traits. Problems of mathematical existence, for example, can never be settled by appeal to any mathematical dogma. Indeed, they have no validity except as related to special foundations theories. The question as to the existence of choice sets, for instance, is not the same for an Intuitionist as for a Formalist. The Intuitionist can justifiably assert that "there is no such problem as the continuum problem" provided he adds the words "for an Intuitionist"—otherwise he is talking nonsense. *Because of its cultural basis, there is no such thing as the absolute in mathematics; there is only the relative.*

But we must not be misled by these considerations and jump to the conclusion that what constitutes mathematics in our culture is purely arbitrary;

that, for instance, it can be defined as the "science of *p* implies *q*", or the science of axiomatic systems. Although the individual person in the cultural group may have some degree of variability allowed him, he is at the same time subject to the dominance of his culture. The individual mathematician can play with postulational systems as he will, but unless and until they are related to the existing state of mathematics in his culture they will only be regarded as idiosyncrasies. Similar ties, not so obvious however, join mathematics to other cultural elements. And these bonds, together with those that tie each and every one of us to our separate mathematical interests, cannot be ignored even if we will to do so. They may exert their influence quite openly, as in the case of those mathematicians who have recently been devoting their time to high speed computers, or to developing other new and unforeseen mathematics induced by the recent wartime demands of our culture. Or their influence may be hidden, as in the case of certain mathematical habits which were culturally induced and have reached the symbolic reflex level in our reactions. Thus, although the postulational method may turn out to be the most generally accepted mode of founding a theory, it must be used with discretion; otherwise the theories produced will not be mathematics in the sense that they will [not] be a part of the mathematical component of our culture.

But it is time that I closed these remarks. It would be interesting to study evidence in mathematics of *styles* and of *cultural patterns*; these would probably be interesting subjects of investigation for either the mathematician or the anthropologist, and could conceivably throw some light on the probable future course of the field. I shall have to pass on, however, to a brief conclusion:

In man's various cultures are found certain elements which are called *mathematical*. In the earlier days of civilization, they varied greatly from one culture to another so much so that what was called "mathematics" in one culture would hardly be recognized as such in certain others. With the increase in diffusion due, first, to exploration and invention, and, secondly, to the increase in the use of suitable symbols and their subsequent standardization and dissemination in journals, the mathematical elements of the most advanced cultures gradually merged until, except for minor cultural differences like the emphasis on geometry in Italy, or on function theory in France, there has resulted essentially one element, common to all civilized cultures, known as mathematics. This is not a fixed entity, however, but is subject to constant change. Not all of the change represents accretion of new material; some of it is a shedding of material no longer, due to influential cultural variations, considered mathematics. Some so-called "borderline" work, for example, is difficult to place either in mathematics or outside mathematics.

From the extension of the notion of number to the transfinite, during the latter half of the 19th century, there evolved certain contradictions around the turn of the century, and as a consequence the study of Foundations questions, accompanied by a great development of mathematical logic, has increased during the last 50 years. Insofar as the search for satisfactory Foundation theories aims at any absolute criterion for truth in mathematics or fixation of mathematical method, it appears doomed to failure, since recognition of the cultural basis of mathematics compels the realization of its variable and growing character. Like other culture traits, however, mathematics is not a thoroughly arbitrary construction of the individual mathematician, since the latter is restricted in his seemingly free creations by the state of mathematics and its directions of growth during his lifetime, it being the latter that determines what is considered "important" at the given time.

In turn, the state and directions of growth of mathematics are determined by the general complex of cultural forces both within and without mathematics. Conspicuous among the forces operating from without during the past 50 years have been the crises through which the cultures chiefly concerned have been passing; these have brought about a large exodus of mathematicians from Western Europe to the United States, thereby setting up new contacts with resulting diffusion and interaction of mathematical ideas, as well as in the institution of new directions or acceleration of directions already under way, such as in certain branches of applied mathematics.

What the next 50 years will bring, I am not competent to predict.In his *Decline of the West*, Spengler concluded [15tr; pp. 89–90] that in the notion of *group*, Western "mathematic" had achieved its "last and conclusive creation," and he closed his second chapter, entitled "The meaning of numbers," with the words: "—the time of the *great* mathematicians is past. Our tasks today are those of preserving, rounding off, refining, selection—in place of big dynamic creation, the same clever detail-work which characterized the Alexandrian mathematic of late Hellenism." This was published in 1918—32 years ago—and I leave it to your judgment whether he was right or not. It seems unlikely that the threatened division into two opposing camps of those nations in which mathematical activity is chiefly centered at present will be of long enough duration to set up two distinct mathematical cultures—although in other fields, such as botany, such a division appears to be under way. Nevertheless, as individual mathematicians we are just as susceptible to cultural forces as are botanists, economists, or farmers, and long separation in differing cultures can result in variations of personality that cannot fail to be reflected in our mathematical behavior. Let us hope that at the turn of the century 50 years hence, mathematics will be as active and unique a cultural force as it is now, with that free dissemination of ideas which is the chief determinant of growth and vitality.

ACKNOWLEDGMENTS

I am indebted to my colleague, Professor L.A. White, of the Anthropology Department, University of Michigan, and to Betty Ann Dillingham, for reading this paper in manuscript and offering most helpful criticism and advice. However, responsibility for errors and opinions expressed herein is entirely my own, of course.

BIBLIOGRAPHY

[1] W.W.R. Ball, *A short account of the history of mathematics*, London, Macmillan, 1888; 4th ed., 1908.

[2] E.T. Bell, *The development of mathematics*, New York, McGraw-Hill, 2d ed., 1945.

[3] P.W. Bridgman, *The logic of modern physics*, New York, Macmillan, 1927.

[4] L.E.J. Brouwer, *Intuitionism and formalism*, Bull. Amer. Math. Soc. vol. 20 (1913–1914) pp. 81–96 (tr. by A. Dresden).

[5] F. Cajori, *A history of mathematics*, New York, Macmillan, 1893; 2d ed., 1919.

[6] A. Dresden, *Some philosophical aspects of mathematics*, Bull. Amer. Math. Soc. vol. 34 (1928) pp. 438–452.

[7] J. Hadamard, *The psychology of invention in the mathematical field*, Princeton, Princeton University Press, 1945.

[8] G.H. Hardy, *A mathematician's apology*, Cambridge, England, Cambridge University Press, 1941.

[9] C.J. Keyser, *Mathematics as a culture clue*, Scripta Mathematica vol. 1 (1932–1933) pp. 185–203; reprinted in a volume of essays having same title, New York, Scripta Mathematica, 1947.

[10] A.L. Kroeber, *Anthropology*, rev. ed., New York, Harcourt, Brace, 1948.

[11] D.D. Lee, *A primitive system of values*, Philosophy of Science vol. 7 (1940) pp. 355–378.

[12] R. Linton, *The Study of man*, New York, Appleton-Century, 1936.

[13] Y. Mikami, *The development of mathematics in China and Japan*, Leipzig, Drugulin 1913.

[14] J.S. Mill, *Inaugural address*, delivered to the University of St. Andrews, Feb. 1, 1867, Boston, Littell and Gay.

[15] O. Spengler, *Der Untergang des Abendlandes*, München, C.H. Beck, vol. I, 1918, (2d ed., 1923), vol. II, 1922. [15tr] English translation of [15] by C.F. Atkinson, under the title *The decline of the West*, New York, Knopf, vol. I, 1926, vol. II, 1928.

[16] D.J. Struik, *A concise history of mathematics*, 2 vols., New York, Dover, 1948.

[17] L.A. White, *The locus of mathematical reality*, Philosophy of Science vol. 14 (1947) pp. 289–303; republished in somewhat altered form as Chapter 10 of [18].

[18] ———, *The science of culture*, New York, Farrar, Straus, 1949.

JUDITH V. GRABINER

Is Mathematical Truth Time-Dependent?

In her essay, Grabiner echoes points made by Lakatos and Hersh. She begins by speaking of errors discerned in the course of history and concludes with a vision of mathematics as subject to ongoing revolution.

> Mathematics grows in two ways: not only by successive increments, but also by occasional revolution. Only if we accept the possibility of present error can we hope that the future will bring a fundamental improvement in our knowledge.

To be sure, foundationalists could acknowledge the existence of *past* revolutions in mathematics, but this was ancient history. Present mathematics is supposedly shielded from them by the Great Revolution, the solution to the crises and the discovery of foundations. Grabiner, by contrast, suggests that the future will be rather like the past, that revolutions are part of mathematical practice in the long run. Thus, her thesis is very close to Thomas Kuhn's theory that scientific revolutions are a fundamental part of scientific development. However, while Kuhn exempted mathematics from his thesis Grabiner insists:

> Mathematics is *not* the unique science without revolutions. Rather mathematics is that area of human activity which has at once the least destructive and still the most fundamental revolutions.

The body of her essay investigates a particular mathematical revolution, the shift in standards of rigor between eighteenth- and ninteenth-century mathematicians' approaches to the calculus. Her thesis is that the shift was due in part to a change of attitudes (Kuhn speaks of world view) shaped by both internal and external factors but played out in the arena of mathematics. Some of the internal factors are widely recognized: the need to avoid errors which became more pressing as mathematics developed into more complex areas, the desire to generalize and unify results, and the aspirations to Euclidean rigor. Less widely recognized is the changing economic circumstances of mathematicians. Grabiner suggests that mathematicians ceased to be patronized by courts or to be independently wealthy and, in the main, came to

Reprinted, with permission, from American Mathematical Monthly, Vol. 81, No. 4, April 1974, pp. 354–365.

earn their living by teaching. Thus, teaching, particularly in a university setting, came to be a main component of mathematical practice and brought with it new standards of mathematical explanation. This, Grabiner argues, was the final catalyst in the change of attitudes.

Grabiner proceeds to show how some of the principles used by eighteenth-century mathematicians were transformed by their successors. The principles at issue were those dealing with approximations, both the actual approximation procedures and the computation of error estimates. Where the eighteenth-century mathematicians had assumed solutions without proof and had concentrated on procedures for approximating those solutions, the nineteenth-century mathematicians took these approximating procedures and built them into existence proofs.

Of course, one case study, however suggestive, does not by itself ground general conclusions. But it can exemplify a new approach to understanding mathematics based on a judicious mixture of practice and theory, mathematical techniques and historical understanding. Grabiner's essay does this very well.

• • • • •

1 INTRODUCTION

Is mathematical truth time-dependent? Our immediate impulse is to answer no. To be sure, we acknowledge that standards of truth in the natural sciences have undergone change; there was a Copernican revolution in astronomy, a Darwinian revolution in biology, an Einsteinian revolution in physics. But do scientific revolutions like these occur in mathematics? Mathematicians have most often answered this question as did the nineteenth-century mathematician Hermann Hankel, who said, "In most sciences, one generation tears down what another has built, and what one has established, the next undoes. In mathematics alone, each generation builds a new story to the old structure." [20, p. 25.]

Hankel's view is not, however, completely valid. There have been several major upheavals in mathematics. For example, consider the axiomatization of geometry in ancient Greece, which transformed mathematics from an experimental science into a wholly intellectual one. Again, consider the discovery of non-Euclidean geometries and non-commutative alegbras in the nineteenth century; these developments led to the realization that mathematics is not about anything in particular; it is instead the logically connected study of abstract systems. These were revolutions in thought which changed mathematicians' views about the nature of mathematical truth, and about what could or should be proved.

Another such mathematical revolution occurred between the eighteenth and nineteenth centuries, and was focussed primarily on the calculus. This change was a rejection of the mathematics of powerful techniques and novel results in favor of the mathematics of clear definitions and rigorous proofs. Because this change, however important it may have been for mathematicians themselves, is not often discussed by historians and philosophers, its revolutionary character is not widely understood. In this paper, I shall first try to show that this major change did occur. Then, I shall investigate what brought it about. Once we have done this, we can return to the question asked in the title of this paper.

2 EIGHTEENTH-CENTURY ANALYSIS: PRACTICE AND THEORY

To establish what eighteenth-century mathematical practice was like, let us first look at a brilliant derivation of a now well-known result. Here is how Leonhard Euler derived the infinite series for the cosine of an angle. He began with the identity

$$(\cos z + i \sin z)^n = \cos nz + i \sin nz.$$

He then expanded the left-hand side of the equation according to the binomial theorem. Taking the real part of that binomial expansion and equating it to cos nz, he obtained

$$\cos nz = (\cos z)^n - \frac{n(N-1)}{2!}(\cos z)^{n-2}(\sin z)^2 + \frac{n(n-1)(n-2)(n-3)}{4!}(\cos z)^{n-4}(\sin z)^4 - \dots .$$

Let z be an infinitely small arc, and let n be infinitely large. Then:

$$\cos z = 1,\ \sin z = z,\ \mathrm{n}(n-1) = n^2,\ n(n-1)(n-2)(n-3) = n^4, \text{ etc.}$$

The equation now becomes recognizable:

$$\cos nz = 1 - \frac{n^2z^2}{2!} + \frac{n^4z^4}{4!} - \dots .$$

But since z is infinitely small and n infinitely large, Euler concludes that nz is a finite quantity. So let $nz = v$. The modern reader may be left slightly breathless; still, we have

$$\cos v = 1 - \frac{v^2}{2!} + \frac{v^4}{4!} - \dots .$$

(See [16, sections 133–4] and [32, pp. 348–9].)

Now that we have worked through one example, we shall be able to appreciate some generalizations about the way many eighteenth-century mathematicians worked. First, the primary emphasis was on getting results. All mathematicians know many of the results from this period, results which bear the names of Leibniz, Bernoulli, L'Hôpital, Taylor, Euler, and Laplace. But the chances are good that these results were originally obtained in ways utterly different from the ways we prove them today. It is doubtful that Euler and his contemporaries would have been able to derive their results if they had been burdened with our standards of rigor. Here, then, is one major difference between the eighteenth-century way of doing mathematics and our way.

What led eighteenth-century mathematicians to think that results might be more important than rigorous proofs? One reason is that mathematics participated in the great explosion in science known as the Scientific Revolution [19]. Since the Renaissance, finding new knowledge had been a major goal of all the sciences. In mathematics, ever since the first major new result—the solution to the cubic equation published in 1545—increasing mathematical knowledge had meant finding new results. The invention of the calculus at the end of the seventeenth century intensified the drive for results; here was a powerful new method which promised vast new worlds to conquer. One can imagine few more exciting tasks than trying to solve the equations of motion for the whole solar system. The calculus was an ideal instrument for deriving new results, even though many mathematicians were unable to explain exactly why this instrument worked.

If the overriding goal of most eighteenth-century mathematics was to get results, we would expect mathematicians of the period to use those methods which produced results. For eighteenth-century mathematicians, the end justified the means. And the successes were many. New subjects arose in the eighteenth century, each with its own range of methods and its own domain of results: the calculus of variations, descriptive geometry, and partial differential equations, for instance. Also, much greater sophistication was achieved in existing subjects, like mathematical physics and probability theory.

The second generalization we shall make about eighteenth-century mathematics and its drive for results is that mathematicians placed great reliance on the power of symbols. Sometimes it seems to have been assumed that if one could just write down something which was symbolically coherent, the truth of the statement was guaranteed. And this assumption was not applied to finite formulas only. Finite methods were routinely extended to infinite processes. Many important facts about infinite power series were discovered by treating the series as very long polynomials [30].

This trust in symbolism in the eighteenth century is somewhat anomalous in the history of mathematics, and needs to be accounted for. It came both from the success of algebra and the success of the calculus. Let us first consider algebra. General symbolic notation of the type we now take for granted was introduced in 1591 by the French mathematician François Viète [6, pp. 59–65] and [32, pp. 74–81]. This notion proved to be the greatest instrument of discovery in the history of mathematics. Let us illustrate its power by one example. Consider the equation

$$(2.1) \qquad (x-a)(x-b)(x-c) = x^3 - (a+b+c)x^2 + (ab+ac+bc)x - abc.$$

Symbolic notation lets you discover what dozens of numerical examples may not: the relation between the roots and the coefficients of any polynomial equation of any degree. Equation (2.1), furthermore, has degree three, and has three roots. Relying on results like (2.1), Albert Girard in 1629 stated that an nth degree equation had n roots—the first formulation of what Gauss later called the Fundamental Theorem of Algebra.

But why are algebraic formulas like (2.1) considered true by eighteenth-century mathematicians? Because, as Newton put it, algebra is just a "universal arithmetic" [29]. Equation (2.1) is valid because it is a generalization about valid arithmetical statements. What, then, about infinite arguments, like the one of Euler's we examined earlier? The answer is analogous. Just as there is an arithmetic of infinite decimal fractions, we may generalize and create an algebra of infinite series [28, p. 6]. Infinite processes are like finite ones—except that they take longer.

The faith in symbolism nourished by algebra was enhanced further by the success of the calculus. Leibniz had invented the notations dy/dx and $\int y\,dx$ expressly to help us do our thinking. The notation serves this function well; we owe a debt to Leibniz every time we change variables under the integral sign. Or, suppose y is a function of x and that x is a function of t; we want to know dy/dt. It is not Leibniz, but Leibniz's notation that discovers the chain rule:

$$dy/dt = (dy/dx)(dx/dt).$$

The success of Leibniz's notation for the calculus reinforced mathematicians' belief in the power of symbolic arguments to give true conclusions.

In the eighteenth century, belief in the power of good notation extended beyond mathematics. For instance, it led the chemist Lavoisier to foresee a "chemical algebra," in the spirit of which Berzelius in 1813 devised chemical symbols essentially like those we use today. Anybody who has balanced chemical equations knows how the symbols do some of the thinking for us. The fact that the idea of the validity of purely symbolic arguments spread from mathematics to other areas shows us how prevalent an idea it must have been.

What has been said so far should not lead the reader to believe that eighteenth-century mathematicians were completely indifferent to the foundations of analysis. They certainly discussed the subject, and at length. I shall not here summarize the diverse eighteenth-century attempts to explain the nature of dy/dx, of limits, of the infinite, and of integrals, during a century that Carl Boyer has rightly called "the period of indecision" as far as foundations were concerned [7, Chapter VI]. What must be emphasized for our present purposes is that discussions of foundations were not the basic concern of eighteenth-century mathematicians. That is, discussions of foundations do not generally appear in research papers in scientific journals; instead, they are relegated to Chapter I of textbooks, or found in popularizations. More important, the practice of mathematics did not depend on a perfect understanding of the basic concepts used. But this was no longer the situation in nineteenth-century mathematics, and, of course, is not the situation today.

Nineteenth-century analysts, beginning with Cauchy and Bolzano, gave rigorous, inequality-based treatments of limit, convergence, and continuity, and demanded rigorous proofs of the theorems about these concepts. We know what these proofs were like; we still use them. This new direction in nineteenth-century analysis is not just a matter of differences in technique. It is a major change in the way mathematics was looked at and done. Now that we have sketched the eighteenth-century approach, we are ready to deal with what are—from the historical point of view—the most interesting questions of this paper. What made the change between the old and new views occur? How did mathematics get to be the way it is now?

Two things were necessary for the change. Most obviously, the techniques needed for rigorous proofs had to be developed. We shall discuss the history of some major techniques in Section 4, below. But also, there had to be a change in attitude. Without the techniques, of course, the change in attitude could never have borne fruit. But the change in attitude, though not sufficient, was a necessary condition for the establishment of rigor. Our next task, accordingly, will be to explain the change in attitude toward the foundations of the calculus between the eighteenth and nineteenth centuries. Did the very nature of mathematics force this change? Or was it motivated by factors outside of mathematics? Let us investigate various possibilities.

3 WHY DID STANDARDS OF MATHEMATICAL TRUTH CHANGE?

The first explanation which may occur to us is like the one we use to justify rigor to our students today: the calculus was made rigorous to avoid errors, and to correct errors already made. But this is not quite what happened. In fact, there are surprisingly few mistakes in eighteenth-century mathematics. There are two main reasons for this. First, some results could be verified numerically, or even experimentally; thus, their validity could be checked without a rigorous basis. Second, and even more important, eighteenth-century mathematicians had an almost unerring intuition. Though they were not guided by rigorous definitions, they nevertheless had a deep understanding of the properties of the basic concepts of analysis. This conclusion is supported by the fact that many apparently shaky eighteenth-century arguments can be salvaged, and made rigorous by properly specifying hypotheses. Nevertheless, we must point out that the need to avoid errors became more important near the end of the eighteenth century, when there was increasing interest among mathematicians in complex functions, in functions of several variables, and in trigonometric series. In these subjects, there are many plausible conjectures whose truth is relatively difficult to evaluate intuitively. Increased interest in such results may have helped draw attention to the question of foundations.

A second possible explanation which may occur to us is that the calculus was made rigorous in a spirit of generalization. The eighteenth century had produced a mass of results. The need to unify such a mass of results could have led automatically to a rigorous, axiomatic basis. But there had been large numbers of results for a hundred years before Cauchy's work. Besides, unifying results does not always make them rigorous; moreover, the function of rigor is not just to unify, but to prove. Still, there is something to be said for the hypothesis that the calculus became rigorous partly to unify the wealth of existing results. At the end of the eighteenth century, several mathematicians thought that the pace of getting new results was decreasing. This feeling had some basis in fact; most of the results obtainable by the routine application of eighteenth-century methods had been obtained. Perhaps, if progress was slowing, it was time to sit back and reflect about what had been done [31, pp. 136–7]. This feeling helped get some mathematicians interested in the question of rigor.

A third possible explanation depends on the prior existence of rigor in geometry. Everybody from the Greeks on knew that mathematics was supposed to be rigorous. One might thus assume that mathematicians' consciences began to trouble them, and that as a result analysts returned their new methods to the old standards. In fact, Euclidean geometry did provide a model for the new rigor. But the old ideas of rigor were not enough in themselves to make mathematicians strive to make the calculus rigorous—as the hundred and fifty years from Newton to Cauchy shows. This is true even though the discrepancy between Euclidean standards and the actual practice of eighteenth-century mathematicians did not go unnoticed. George Berkeley, Bishop of Cloyne, attacked the calculus in 1734, on the perfectly valid grounds that it was not rigorous the way mathematics was supposed to be. Berkeley wanted to defend religion against the attacks of unreasonableness levelled against it by eighteenth-century scientists and mathematicians. Berkeley said that his opponents did not even reason well about mathematics. He conceded that the results of the calculus were valid, but attacked its methods. Berkeley's attack, *The Analyst,* is a masterpiece of polemics [32, pp. 333–338] and [3]. He said of the "vanishing increments" that played so crucial a role in Newton's calculus, "And what are these . . . vanishing increments? They are neither finite quantities, nor qualities infinitely small, nor yet nothing. May we not call them the ghosts of departed quantities?" Berkeley's attack—which included point-by-point mathematical criticisms of some basic arguments of Newton's calculus—provoked a number of mathematicians to write refutations. However, neither Berkeley's attack nor the replies to it produced the change in attitude toward rigor which we are trying to explain. First of all, the replies are not very convincing [8]. Besides, the subject of foundations was still not considered serious mathematics. Berkeley did get people thinking, more than they would have without him, about the problem of foundations. The discussions of foundations by Maclaurin, D'Alembert, and Lagrange were all at least somewhat influenced by Berkeley's work. Nevertheless, Berkeley's attack in itself was not enough to cause foundations to become a major mathematical concern.

In bringing about the change, there is one other factor which, though seldom mentioned in this connection, was important: the mathematician's need to teach. Near the end of the eighteenth century, a major social change occurred. Before the last decades of the century, mathematicians were often attached to royal courts; their job was to do mathematics and thus add to the glory, or edification, of their patron. But almost all mathematicians since the French Revolution have made their living by teaching [31, p. 140] [2, p. 95,108].

This change in the economic circumstances of mathematicians had other causes than the decline of particular royal courts. In the eighteenth century, science was expanding. This was the "age of Newton" and the success of Newtonian science. Governments and businessmen felt that science was important and could be useful; scientists encouraged them in these beliefs. So governments founded educational institutions to promote science. Military schools were founded to provide prospective officers with knowledge of applied science. New scientific chairs were endowed in existing universities. By far the most important new institution for scientific instruction, one which served as a model to several nations in the nineteenth century, was the *École polytechnique* in Paris, founded in 1795 by the revolutionary government in France.

Why might the new economic circumstances of mathematicians—the need to teach—have helped promote rigor? Teaching always makes the teacher think carefully about the basis for the subject. A mathematician could understand enough about a concept to use it, and could rely on the insight he had gained through his experience. But this does not work with freshmen, even in the eighteenth century. Beginners will not accept being told, "After you have worked with this concept for three years, you'll understand it."

What is the evidence that teaching helped motivate eighteenth and nineteenth century mathematicians to make anlaysis rigorous? First, until the end of the eighteenth century, most work on foundations did not appear in scientific journals, apparently because foundations were not considered to pose major mathematical (as opposed to philosophical) questions. Instead, such work appeared in courses of lectures, in textbooks, or in popularizations. Even in the nineteenth century, when foundations had been established as essential to mathematics, their origin was often in teaching. The work on foundations of analysis of Lagrange [23,26], of Cauchy [10,11], of Weierstrass [21, pp. 283–4] [7, pp. 284–7], and of Dedekind [14, p. 1], all originated in courses of lectures.

Each of the points we have made so far helps explain what motivated mathematicians to shift from the result-oriented view of the eighteenth century to the more rigorous standards of the nineteenth. One more catalyst of the change should be identified: Joseph-Louis Lagrange. Lagrange's own interest in the problem of foundations was first engaged by having to teach the calculus at the military school in Turin [24]. In 1784, by proposing the foundations of the calculus as a prize problem for the Berlin Academy of Sciences, he stimulated the first major booklength contributions to foundations of the calculus written on the Continent. (See [27] [9] [7, p. 254–255] and [18, pp. 149–150].) Above all, Lagrange's lectures at the *École polytechnique,* published in two widely influential books, attempted to give a general and algebraic framework for the calculus [26] [23]. Lagrange did not correctly solve the problem of foundations—we can no longer accept his *definition* of $f'(x)$ as the coefficient of h in the Taylor series expansion of $f(x + h)$. Nevertheless, his vision of reducing the calculus to algebra decisively influenced the work of Bolzano [5] and—as we shall see—of Cauchy.

The change in attitude we have been discussing was not enough in itself to establish rigor in the calculus—as the example of Lagrange shows. Having decided that we want to make a subject rigorous, what else do we need? Two more things are required: the right definitions, and techniques of proof to derive the known results fom the definitions. We must now answer another question: where did the required definitions and proofs come from?

Eighteenth-century mathematicians themselves had developed many of the techniques, and isolated many of the basic defining properties—even though they did not know that this is what they were doing. It is amazing that so many of the techniques used by Cauchy in rigorous arguments had been around for so long. This fact shows that a real change in point of view was required for the rigorization of analysis; it was not an automatic development out of eighteenth-century mathematics.

4 THE EIGHTEENTH—CENTURY ORIGINS OF NINETEENTH-CENTURY RIGOR

We shall illustrate the eighteenth-century origins of nineteenth-century rigor by giving several examples of eighteenth-century work which was transformed into nineteenth-century definitions and proofs. The principal area of eighteenth-century mathematics we shall investigate is the study of approximations. Eighteenth-century mathematicians, whether solving algebraic equations or differential equations, developed many useful approximation methods. When the goal is results, an approximate result is better than nothing. Paradoxically, eighteenth-century mathematicians were most exact when they were being approximate; their work with inequalities in approximations later became the basis for rigorous analysis.

We shall discuss two classes of eighteenth-century approximation work: the actual working out of approximation procedures, and the computation of error estimates. Let us see what use nineteenth-century analysts made of these.

One new way in which nineteenth-century mathematicians looked at eighteenth-century approximations was to see the approximate solution as a construction of that solution, and therefore as a proof of its existence. For instance, Cauchy did this in developing what is now called the Cauchy-Lipschitz method of proving the existence of the solution to a differential equation; the proof is based on an approximation method developed by Euler [15, pp. 424–5] [12, p. 399 ff]. Similarly Cauchy's elegant proof of the intermediate-value theorem for continuous functions was based on an eighteenth-century approximation method [22, pp. 260–1] [25, sections 2,6] [10, pp. 378–80]. For a continuous function $f(x)$, Cauchy took $f(a)$ and $f(b)$ of opposite sign, divided the interval $[a,b]$ into n parts, and concluded that there were at least two values of x on $[a,b]$, differing by $(b - a)/n$, which yielded opposite sign for $f(x)$. He then repeated the procedure on the interval between these two new values, on an interval of length $(b - a)/n$, which gives two more values, differing by $(b - a)/n^2$, and so on. Where Lagrange had used this technique to approximate to the root ξ of a polynomial included between $x = a$ and $x = b$, Cauchy used it to argue for the existence of the number ξ as the common limit of the sequences of values of x which gave positive sign for f, and negative sign for f. The origin of Cauchy's proof in algebraic approximations is further demonstrated by the context in which he gave it: a "*Note*" devoted to discussing the approximate solution of algebraic equations [10, p. 378 ff].

Another example of the conversion of approximations into existence proofs is given by Cauchy's theory of the definite integral. In the eighteenth century, it was customary to define the integral as the inverse of the derivative. It was known, however, that the value of the integral could be approximated by a sum. Cauchy took Euler's work on approximating the values of definite integrals by sums [15, pp. 184–7], and looked at it from an entirely new point of view. Cauchy *defined* the definite integral as the limit of a sum, proved the existence of the definite integral of a continuous (actually, uniformly continuous) function, and then used his definition to prove the Fundamental Theorem of Calculus [11, pp. 122–5, 151–2].

Now let us consider another type of result in eighteenth-century approximations: approximations given along with an error estimate. These results took a form like this: given some n, the mathematician could compute an upper bound on the error made in taking the nth approximation for the true value. Near the end of the eighteenth century, the algebra of inequalities was exploited with great skill in computing such error estimates [13, pp. 171–183] and [25, pp. 46–7, p. 163]. Cauchy, Abel, and their followers turned the approximating process around. Instead of being given n and finding the greatest possible error, we are *given* what is in effect the "error"—epsilon—and, provided that the process converges, we can always find n such that the error of the nth approximation is less than epsilon. (This seems to be the reason for the use of the letter "epsilon" in its usual modern sense by Cauchy [10, pp. 64–5 *et passim*].) [1] [10, pp. 400–415]. Cauchy's definition of convergence—which is essentially ours—is based on this principle [10, Chapter VI].

Another way in which nineteenth-century mathematicians changed eighteenth-century views of results using inequalities was to take facts known to eighteenth-century mathematicians in special cases and to make them legitimate in general. For instance, D'Alembert and others had shown that some particular series converged by showing that they were, term-by-term, less than a convergent geometric progression [13]. Guass in 1813 used this criterion to investigate, in a rigorous manner, the convergence of the hypergeometric series [17]. Cauchy used the comparison of a given series with a geometric one to derive and to prove some general tests for the convergence of any series; the ratio test, the logarithm test, and the root test [10, pp. 121–127].

Let us look at one last example—a very important one—of an eighteenth-century result which became something different in the nineteenth century: the property of the derivative expressed by

$$(4.1) \qquad f(x + h) = f(x) + hf'(x) + hV,$$

where V goes to zero with h. As we have remarked, Lagrange had defined $f'(x)$ as the coefficient of h in the Taylor expansion of $f(x + h)$. He then "derived" (4.1) from that Taylor series expansion, considering V to be a convergent infinite series in h. Lagrange used (4.1) to investigate many properties of the derivative. To do this, he interpreted "V goes to zero with h" to mean that, for any given quantity D, we can find h sufficiently small so that $f(x + h) - f(x)$ "will be included between" $h[f'(x) - D]$ and $h[f'(x) + D]$ [23, p. 87]. First Cauchy, and then Bolzano and Weierstrass, made (4.1) and its associated inequalities into the *definition* of $f'(x)$. (Cauchy's definition was actually verbal, but he translated it into the language of inequalities in proofs.) [11, pp. 44–5; 122–3], [4, Chapter 2] and [7, pp. 285–7].

This definition made legitimate the results about $f'(x)$ that Lagrange had derived from (4.1)—for instance, the mean-value theorem for derivatives. (Except, we must note, for a few errors, especially the confusion between convergence and uniform convergence, which was not cleared up until the 1840s.)

Of course, we do not mean to imply that Gauss, Cauchy, Bolzano, Abel, and Weierstrass were not original, creative mathematicians. They were. To show that major changes in point of view occur in mathematics, we have concentrated in this section on what these men owed to eighteenth-century techniques. But, besides transforming what they borrowed, they contributed much of their own that was new. Cauchy, in particular, devised beautiful proofs about convergent power series in real and complex variables, about real and complex integrals, and, of course, contributed to a variety of subjects besides analysis. Nevertheless, for our present purposes, we need the biased sample we have chosen—things accomplished either by taking what the eighteenth century knew for particular cases and making it general, or by taking what the eighteenth century had derived for one purpose and putting it to a more profound use.

Much effort was needed to transform eighteenth-century techniques in the ways we have discussed. But it was more than just a matter of effort. It took asking the right questions *first;* and then using—and expanding—the already existing techniques to answer them. It took—and was—a major change in point of view. The reawakening of interest in rigor was just as necessary as the availability of techniques to produce the point of view of Balzano and Cauchy—the point of view which has been with us ever since. Mathematics requires not only results, but clear definitions and rigorous proofs. Individual mathematicians may still concentrate on the creation of fruitful methods and ideas to be exploited, but the mathematical community as a whole can no longer be indifferent to rigor.

5 CONCLUSION

We began by asking whether mathematical truth was time-dependent. Perhaps mathematical truth is eternal, but our knowledge of it is not. We have now seen an example of how attitudes toward mathematical truth have changed in time. After such a revolution in thought, earlier work is re-evaluated. Some is considered worth more; some, worth less.

What should a mathematician do, knowing that such re-evaluations occur?

Three courses of action suggest themselves. First, we can adopt a sort of relativism which has been expressed in the phrase "Sufficient unto the day is the rigor thereof." Mathematical truth is just what the editors of the *Transactions* say it is. This is a useful view at times. But this view, if universally adopted, would mean that Cauchy and Weierstrass would never have come along. Unless there were the prior appearance of major errors, standards could never improve in any important way. So the attitude of relativism, which would have counselled Cauchy to leave foundations alone, will not suffice for us.

Second, we can attempt to set the highest conceivable standard: never use an argument in which we do not completely understand what is going on, dotting all the *i*'s and crossing all the *t*'s. But this is even worse. Euler, after all, knew that there were problems in dealing with infinitely large and infinitely small quantities. According to this high standard, which textbooks sometimes urge on students, Euler would never have written a line. There would have been no mathematical structure for Cauchy and Weierstrass to make rigorous.

So I suggest a third possibility: a recognition that the problem I have raised is just the existential situation mathematicians find themselves in. Mathematics grows in two ways: not only by successive increments, but also by occasional revolutions. Only if we accept the possibility of present error can we hope that the future will bring a fundamental improvement in our knowledge. We can be consoled that most of the old bricks will find places somewhere in the new structure. Mathematics is *not* the unique science without revolutions. Rather, mathematics is that area of human activity which has at once the least destructive and still the most fundamental revolutions.

ACKNOWLEDGMENTS

This paper was originally delivered at the Mathematical Association of America, Southern California Section, March 1972. The author wishes to thank Elmer Tolsted for encouragement and suggestions.

NOTES

1. N.H. Abel, Recherches sur la série

$$1 + (m/1)x + [m(m-1)/1.2]x^2 + [m(m-1)(m-2)/1.2.3]x^3 + \dots,$$

Oeuvres complètes, Vol. I, Christiania, 1881.

2. J. Ben David, The Scientist's Role in Society, Prentice-Hall, Englewood Cliffs, 1971.

3. G. Berkeley, The Works of George Berkeley, Vol. IV, ed. A.A. Luce and T.E. Jessop, Edinburgh, 1948–1957.

4. B.Bolzano, Functionenlehre, Schriften, Band I, Prague, 1930.

5. ________, Rein analytischer Beweis des Lehrsatzes, dass zwischen je zwei Werthen, die ein entgegengesetztes Resultat gewaehren, wenigstens eine reelle Wurzel der Gleichung liege, 1817, Englemann, Leipzig, 1905.

6. Carl Boyer, History of Analytic Geometry, Scripta Mathematica, New York, 1956.

7. ________, History of the Calculus and its Conceptual Development, Dover, New York, 1959.

8. F. Cajori, A History of the Conceptions of Limits and Fluxions in Great Britain from Newton to Woodhouse, Open Court, Chicago, 1931.

9. L.N.M. Carnot, Réflexions sur la métaphysique du calcul infinitésimal, Duprat, Paris, 1797.

10. A.-L. Cauchy, Cours d'analyse de l'école royale polytechnique, Imprimerie royale, Paris, 1821, in Oeuvres Complètes, Series 2, Vol. III, Gauthier-Villars, Paris, 1897.

11. A.-L. Cauchy, Résumé des leçons données à l'école royale polytechnique sur le calcul infinitésimal, Imprimerie royale, Paris, 1823, in Oeuvres Complètes, Series 2, Vol. IV, Gauthier-Villars, Paris, 1899.

12. A.-L. Cauchy, Exercises d'analyse, 1840, in Oeuvres, Series 2, Vol. XI.

13. Jean D'Alembert, Réflexions sur les suites et sur les racines imaginaires, Opuscules mathématiques, vol. V, Paris 1768, pp. 171–215.

14. Richard Dedekind, Essays on the theory of numbers, Dover, New York, 1963.

15. Leonhard Euler, Institutiones calculi integralis 1768, Opera Omnia, Series 1, vol. XI, Teubner, Leipzig and Berlin, 1911.

16. _________, Introductio in analysin infinitorum 1748, Opera Omnia, Series, 1, vols. 8–9.

17. K.F. Gauss, Disquisitio generales circa seriem infinitam

$$1 + \frac{\alpha \cdot \beta}{1 \cdot \gamma}x + \frac{\alpha(\alpha + 1)\beta(\beta + 1)}{1 \cdot 2 \cdot \gamma(\gamma + 1)}x^2 + \frac{\alpha(\alpha + 1)(\alpha + 2)\beta(\beta + 1)(\beta + 2)}{1 \cdot 2 \cdot 3 \cdot \gamma(\gamma + 1)(\gamma + 2)}x^3 + \ldots,$$

[1813], Werke, Vol. 3, pp. 123–162; German translation, Berlin, 1888.

18. C.C. Gillispie, Lazare Carnot Savant, Princeton, 1971.

19. A.R. Hall, The Scientific Revolution, 1500–1800, Beacon, Boston, 1966.

20. H. Hankel, Die Entwicklung der Mathematik im letzten Jahrhundert, 1884, quoted by M. Moritz, On Mathematics and Mathematicians, Dover, New York, 1942, p. 14.

21. F. Klein, Vorlesungen über die Entwicklung der Mathematik im 19. Jahrhundert, 1926, reprinted by Chelsea, New York, 1967.

22. J.-L. Lagrange, Leçons élémentaires sur les mathématiques, données à l'école normale en 1795. Oeuvres, VIII, Gauthier-Villars, Paris, 1867–1892, pp. 181–288.

23. _________, Leçons sur le calcul des fonctions, 2d edition, 1806, Oeuvres, X.

24. _________, Letter to Euler, 24 November 1759, Oeuvres, XIV, pp. 170–174.

25. _________, Traité de la résolution des équations numériques de tous les degrés, 1808, Oeuvres, VIII.

26. _________, Théorie des fonctions analytiques, 2d. edition, 1813, Oeuvres, IX.

27. S. L'Huilier, Exposition élémentaire des principes des calculs supérieurs, Decker, Berlin, 1787.

28. Isaac Newton, On the analysis by equations of an infinite number of terms, 1669, in D.T. Whiteside, ed., The Mathematical Works of Isaac Newton, Johnson Reprint, London and New York, 1964, vol. I.

29. Isaac Newton, Universal Arithmetic, 1707, in D.T. Whiteside ed., The Mathematical Works of Isaac Newton, vol. II, Johnson, London and New York, 1970.

30. R. Reiff, Geschichte der unendlichen Reihen, Tübingen, 1889.

31. D.J. Struik, Concise History of Mathematics, Dover, New York, 1967.

32. D.J. Struik, ed., A Source Book in Mathematics, 1200–1800, Harvard, Cambridge, 1967.

PHILIP KITCHER

Mathematical Change and Scientific Change

Wilder and Grabiner encourage us to look at mathematics in a new way, as a social or cultural practice that evolves over time. Such a viewpoint on mathematics might seem strange at first. However, it seemed a strange approach to natural science at one time, yet now it is a standard position in the philosophy of science. Can the philosophy of mathematics learn anything from the philosophy of science in this regard? The answer depends on the similarities between science and mathematics. No one has investigated the relation between these two fields more thoroughly than the philosopher, Philip Kitcher. The following selection, "Mathematical Change and Scientific Change," is the seventh chapter of his recent book, *The Nature of Mathematical Knowledge.*

In his essay, Kitcher compares mathematics to science with regard to their patterns of development. He begins by considering what appear to be major differences between mathematical change and scientific change. One is the idea that science changes essentially by making new observations and that observation is irrelevant to mathematics. Kitcher argues that both parts of this idea are incorrect.

A second apparent difference is that mathematical change seems cumulative in a way that scientific change does not. After criticizing several preliminary formulations of the cumulative aspect of mathematics, Kitcher admits a sense in which mathematics is cumulative. Mathematics has a mechanism of reinterpretation that resolves threats of competition. For example, the discovery of non-Euclidean geometries did not force mathematicians to choose between these and Euclidean geometry. Instead mathematicians reinterpreted geometry so that both the Euclidean and non-Euclidean varieties could be included in a systematic relation.

I suggest in passing that Kitcher might have pressed his case further by observing reinterpretation at work in the natural sciences. Newtonian physics has not been displaced by relativity theory in anything like the way in which the phlogiston theory or Lamarkian evolution have been discarded. Quite the contrary, Newtonian physics continues to be taught and used today, reinterpreted as a 'special case' of

---

relativity theory. Perhaps many natural sciences could be better interpreted as the development of alternative models (like geometry) rather than as competitions to settle on a single correct model.

In any case, the parallels between mathematics and science are sufficiently strong to induce Kitcher to apply some lessons from the philosophy of science to the philosophy of mathematics. He begins this project in the third section of his essay. From the philosophy of science, Kitcher obtains the Kuhnian notion of a paradigm, which he in turn analyzes in terms of practice and changes in practices. The notion of a paradigm is important insofar as it offers a richer conception of a field than the conception of a field as merely a set of statements. Paradigms include practice and methodology, both general principles and concrete exemplars. However, Kuhn tied his concept of a paradigm to the existence of scientific revolutions. For Kuhn, normal science proceeds under a stable set of paradigms, while scientific revolutions occur when scientists switch paradigms. Kitcher is able to sidestep the controversial distinction between normal science and revolutionary science by focusing on the practices of a discipline at any given time and examining the kinds of changes such practices can undergo. We can leave it to the historians to decide which changes were truly revolutionary and which changes were merely continuous developments.

Whatever the merits of analogizing mathematics to science, it has the drawback of importing into the philosophy of mathematics some of the ongoing controversies of the philosophy of science. The controversy that Kitcher contends with in section four of his essay might be labeled as the dilemma between stupidity and incommensurability. Let me sketch the dilemma as it might apply to mathematics. The problem arises when we try to compare the mathematics of different eras. From a foundational perspective, pre-foundational mathematicians were quite primitive, if not quite stupid. (This is a point Lakatos often makes.) Where pre-twentieth-century mathematicians did hit on correct results, the foundationalists would say, their reasoning was often hopelessly inadequate when measured by modern standards. In short this view characterizes other mathematics as better, or more often worse, approximations to ours. An alternative to this rather chauvinistic attitude is to regard other mathematicians as not primitive or stupid, but as expert practitioners of a practice of mathematics that differs from ours. Unfortunately, this has the effect of supposing that other mathematicians lived in a different mathematical world from us. We no longer can interpret them as lucky guessers—because we can no longer interpret them at all! Previous mathematics is not comparable to ours. Obviously, neither horn of the dilemma is very palatable. Kitcher attempts to resolve the puzzle by introducing the concept of 'reference potential'. He broadens the philosophically popular causal theory of reference to include attention not just to the actual referent a term might have, but also the potential reference of particular uses.

In the final section of his essay, Kitcher uses the concept of reference potential to help explain such major shifts in mathematics as the introduction of complex numbers and the introduction of transfinite numbers. Regardless of one's opinion of the details of Kitcher's analysis, there can be no doubt, I think, that he demonstrates the technical feasibility of a rigorous and uniform presentation of quasi-empiricism.

• • • • •

I

The existence of mathematical change is obvious enough. Contemporary mathematicians accept as true statements which our predecessors did not accept. In 1400, the members of the mathematical community did not believe that every polynomial equation with rational coefficients has roots; their nineteenth-century descendants did. Conversely, later writers sometimes abandon claims which have been espoused earlier. Leibniz and some of his followers believed that $1 - 1 + 1 - 1 + 1 \ldots = 1/2$. Cauchy and Abel scornfully rejected this and kindred statements. Yet the shifting allegiance to some statements is only one facet of mathematical change. Equally evident are alterations in mathematical language, variations in style and standards of reasoning, changes of emphasis on kinds of problems, even modifications of views about the scope of mathematics. The fact of mathematical change provokes a series of questions. Why do mathematicians propound different statements at different times? Why do they abandon certain forms of language? Why do certain questions wax and wane in importance? Why are standards and styles of proof modified? In short, what kinds of changes occur in the development of mathematics, and what general considerations motivate them?

To raise these questions is to begin to investigate the methodology of mathematics, in a way which is parallel to recent and contemporary inquiries about the methodology of the natural sciences. Neglect of the methodology of mathematics stems from distrust of the parallel. In turn, that distrust gains powerful support from mathematical apriorism. Yet, even if we reject the apriorist conception of mathematical knowledge, we may still wonder whether the development of mathematical knowledge is analogous to that of natural scientific knowledge. My goal in this chapter is to investigate the similarities and differences between mathematical change and scientific change. By doing so, I hope to dispose of some myths about mathematical change and to use the comparison with natural science to formulate more sharply the enterprise of investigating the methodology of mathematics.

Suspicion about the kinship of mathematical change and scientific change, when it is not simply a by-product of apriorist doctrine, is prompted by two important observations. One apparent major difference between the growth of scientific knowledge and the growth of mathematical knowledge is that the natural sciences seem to evolve in response to experience. As observations and experiments accumulate, we find ourselves forced to extend and modify our corpus of beliefs. In mathematics, however, the observation of previously unobserved phenomena and the contrivance of experiments seem to play no important role in stimulating change of belief. So we are easily led to conclude that the springs of change are different in the two cases. A second feature of the growth of mathematical knowledge is the appearance of cumulative development in mathematics in ways which seem absent in the natural sciences. Because contemporary mathematics appears to preserve so much more of what was accepted by the mathematicians of the past, it is tempting to suppose that the manner in which mathematical knowledge evolves must be fundamentally different from that in which scientific knowledge grows. Mathematical methods must be more sure-footed than those used by natural scientists.

In this section, I want to consider the first of these apparent disanalogies. I shall consider the issue of the cumulative character of mathematical knowledge in Section II. Our first task will be to uncover the picture of scientific change which underlies the complaint that, unlike the natural sciences, mathematics does not grow by responding to observation and experiment.

Consider the simplest empiricist view of the growth of scientific knowledge.[1] According to this picture, the statements accepted by the scientists of a given period can be divided into two classes: there are observation statements (*O-statements*) and theoretical statements (*T-statements*); the former are accepted on the basis of observation and are unrevisable; the latter are adopted on the basis of inference from the accepted O-statements, indeed on the basis of inferences which accord with principles of the "logic of scientific inquiry," principles which hold for all scientists at all times.[2] As science develops, the change in the corpus of O-statements is by accumulation. New O-statements are added, but old O-statements are never deleted. However, amendment of the class of T-statements is not by accumulation. Even though a particular set of T-statements may have been justified in the light of the limited set of O-statements adopted at an earlier stage, extension of the corpus of O-statements can force us to retract what we formerly believed, substituting a quite different set of T-statements in its place. There are two features of this picture of scientific change to which I wish to draw attention: (i) the match between observation and theory at any stage in the history of science is assumed to be perfect (the adopted O-statements justify the accepted T-statements in the light of the universal principles of the "logic of scientific inquiry"); (ii) addition of new O-statements can disrupt the match, forcing the modification of the corpus of T-statements to accommodate the broader class of O-statements. Together, these features combine to distinguish observation as the source of scientific change. Without new observations, science would be static.

I do not know whether anyone has held exactly this picture of scientific change, but something very close to it seems to be implicit in the writings of many logical empiricist philosophers of science. A variety of considerations makes it clear that this simple empiricist picture of scientific change cannot be sustained.

In the first place, there have been severe (and, to my mind, conclusive) attacks on the thesis that there is a class of unrevisable reports of observation, with consequent denial that the history of science can be viewed as a series of responses to an observational corpus which develops cumulatively.[3] Yet this critique, in and of itself, does not compel us to abandon those features of the simple empiricist picture which generate the view that observation is the source of scientific change, and thereby foster our suspicion that mathematical change is importantly different from scientific change. We may continue to suppose that the science of an epoch is a collection of statements determined jointly by the stimuli which have so far impinged upon those who adopt it and the canons of scientific inquiry. New stimuli can still be viewed as the sole inducers of modification of the corpus of beliefs, even though we agree that there is no level at which modification must be cumulative.

A second major assault on the simple empiricist picture challenges us to understand the large upheavals in science—such "revolutions" as the transition from Aristotelian cosmology to Copernician cosmology, the overthrow of the phlogiston theory, and the replacement of Newtonian physics with the special and general theories of relativity—using the terms which simple empiricism supplies.[4] Can we account for these episodes as consisting in the modification of a corpus of statements in the light of new stimuli and a set of universal canons of scientific inquiry? A number of writers, most notably Paul Feyerabend, Stephen Toulmin, and Thomas Kuhn, have argued that we cannot, and their writings have provoked several attempts to offer a view of scientific change which will do justice to scientific revolutions. Among these writers I shall take Kuhn as the most important representative, since his views are at once most systematic and most sensitive to the history of science. Kuhn's seminal book, *The Structure of Scientific Revolutions*, argues for a conception of scientific revolutions which is at odds with simple empiricism and which has been much discussed by philosophers. On Kuhn's account, scientific revolutions involve: *conceptual changes*, which can render impossible the formulation of prerevolutionary and postrevolutionary theories in a common language; *perceptual changes*, which produce new ways of seeing familiar phenomena; and, perhaps most important, *methodological changes*, which, by amending the rules of justification for scientific theories, make the rational resolution of the differences between earlier and later theories impossible. The simple empiricist picture of science as developing by rational adjustment to observation is completely undetermined if this account of revolutions is accurate. Scientists engaged in revolutionary debate do not share enough rules of justification to reach agreement, even if they could begin from shared observations. But they do *not* begin from shared observations. Moreover, their rival claims cannot be formulated in a common language. Small wonder, then, that, in one of the most cited discussions in his much-quoted book, Kuhn talks of scientific decision in terms of "conversion experience" and "faith."[5]

Despite the fact that Kuhn's account of revolutions is obviously important, what concerns me is not the correctness of the view of revolutions just sketched, but whether that view alters our previous estimate of the distinction between mathematical change and scientific change. I think it does not. For, as I have so far presented it, the central thrust of the view is that observation does not rationally compel us to modify our scientific beliefs. Unless we yearn for a change of fashion, faith in the old corpus can be maintained. To accept this thesis is not to abandon the claim that observation is the source of scientific change, but only to contend that not even new observation need provoke us to amend our old ways.

Yet my presentation of the historically inspired attack on the simple empiricist picture of scientific change has been deliberately one-sided. In the last paragraph I have briefly rehearsed the view which most philosophers have found in *The Structure of Scientific Revolutions*.[6] However, besides its apparent commitment to the thesis that scientific revolutions can only be resolved "by faith," Kuhn's book contains another very important claim, which not only controverts the simple empiricist picture but is also relevant to our project here. To put the point in its simplest terms, Kuhn contends that almost all theories are falsified at almost all times. Thus, contrary to feature (i) which we distilled from the simple empiricist picture, the match between theory and observation is *not* perfect. In the discrepancy between theory and observation, or, more generally, between different *parts* of theory, Kuhn finds the source of the problems which occupy scientists for most of their careers. On this account, scientists (justifiably) accept a general form for theory-construction in a particular field, adopting particular pieces of work as paradigmatic, selecting certain questions as important, choosing rules for answering those questions, and so forth. Given this set of background views, they put forward proposals, modifying and articulating them so as to achieve, insofar as possible, successful conformity both to the canons which govern all scientific activity and to the rules of their own particular enterprise. Discrepancies are always with them, presenting challenges even in the absence of new observations.[7] The problems may be more or less empirical (for example, puzzles about unanticipated experimental data) or they may be highly theoretical. The latter are of especial concern to us. Scientists are frequently challenged to answer a question posed by existing theory. Newton struggled with the issue of whether his theory of gravitation could be reconciled with the thesis that all action is by immediate contact. Darwin was confronted with the difficulty of resolving conflicts between his account of rates of evolution and geophysical estimates of the age of the Earth. Wegener and his early adherents were challenged to propose a mechanism which could move the continents. Contemporary evolutionary theorists have exhibited considerable ingenuity in devising theoretical models to show how apparently maladaptive traits may become fixed in a population. Molecular biology still faces the problem of reconciling our knowledge of the differential development of the cells of an embryo with our understanding of the synthesis of intracellular products. The examples could be multiplied almost indefinitely. They show that the simple empiricist picture of scientific change is badly mistaken. Even without the provocation of new observations, factors to stimulate scientific change are always present.

We are now in a position to become clearer about the complaint from which we began. It would be futile to deny that observation is *one* source of scientific change. The burden of the last paragraph is that observation is not the *only* such source. There are always "internal stresses" in scientific theory, and these provide a spur to modification of the corpus of beliefs. I propose to think of mathematical change as akin to this latter type of modification.[8] Just as the natural scientist struggles to resolve the puzzles generated by the current set of theoretical beliefs, so too mathematical changes are motivated by analogous conflicts, tensions, and mismatches.

To oversimplify, we can think of mathematical change as a skewed case of scientific change: all the relevant observations are easily collected at the beginning of inquiry; mathematical theories develop in response to these and *all* the subsequent problems and modifications are theoretical. This is an oversimplification because new observations are sometimes important even in mathematics. The efforts of the inhabitants of Königsberg to cross all of the famous seven bridges without retracing their steps suggested to Euler a mathematical problem, for which he found a solution, integrated by later mathematicians into a new branch of mathematics. Nor is this an isolated case. Pascal's investigations in probability theory, the study of possibilities of map coloring, and the recent work in catastrophe theory (whatever its merits) can all be viewed as mathematical responses to observable features of everyday situations. Moreover, as with the natural sciences, the "new" observation is often concerned with some familiar phenomenon whose significance has not hitherto been appreciated.

Before leaving the issue of the relation between observation and mathematical change, we should take note of the *indirect* ways in which experiment and observation may affect the development of mathematics. Sometimes difficulties in mathematical concepts or principles are first recognized when trouble arises in applying them in scientific cases. Thus in the eighteenth- and nineteenth-century study of functions, variational problems, and differential equations, modification both of physical theory and the mathematics presupposed by it go hand in hand. We shall examine one example of this interplay in Chapter 10.

Our initial concern was that an account of mathematical change must be very different from an account of scientific change in that the main force of scientific change is the pressure of new observations. I have responded to this in two different ways. The last two paragraphs indicate that new observations may be relevant (directly or indirectly) to the evolution of mathematical knowledge. But my principal point is that the concern thrives on a misunderstanding of scientific change. Many important episodes in the evolution of scientific knowledge are best viewed not as responses to new observations but as attempts to resolve pre-existing intra-theoretic tensions. The same applies to mathematics—and applies with a vengeance. Later in this chapter, I shall try to explain how this idea of intra-theoretic stress can be conveniently represented. Before I do so, I want to examine the second concern voiced above, the worry that mathematical change is cumulative in ways that scientific change is not.

II

In what sense is the development of mathematics cumulative and the development of science not? The idea that there is a difference here can receive a number of formulations: (a) there are no "revolutionary debates" in the history of mathematics; when mathematicians engage in dispute at least one party is being irrational or stubborn;[9] (b) many mathematical truths have been accepted since antiquity; (c) when mathematical statements are accepted at one time and rejected at a later time, those who originally accepted the statements were unjustified in doing so. In each case the formulation suggests a contrast with the natural sciences. Since reading Kuhn, Feyerabend, and others, philosophers have recognized that those episodes during which the natural sciences seem to make their greatest advance are marked by disputes in which the conservative protagonists cannot simply be labelled as "prejudiced," "irrational," or "stubborn." Moreover, increasing understanding of the history of science has enabled us to see that many of the scientific concepts and principles of our predecessors have been discarded or modified. Finally, our study of science finds room for the notion of a justifiable mistake. We are prepared to admit that the scientists of earlier ages held justified false beliefs. Hence each of the theses (a), (b), (c) can serve to expose a contrast between the cumulative development of mathematics and the non-cumulative development of natural science.

These ideas of an important contrast stem from the available historical studies. Hence an appropriate first response to them is to suggest that the appearance of harmony and straightforward progress may be an artifact of the histories of mathematics which have so far been written. Until the history of natural science came of age, it was easy to believe that the course of true science ever had run smooth. Unfortunately the history of mathematics is underdeveloped, even by comparison with the history of science.[10] Only in the last few years have there appeared studies which advanced beyond biographical details and accounts of names, dates, and major achievements. One difficulty for the historian has been the prevailing philosophical view of the nature of mathematics, with its emphasis on mathematics as a body of a priori knowledge. That emphasis has diverted attention from the rejected theories, the plausible but unrigorous pieces of reasoning, the inter-theoretical struggles.

Even the most cursory look at some primary sources will dispose of a *very* naîve conception of the cumulative character of mathematics, the idea that mathematics literally proceeds by accumulation, that new claims are added but old claims are never abandoned. Eighteenth-century analysis abounds with statements that we have rejected. The history of the investigation of the distribution of prime numbers contains many false starts and blind alleys. Other cases are more subtle. If one compares a contemporary text in analysis with a classic text of the early part of the century (say Whittaker and Watson's *Course of Modern Analysis*) it is impossible to regard the later work as a simple extension of the earlier. True, there is significant overlap in material, but the modern text approaches the subject from a different perspective, generalizing the treatment of some theorems and omitting other topics altogether. *In some sense*, most of nineteenth-century analysis survives in the contemporary treatment, but it does not do so in any straightforward way: we no longer care for the systematic exploration of special functions which our Weierstrassian predecessors loved so well.

The formulations I have given to the idea that mathematics is cumulative in a way that natural science is not are more sophisticated than the position just considered, and less easy to dismiss. Nevertheless, we can point to episodes from the history of mathematics which call each of them into question. Just as there are protracted disputes in the history of science in which we are reluctant to characterize any of the protagonists as stupid or wrong-headed, so too in mathematics there are parallel controversies. Consider, for example, some of the debates which surround the early calculus. Newtonians and Leibnizians each proclaimed the superiority of their method to that practiced by the rival tradition. The Leibnizians pointed proudly to their problem-solving efficiency; Newtonians emphasized their ability to preserve important features of previous mathematics. We should no more castigate Newton and his successors for clinging to a style of mathematics which the calculus was eventually to transform than we should condemn Priestley for his attempt to salvage the phlogiston theory and to use it to account for his own experimental results. As a further illustration, we can turn to the late nineteenth-century dispute about the legitimacy of various construals of the real numbers and of Cantor's transfinite set theory. We disagree with those, like Kronecker, who insisted on a literal application of the slogan that analysis should be arithmetized. Yet we would find it just as hard to convict Kronecker of irrationality and dogmatism as to press the same charges on the more subtle of the Aristotelians who debated Galileo. Hence I conclude that we should not articulate the contrast between mathematics and natural science along the lines suggested by (a).

Let us now examine (b). Even if we grant that standard presentations of the history of mathematics conceal the existence of genuine disputes and noncumulative changes, it appears at first that vastly more of ancient mathematics than of ancient science has survived intact into the present. We have not abandoned the truths of arithmetic, or Euclid's theorems, or the solutions to quadratic equations obtained by the Babylonians. Does this not indicate an important difference between the development of mathematics and the development of science? It is crucial here to find the right scientific analogs for these mathematical results. Let us recognize that many statements have in fact persisted through the history of science. We continue to share with our ancestors a wealth of beliefs about the ordinary properties of ordinary things. To claim that there is no privileged level of observational reporting, that all our observation statements are revisable, is quite consistent with the admission that many of the claims we make on the basis of observation coincide with judgments that have been made for centuries. I anticipate an objection. When we say, for example, that feathers float on water or that the sun rises in the east, can we really be taken to agree with our predecessors? Perhaps the translation of their utterances by these sentences of ours blurs important conceptual differences which separate us from them. I believe that such worries are unfounded. When the notion of conceptual change in science is properly understood, we see that it is possible to allow for the existence of conceptual differences between ourselves and our ancestors while claiming that we can record some of their beliefs in sentences of contemporary language to which we would assent. However, even if this were not so, the objection would not be pertinent to our present discussion. For any argument for shifts in our concepts of the ordinary things around us and of their ordinary properties could be mirrored by an argument for parallel shifts in our concept of number. If, for example, we suppose that our concept of water has been transmuted by the discovery that matter is discontinuous, so too we may take our concept of number to have been altered by the introduction of negative, rational, real, complex, and transfinite numbers. Hence it would be wrong to claim that our arithmetical beliefs have been preserved through the centuries, while our everyday physical beliefs have not.

Finally, we must address the suggestion that mathematicians, unlike natural scientists, cannot justifiably hold false beliefs (the suggestion offered by (c)). Were we to adopt this suggestion we would be forced to some harsh judgments concerning those mathematicians who have advanced inductively based conjectures about formulas for generating prime numbers. More importantly, we would fail to do justice to the numerous occasions on which acceptance of a simplified principle paves the way for the development of concepts which can be used to correct that principle. Euler and Cauchy justifiably believed, for example, that trigonometric series representations of arbitrary functions could not be given. Only in the wake of Cauchy's attempt to articulate the reasons which he drew from Euler could it become apparent how the claim was incorrect. To develop the concepts required to correct Cauchy's mistake took approximately a quarter of a century. Here, and in many other cases, we find mathematicians making the best use of their epistemic situations to advance false claims, whose falsity only becomes understood through the efforts of those very mathematicians to articulate their reasons. If we accept (c) we shall not only divorce the notion of justification in mathematics from justification in other fields, but also make the progressive uncovering of subtle errors look like a sequence of blunders which culminates, miraculously, in apprehension of the truth.

So far, then, we have failed to discover a sense in which the growth of mathematical knowledge is cumulative and the growth of scientific knowledge is not. However, I believe that there is something to the suggestion that we have so far failed to credit. Mathematical *theories* seem to have a far higher rate of survival than scientific theories. Newton's "method of fluxions" is very different from contemporary calculus, and Hamilton's theory of quaternions is by no means identical with modern linear algebra; yet, in some sense, both Newton's and Hamilton's ideas live on in modern mathematics. Obviously, similar remarks can be made about some past scientific theories. What we do not seem to find in mathematics are the analogs of the discarded theories of past science: there appear to be no counterparts of Aristotle's theory of motion, the phlogiston theory of combustion, or theories of blending inheritance. I shall now try to explain why this is so.

Consider the difference between the development of non-Euclidean geometry and the (roughly contemporary) development of the oxygen theory of combustion. In the former case, after nearly two millennia of attempts to prove Euclid's fifth postulate (which is *equivalent* to the statement that, given a line in a plane and a point of the plane which does not lie on the line, there is a unique line through the point which is parallel to the given line), three mathematicians, Lobatschevsky, Bolyai, and Gauss, decided to investigate the consequences of adding to the first four postulates a statement asserting the existence of many parallels. Their efforts produced the non-Euclidean geometry we call "Lobatschevskian." Once they became convinced that the new geometry was consistent, mathematicians accepted it as part of mathematics, and they set about proving Lobatschevskian theorems, trying to find characteristics which would distinguish Lobatschevskian geometry from Euclidean geometry, attempting to generalize geometrical theories, and so forth. As far as mathematics is concerned, there was no need to choose between Lobatschevsky and Euclid (although tradition credits Gauss with an investigation designed to determine if space is Euclidean). Contrast this course of events with the debate over theories of combustion. The phlogiston theory claimed that something—phlogiston—is emitted from substances when they burn. Lavoisier's oxygen theory contends that combustion involves not emission but absorption of a constituent of the air. By 1800, the scientific community had decided in favor of the oxygen theory, and, after Priestley's death in 1804, no major scientist explored further consequences of the phlogiston theory.

What appears at first to be mathematical competition issues in peaceful co-existence. By contrast, scientific competition ends in the death of one theory. Lobatschevsky's geometry sits alongside Euclid's in the pantheon of mathematical theories, because for the mathematician both theories are correct descriptions of different things; Lobatschevsky, Bolyai, and Gauss provided an accurate account of a particular kind of non-Euclidean space; Euclid's geometry remains the correct theory of Euclidean space; the question of which kind of geometrical space is realized in physical space is given to the physicists (or, if the apocryphal story about Gauss is true, to mathematicians moonlighting as physicists). Yet we should appreciate that this distinction of questions is a consequence of the construction of non-Euclidean geometry. Both geometries survive because both are interpreted differently from the way in which geometry had previously been construed. Between the time of Descartes and the investigations of Lobatschevsky, Bolyai, and Gauss, mathematicians did not distinguish geometrical space from physical space. Euclid's geometry was, at once, part of mathematics and part of physical science. The mathematical investigation showed that there was (apparently) a rival theory of physical space.[11] The mathematicians equipped both the old and the new geometry with a new style of interpretation, and left the physicists to determine which theory was true on the old construal.

The move is typical of mathematics, especially of the recent history of mathematics. Yet the root idea is readily comprehensible in terms of a division of labor which began in ancient science.[12] Initially, mathematics included optics, astronomy, and harmonics as well as arithmetic and geometry: our contemporary division of fields does little justice to the classificatory system of the ancient world. What has occurred since is a continued process of dividing questions among specialists. The old mathematical investigations of light, sound, and space are partitioned into explorations of the *possibilities* of theory construction (the province of the mathematician) and determinations of the correct theory (the province of the natural scientist). This division of labor accounts for the fact that mathematics often resolves threats of competition by reinterpretation, thus giving a greater impression of cumulative development than the natural sciences.

Consider this practice in light of the picture of mathematical reality advanced in the last chapter. Mathematics begins from studying physical phenomena, but its aim is to delineate the structural features of those phenomena. Our early attempts to produce mathematical theories generate theories which, we later discover, can be amended to yield theories of comparable richness and articulation. When this occurs, we regard both the original theory and its recent rival as concerned with different structures, handing over to our scientific colleagues the problem of deciding which structure is instantiated in the phenomena we set out to investigate. Our consideration of "neighboring" structures is scientifically fruitful both for enabling us to formulate and test scientific hypotheses about which structures are instantiated in the actual world, and for advancing our understanding of those structures which are instantiated.

The case of Lobatschevskian geometry is worth examining at slightly greater length, for it may appear that the status of that geometry is problematic. After all, someone may complain, Lobatschevskian geometry does *not* apply to the world, and so how can it be claimed that, in developing that geometry, Lobatschevsky, Bolyai, and Gauss were unfolding part of the mathematical structure of reality? My answer draws on the interpretation of the thesis that mathematics describes the structure of the world which I gave in the last chapter. Mathematics consists in a series of specifications of the constructive powers of an ideal subject. These specifications must be well grounded, that is, they must be successful in enabling us to understand the physical operations which we can in fact perform upon nature. What makes an idealization appropriate is its relation to prior idealizations and, ultimately, to the concrete manipulations in which we engage. We attribute to the ideal mathematical subject a power to perform Lobatschevskian as well as Euclidean operations because, by doing so, we are able to enhance our understanding of powers which have alreaady been attributed. It is important to emphasize that, in doing this, we adopt an inclusive policy of attributing powers to the ideal subject. We extend our account of the powers of that subject in any way which is illuminating or fruitful. Thus whether or not Lobatschevskian geometry finds instances in the physical world, that geometry counts as part of mathematics because it is an appropriate idealization to introduce in our inquiries into the physical world, and what makes it an appropriate idealization is its relation to prior idealizations which were themselves properly grounded.

There is a tendency to be drawn in one of two directions. On the one hand, someone may suggest that mathematics is the investigation of the consequences of arbitrary stipulations.[13] This proposal has the advantage of accounting for those episodes in which prior mathematical theories are reinterpreted to resolve the problem of a threatened dispute. Yet, as I have already argued at some length, it fails to be epistemologically satisfactory. Moreover, one might note that the historical develpoment of mathematics does not reveal a *random* set of investigations of the consequences of arbitrary stipulations. The opposite pull is to anchor mathematics in what actually exists, to suggest that mathematics describes those entities (Platonic objects, structures, operations) which the world contains. I have offered what I hope is a middle course. Mathematics consists in idealized theories of ways in which we can operate on the world. To produce an idealized theory is to make some stipulations—but they are stipulations which must be appropriately related to the phenomena one is trying to idealize. I maintain *that* the idealizations which have been offered in the course of the history of mathematics satisfy this latter condition, and, in taking the methodology of mathematics seriously, I shall try to understand *in what* the satisfaction of that condition consists.

Mathematics is cumulative in a way that natural science is not, because threats of competition are often resolved by reinterpretation. Furthermore, this important role of reinterpretation does indicate the significance of stipulation in mathematics. Yet we should not conclude from this that mathematical method is simple, that all the mathematician has to do is set down his stipulations and work out the consequences. The power to stipulate is constrained by canons of mathematical method, akin to those which govern the practice of natural science. Hence my concession to the thesis that mathematics is cumulative should not be taken to invalidate the project of describing mathematical methodology. Nor, since science also proceeds by achieving idealizations, should it convince us that parallels between scientific change and mathematical change are not worth pursuing.

III

The previous sections of this chapter have attempted to clear some ground. My next step will be to use recent insights about scientific change to pose in a more precise form the question of how mathematical knowledge grows. One of the most important contributions of those philosophers of science who have been sensitive to the historical details of scientific change has been their recognition that the great clashes of opposing views involve more than a simple opposition of theoretical statements, and that, by the same token, the development of a field of science during periods of relative calm proceeds against the background of shared extratheoretical assumptions which expedite the resolution of disagreements.[14] The simple empiricist picture (as well as the most obvious refinements of it) aims to understand scientific change by finding principles which govern the modifications of sets of theoretical statements in response to observational changes. One way to reject this picture is to give up its view of the units of change. So, for example, we might replace empiricist talk of modifications of theory with Kuhnian talk about articulations and changes of "paradigms."

The concept of a paradigm is as suggestive as it is unclear.[15] It would be tangential to my main theme to offer detailed exegesis of Kuhn's discussions of paradigms. What I wish to emphasize is that the notion of a paradigm is designed to fulfil two different philosophical purposes. First, and perhaps most obviously, his references to paradigms enable Kuhn to divide the history of science into large segments. The distinction between normal and revolutionary science separates those periods in which paradigms are articulated from those in which paradigms are abandoned, and, taken at face value, Kuhn's book encourages us to apply this distinction throughout the history of science. However, in the linguistic move from the empiricist mode of discussing scientific change as theory change to the Kuhnian idiom of paradigm change, we find a second function which paradigms serve. Kuhn intends to deny that we can understand the history of science simply by talking about modifications of the set of statements which the scientists of an era accept. To chart the development of a field we need more indices of its state at any given time. Hence, Kuhn introduces the richer—and vaguer—notion of a paradigm in place of the empiricist concept of a theory or corpus of beliefs.

The first point I wish to make is that the second function of the paradigm concept is independent of the first. It is quite possible for someone to be sceptical about the possibility of subsuming all episodes in the history of science under Kuhn's normal/revolutionary distinction while consistently maintaining that scientific change should be understood in terms of the modification of more than a set of accepted statements. To suppose that the science of a time is to be regarded as multi-faceted is not to endorse the idea that the history of science must reveal discontinuities, or that changes in some components of the science are so fundamental that those changes should be hailed as revolutionary. We can disregard Kuhn's doctrines about the segmentation of history, while retaining his insight that the units of change are more complicated than empiricists have traditionally supposed.

Let me elaborate on this point by drawing an analogy between an evolutionary account of human knowledge and the evolutionary theories which have been propounded in the natural sciences. With any evolutionary theory, there is a danger that one will fail to isolate the principles which govern the development of the system under study because one has failed to pick out all the relevant variables. A physicist who tried to chart the changes in pressure of a gas by attending only to temperature variations, or an ecologist who studied the career of a population by considering only food supply and neglecting threats posed by predators, would be engaged in a hopeless enterprise. Evolutionary theories, whether they are concerned with the thermal behavior of gases, the modification of organic phenotypes or the development of human knowledge, hope to understand the state of the system at later times by relating it to previous states of the system by laws of development, and to achieve their goal they must provide a sufficiently detailed characterization of the states of the system.

I interpret Kuhn's challenge to simple empiricism as applying this point to the growth of scientific knowledge. Kuhn denies that we can understand scientific change by focusing simply on the shifts in allegiance to theoretical principles. Instead we must view what changes as a *scientific practice* with many components: language, theoretical principles, examples of experimental and theoretical work which are deemed worthy of emulation, approved methods of reasoning, problem-solving techniques, appraisals of the importance of questions, metascientific views about the nature of the enterprise, and so forth. Unfortunately, Kuhn fuses this important idea with a claim that certain types of changes in practice are intrinsically different from others, so that the notion of a paradigm is expected to cover those sequences of practices in which no "fundamental" transitions occur.[16]

I wish to salvage the notion of a practice and jettison the concept of a paradigm which Kuhn generates from it. One of Kuhn's major insights about scientific change is to view the history of a scientific field as a sequence of practices. I propose to adopt an analogous thesis about mathematical change. I suggest that we focus on the development of *mathematical practice*, and that we view a mathematical practice as consisting of five components: a language, a set of accepted statements, a set of accepted reasonings, a set of questions selected as important, and a set of metamathematical views (including standards for proof and definition and claims about the scope and structure of mathematics). As a convenient notation, I shall use the expression "<L,M,Q,R,S>" as a symbol for an arbitrary mathematical practice (where L is the language of the practice, M the set of metamathematical views, Q the set of accepted questions, R the set of accepted reasonings, and S the set of accepted statements). The problem of accounting for the growth of mathematical knowledge becomes that of understanding what makes a transition from a practice <L,M,Q,R,S> to an immediately succeeding practice <L′,M′,Q′,R′,S′> a rational transition.

In regarding a mathematical practice as a quintuple of this kind, I have selected those features of mathematical activity which seem to undergo significant change. Obviously it is possible that I may have chosen more components than I need or, conversely, that other features of mathematical activity need to be included if we are to obtain an adequate understanding of mathematical change. If I have erred in the former direction then we should find that it is possible to understand changes in some subset of the components without appealing to components which do not belong to this subset. A mistake of the latter type should be reflected in inability to reconstruct certain kinds of mathematical change. Later chapters will provide support for my analysis, both by showing how important types of mathematical change involve interconnections among all the components I have listed, and by demonstrating its capacity for handling a range of examples.

Let me conclude this section by using my reformulation of the problem of mathematical change to present more precisely the points about the similarities and differences between mathematical and scientific change which were made in Sections I and II. In the first place, scientific practices can change in response to new observations. But they can also change as the result of the existence of discrepancies among the various components of the practice. To exploit the analogy with developing systems, we may say that the movement to a new practice may result from the fact that the old practice was not in equilibrium. This type of change is the rule in mathematics. As we shall see, the components of a mathematical practice are never in complete harmony with one another, and the striving for concordance generates mathematical change. Second, we shall account for the apparently greater cumulative development of mathematics, by recognizing the existence of a particular type of linguistic change in mathematics which enables the resolution of apparent conflicts. So, where in the case of science we find the *replacement* of one theory by another (as in the case of the replacement of the phlogiston theory by the oxygen theory), in the mathematical case there is an adjustment of language and a distinction of questions, so that the erstwhile "rivals" can coexist with each other. Mathematical change is cumulative in a way that scientific change is not, because of the existence of a special kind of interpractice transition. As I have already suggested, this type of transition is found in mathematics because the task of the mathematician is to unfold the possibilities for theory construction, a task which consists in advancing appropriate stipulation of the powers of the ideal mathematical subject. We engage in this task by following an inclusive policy of attributing powers, further articulating our account of the subject in any ways which advance our understanding of the attributions already made.[17]

IV

I have used the comparison between mathematical change and scientific change to offer a very general hypothesis about the growth of mathematical knowledge. Mathematical knowledge develops through the rational modification of mathematical practices, and mathematical practices are to be understood as having five components. I now want to examine one type of interpractice transition which is especially important. To fill out the specific details of my hypothesis, we shall need to pay attention to the question of how mathematical language develops.

One of the principal obstacles to a satisfactory account of scientific knowledge has been the difficulty of understanding conceptual change in science. Any adequate study of the history of science must come to terms with the fact that the language used in the same field of science at different times seems to undergo subtle shifts. We find our predecessors using the words we use, but when we try to translate them we discover that it is difficult to record their beliefs without attributing blatant errors to them. A radical response to this predicament is to declare that the languages used in the same field at different times (at times separated by a revolution) are *incommensurable*, that statements made in one cannot be adequately translated by statements made in the other.[18] I believe that we can do justice to our predicament without making this radical response. I shall try to provide an account of conceptual change which will avoid the declaration of incommensurability, applying this account to cope with the problem as it arises in mathematics. As will become clear in later chapters, my discussion will not only help us to understand that type of interpractice transition which consists in the modification of mathematical language. It will be important in explaining other types of interpractice transition as well.

In this section, I shall investigate the general topic of conceptual change. Let us begin with the problem which leads some writers to talk of incommensurability. When we consider the language of Aristotelian physics or of phlogiston theoretic chemistry, we encounter difficulty in giving an adequate translation for central expressions of the language. The standard of adequate translation invoked here is relatively straightforward: an adequate translation for an expression is one which would specify the referent of that expression. Trouble arises from the fact that we do not countenance the entities to which proponents of the old theory seem to have intended to refer, so that obvious attempts to translate their utterances construe their claims as completely false. When we reflect that the old theory seems to have been useful in developing its successor, this blanket dismissal is disconcerting. Consider, for example, the language of the phlogiston theory. We are inclined to say that there is no phlogiston, that 'phlogiston' fails to refer, and that in consequence the complex expressions 'phlogisticated air' and 'dephlogisticated air' fail to refer.[19] We are then embarrassed to find that phlogiston theorists apparently recorded many true claims about oxygen using the term 'dephlogisticated air' and that their achievements in this area were important in the development of Lavosier's theory of combustion. How can we avoid the unfortunate conclusion that *all* phlogiston-theoretic claims are false because the phlogiston theorists were not talking about anything—without embracing the unhelpful suggestion that they were talking about the occupants of "another world" or that their theory has a different ontology from ours?

My answer is to retain the idea that adequate translation of the language of past science should specify the referents of the expressions which were formerly used, but to articulate that idea in the light of recent work on the theory of reference. I shall first review some contemporary insights about reference. This will lead me to a resolution of the problem posed in the last paragraph, and to a general account of conceptual change in science. The application to mathematics will be undertaken in the next section.

Recent studies of reference for proper names and natural kind terms have made it clear that one can refer to an object (or set) without being able to produce any description which identifies the object (or gives the condition of membership in the set) in a nontrivial way.[20] People regularly refer to Einstein without being able to say any more about him than that he was (is!) a physicist, and we can refer to aluminum without knowing any criterion which would distinguish it from molybdenum (or other metals). How is this possible? The first thing to recognize is that many of our references are parasitic on those of others. We refer to an object by intending to refer to that to which our fellows refer. Better, we acquire an ability to refer using a particular term from others who already have an ability to refer using that term. But how does the chain of reference originally start? Here, it is natural to think that the original user attaches the term to its referent either by providing a description of the referent or by applying it to a presented object. Thus we obtain the picture of reference as initiated by a baptismal ceremony in which the expression is fixed to its referent; thereafter, the ability to refer spreads through a community of speakers in virtue of intentions to concur in the references of other speakers (including, ultimately, the original user of the term). Baptismal ceremonies themselves divided into two types, *ostensive* and *descriptive*. In cases of the latter type, the referent is originally singled out by description, and, even though we do not assume that the description is known by all those who use the term, there are at least some members of the community who can give an identifying description of the referent. For terms introduced by ostensive baptismal ceremonies, however, it may happen that *none* of the subsequent users is able to provide an identifying description of the referent.

The history of science supplies a number of examples of terms which appear to be introduced by an ostensive baptismal ceremony. Consider, for example, terms for kinds of substances, such expressions as 'gold,' 'water,' and 'acid.' It is tempting to adopt the hypothesis that the current use of the expressions descends from occasions on which original speakers attached expressions (not necessarily the terms 'gold,' 'water,' and 'acid') to samples of gold, water, and acid respectively, intending thereby to pick out the kind of thing to which the present sample belonged. During the subsequent centuries, their successors struggled to find descriptions which would correctly characterize the kinds to which they were referring, sometimes advancing incorrect descriptions whose shortcomings were exposed by further research. Finally, we have achieved sufficient knowledge of the properties of the referents to be able to give descriptions which identify them correctly.

I think that this picture of the reference of some scientific terms has much to recommend it, but it needs to be refined in two different ways if we are to have an account which will solve the problem of conceptual change. First, we need to allow for the possibility that the links between words and the world may be constantly renewed so that, in time, a term becomes associated with a complex apparatus of referential ties, with the result that different tokens may refer differently. Second, some of the initial links between words and the world, or some of the subsequent connections, may be made by description. Recognition of the role of ostensive baptismal ceremonies should not lead us to neglect the fact that sometimes reference is fixed differently.

Both points are illustrated by the example considered above. The term 'phlogiston' was originally introduced into the language of chemistry by a declaration that phlogiston is to be the substance which is emitted in combustion. The description which is used here to fix the reference of 'phlogiston' is not satisfied by anything at all, so that, given this original establishment of its usage, the term fails to refer. As a result, insofar as the referent of 'phlogiston' is fixed through the description initially given, the term 'dephlogisticated air,' which abbreviates the phrase "the substance obtained when phlogiston is removed from the air," also fails to refer. However, when tokens of 'dephlogisticated air' occur in the writings of theorists such as Priestley and Cavendish, the best interpretation of their remarks is often to construe those tokens as referring to oxygen, a gas which Priestley was the first to isolate. For example, Priestley recounts that dephlogisticated air supports combustion better than ordinary air, that mice thrive in it, and that breathing dephlogisticated air is quite pleasant. There is a natural explanation for such remarks. Having isolated oxygen, Priestley misidentified it as "dephlogisticated air." On this occasion the referent of his token of 'dephlogisticated air' had its referent fixed in the old way: that is, dephlogisticated air is the substance remaining when the substance emitted in combustion is removed from the air (hence the token fails to refer). However, Priestley's misidentification set the stage for a new usage. Thereafter, he sometimes produced tokens of 'dephlogisticated air' whose reference is fixed *via* the misidentification (or perhaps *via* subsequent misidentifications), tokens which refer to the kind of substance which Priestley had isolated, namely to oxygen. Thus the term *type* 'dephlogisticated air' came to acquire two different modes of reference. The reference of its tokens could be fixed through the original "ceremony" in which phlogiston was picked out as the substance emitted in combustion or through encounters with oxygen. Let us call the "ceremony" through which the referent of a token is fixed the *initiating event* for that token. Then our conclusion is that tokens of 'dephlogisticated air' have initiating events of two different kinds. The fact that tokens of 'dephlogisticated air' possess different kinds of initiating events reflect the belief, explicit in Priestley's work and accepted by his fellow phlogistonians, that the different initiating events pick out the same entity. We can generalize the example by defining the *reference potential* of a term type as the set of events which can serve as initiating events for tokens of the type. The *theoretical presupposition* of a term is the thesis that all the initiating events which belong to the reference potential pick out the same entity. After Priestley's work, 'dephlogisticated air' had a heterogeneous reference potential and a false theoretical presupposition.

I want to use this general approach to account for conceptual change in the natural sciences, in general, and in mathematics, in particular. I suggest that we identify concepts as reference potentials and chart changes in concepts by following the modifications of reference potentials. If this approach is to succeed we shall need a firmer grasp on the concept of the fixing of the reference of a token through a particular event, a concept presupposed by my notion of reference potential.

What does it mean to claim that an event is the initiating event for a particular token? The question naturally arises when we try to apply the view of reference which I have offered. Attention to the case of Priestley helps us to see how to answer it. We take some of Priestley's tokens to have their referents fixed through his encounters with oxygen because, by doing so, we achieve the best explanation of why he said what he did. In this we emulate the professional historian. To understand the dicta of our predecessors, we conceive of them by analogy with ourselves, attributing to them the kinds of cognitive faculties we possess and using our knowledge of the stimuli impinging upon them to project the content of their beliefs. We do not expect them always to agree with us, for, despite the similarity of their faculties to ours, the experiences they have may be very different. What we do expect to find is a similar pattern of relationships among beliefs, desires, intentions, experience, and behavior. Claims which identify particular events as the initiating events for particular tokens should be understood in this light. We are proposing that the identification offers the best explanation of the remarks in which we are interested, where the standards for goodness of explanation are fixed by the expectation of similar psychological relations.

It will be helpful for our future discussions to recognize three main types of explanations of a speaker's token. The first is what I will call a *conformity explanation*, when we attribute to the speaker a dominant intention to agree with others and trace the referent of his token to an initiating event involving some other speaker. Although the vast majority of cases of language use require this type of explanation, many of the most interesting cases demand something different. Historical studies of mathematics and science are frequently concerned with the pioneers, those who authored new patterns of usage. Sometimes, when we attend to the utterances of a great mathematician or scientist, it is appropriate to explain her remarks by supposing that the initiating event for her tokens is an event in which she singled out a paradigm object (or paradigm objects) with the dominant intention to refer to a kind exemplified by the paradigm. I shall call these *present paradigm* explanations. They contrast with cases in which our best explanation is to take the remarks as initiated by an event in which the speaker singles out the referent by description, explanations which I shall call *stipulational* explanations. The difference between the present paradigm and stipulational types can easily be dramatized by a fictitious attribution of soliloquy. When we give a present paradigm explanation, our conception of the speaker's psychological stance is that she should say to herself, "I do not care whether or not the descriptions I am inclined to give are misdescriptions—what is important is that I am picking out a genuine kind." On the other hand, when we advance a stipulational explanation it is as if we conceived of the speaker as saying to herself, "It does not matter whether or not I am picking out a genuine kind—what is important is that the referent should satisfy these descriptions." I think that it is worth emphasizing that the attitudes manifested in these fictitious attributions are both reasonable in appropriate contexts. Among the goals of inquiry are the development of a language which will divide the world into kinds (that is, a language which will permit the formulation of simple laws) and the achievement of descriptions which will accurately characterize the referents of our terms. To sacrifice the former goal for the latter is to risk creating cumbersome theories, while the contrary sacrifice courts the danger of vague and ill-understood language. It is sometimes reasonable in the interests of clarity to stipulate explicitly that the referent of a word is to satisfy a particular description.[21] On other occasions, it is equally reasonable to allow that all of one's attempts to identify one's referent may be premature. I conjecture that many scientific and mathematical expressions pass through a period during which it is correct to give present paradigm explanations of the production of some tokens and stipulational explanations of the production of others.

To sum up, conceptual change in science is to be understood as the modification of reference potentials. The reference potential of a term type is the class of events which can initiate the production of tokens of the type. An event counts as the initiating event for the production of a token if the hypothesis that the speaker referred to the entity singled out in that event provides the best explanation for her saying what she did. We can recognize a number of different forms of explanation, two of which, present paradigm explanations and stipulational explanations, will be especially important in applying my account to mathematics.

This approach solves the problem about conceptual change from which we began. Proponents of incommensurability have recognized that reference potentials of terms used by former scientists need not match the reference potentials of any terms in the language of later science. Yet it is wrong to conclude that the referents of the individual tokens are not specifiable in the other language, or that, in some mysterious sense, the two groups of scientists are responding to different worlds. I shall now return from my general discussion to the specific case of mathematics, showing how to resolve some difficulties about the development of mathematical concepts and how to make sense of an important type of interpractice transition.

V

I propose to think of the language component of a mathematical practice as consisting of a syntax coupled with a semantics which includes a set of reference potentials. Some kinds of changes in this component are relatively trivial. Anyone who has attained a modest degree of sophistication in mathematics understands the point of introducing notation to abbreviate expressions of the existing language. To make a proof more perspicuous, or simply to avoid the tedium of writing the same long string of symbols again and again, one decides to adopt an abbreviatory convention, and sometimes the convention spreads through the mathematical community. If such cases were the only kinds of linguistic change which occurred in the development of mathematics, we should need no elaborate account of conceptual change. For these examples are readily understood as occasions on which the syntax of the language is changed by adding a new expression and the semantics is augmented by fixing the referent of the expression through explicit stipulation in previously available terms.

Although these simple changes are very common, the history of mathematics presents us with at least two other types of linguistic change. When we look at the history of analysis, we are inclined to say that the concepts of function, continuity, integrability, and series summation change during the eighteenth and nineteenth centuries; similarly, the history of algebra seems to show the evolution of the concept of a group. I shall attempt to explain what occurs in these examples by using the approach to conceptual change developed in the last section. I shall also consider a more worrying type of case. Sometimes it appears that a new expression is introduced into mathematical language by a stipulation which violates previously accepted theorems. This seems to occur, for example, both with the initial usage of expressions for complex numbers and with Cantor's term 'ω.' Such cases are the mathematical analogs of those episodes which, like the phlogiston-theoretic example of the last section, provoke philosophers of science to appeal to incommensurability. If my approach can yield insight into them then that should count strongly in its favor.

Initially I shall discuss these cases from an ontologically neutral standpoint, without invoking the picture of mathematical reality which I presented in Chapter 6. I shall simply assume that mathematical expressions typically refer and inquire into their mode of reference without adopting my favored view of their referents. There are two advantages to this procedure. First, it will show that the thesis about linguistic change defended here can be accepted independently of any particular picture of mathematical reality. Second, discussion of the examples will be focussed more precisely by concentrating on the types of referential links between words and entities without worrying about the nature of the entities to which the words are linked. However, I shall conclude my discussion by explaining one example from the perspective of the ontological view of the last chapter.

A first approximation to an account of those conceptual changes typified by the evolution of the concepts of function, continuity, integrability, series summation, and group can be given as follows. Originally the reference of the associated terms was fixed through paradigms. Later discussions show a sequence of attempts to give a descriptive characterization of the entities which had previously been picked out. Consider, for example, the concept of function. Leibniz began from the idea that the functions of a *curve* were such things as its length or area, and that the functions of a *point of a curve* were such things as the tangent to the curve at that point. Thus the term 'function' originally had its reference fixed through certain paradigms. As the calculus was developed by Leibniz's successors, the set of things recognized as belonging to the same kind came to include entities which were not obviously subject to characterization in geometrical terms. Euler achieved a *partial* descriptive characterization of the referent of 'function.' In a famous sentence he announced that a function is any expression however made up of variables and constants. I call this a "*partial* descriptive characterization" to highlight the fact that Euler's statement itself contains an expression whose reference is fixed through paradigms. The notion of an expression's "being made up of variables and constants" has its reference fixed by the paradigms of expression formation used in constructing polynomial expressions. Further work was required to determine if "functions" given only by integral or infinite series representation belong to the same kind, and to arrive at the modern general characterization of a function.

This kind of story obviously runs parallel to the accounts we would offer concerning the evolution of the natural scientific concepts of acid, water, and so forth. We regard the evolution of the concepts as consisting in the replacement of reference by way of paradigms with a descriptive characterization of the referent. Although this brings out the main features of the development of the concept, it can be improved by drawing on some of the ideas of the last section. Specifically, we can recognize that the referents of some tokens of the expression under study are fixed through initiating events in which a description which is ultimately rejected as an appropriate characterization is used to single out the referent. In short, the reference potentials of these terms are heterogeneous, and the evolution of the concepts shows an interesting interplay between the addition of new paradigms for use in initiating events and the discarding of descriptions which had previously been taken to give adequate characterizations of the referents.

Continuing the example used above, I suggest that some tokens of 'function' which appear in the writings of eighteenth- and nineteenth-century analysts have their reference fixed descriptively. Thus, for example, the dispute between Euler and d'Alembert concerning complete solutions to partial differential equations (in particular, the equation of motion of the vibrating string) turns in part on their having two different conceptions of function.[22] D'Alembert offers a specification of the referent of 'function' which excludes entities regarded by Euler as belonging to the same kind as those which serve both men as paradigms. The eventual resolution of the dispute involved modification of the reference potential of 'function,' abandoning d'Alembert's favored description as an approrpiate means of fixing the reference of tokens of 'function.'

The cases which are most difficult are not those in which we can discern a clear pattern of development towards characterization of a previously uncharacterized referent, overlaid with occasional uses of what turn out to be inadequate preliminary descriptions, but those in which, from the beginning, there is an apparently crucial obstacle to the provision of a descriptive characterization of the referent of the newly introduced expression. Sometimes it seems that a new symbol, or complex of symbols, has its reference fixed in such a way that, from the perspective of the mathematics of the time, it can have no referent. I shall examine two examples of this type in a little more detail, since the problematic character of such cases provides the best way of exposing the strength of my account of conceptual change.

Consider first Cantor's initial introduction of symbols for transfinite ordinals in 1883. Cantor fixed the referent of his symbol 'ω' by declaring that ω is to be the first number immediately following the series 1, 2, 3,. . . .[23] Cantor seems to have used a description belonging to the previous language of mathematics to fix the referent of a new symbol. Yet it would be wrong to assimilate Cantor's specification to those trivial cases of abbreviation which I noted at the beginning of this section. Many of Cantor's contemporaries were puzzled—and some were outraged—by his procedure. Their response was based on an appeal to an alleged "theorem" to the effect that nothing follows the entire series 1, 2, 3, . . . , a "theorem" that depends on the *prima facie* plausible premises that the series of natural numbers does not come to an end and that it makes no sense to speak of something following an entire series unless the series comes to an end.

When we consider this example without employing the distinctions introduced in the last section we appear to have two options. If we suppose that Cantor used antecedently available language successfully to refer to a transfinite ordinal, then we shall find ourselves with the task of explaining how so many of his contemporaries viewed his specification as deeply puzzling. If, on the other hand, we credit them with a correct understanding of the old language, taking the referents of the expressions Cantor employed to be fixed so as to preclude the possibility that anything satisfies his specification, we shall have trouble seeing how he could have launched himself into the transfinite. The remedy is to recognize the expressions which figure in Cantor's characterization of ω as having heterogeneous reference potentials. Consider first the ways in which the referent of 'number' could be fixed. One way to specify the numbers is to take them to be the complex numbers. Thus we can imagine a late nineteenth-century mathematician fixing the referent of 'number' by saying: "A number is anything denoted by an expression '$a + ib$' where 'a,' 'b' are decimal expressions." Our mythical mathematician would obviously be puzzled by Cantor's claims, since nothing of the kind picked out by this specification follows all the natural numbers. An alternative way to fix the referent of 'number' would be to suppose that numbers are entities on which one can perform certain kinds of operations (saying, for example, that numbers are those things which can be added, subtracted, multiplied, and divided). Given this method of fixing the referent the question of the existence of transfinite numbers is an open question. To settle it, one needs to show how it is possible to define recognizable analogs of the standard operations on ordinary numbers which can be applied to transfinite numbers. The naïve methods of introducing transfinite arithmetic—such as the extension of ordinary division to allow division by zero—had been explored long before Cantor, and shown to lead to paradox. Thus Cantor had to turn back a serious challenge to the possibility of extending arithmetic into the transfinite. Transfinite arithmetic plays so large a role in his papers because Cantor's extension of arithmetical operations shows that the challenge can be met. Cantor produces an analog of ordinary arithmetic, thereby demonstrating that his transfinite numbers are indeed *numbers*, that is, entities to which arithmetical operations are applicable.[24]

Yet this is only to touch on one aspect of the problem involved in extending mathematical language to include reference to the transfinite. So far, I have addressed the worry that Cantor's specification of ω cannot characterize a *number*, but I have not examined the deeper anxiety that it fails to pick out *anything at all.* This anxiety has its source in the idea, to which I alluded above, that it only makes sense to speak of an entity as following an entire series if the series comes to an end. One way to explicate this idea would be to take the referent of '① follows all the members of the series ②' to be fixed in such a way that it only includes pairs whose second member is a series with a last member. Perhaps some of Cantor's contemporaries fixed the referent of the expression in this way, and thus concluded that Cantor's characterization of ω must inevitably be empty. Their objection could be turned back by showing that there are paradigms of succession in which all the members of a series are succeeded even though the series has no last member. In general, points of accumulation (limit points) for infinite open point sets will provide examples. (A specific instance is given by noting that 1 follows all the members of the infinite series $<1/2, 3/4, \ldots, 1 - 1/2^n, \ldots>$.) Hence Cantor could appeal to paradigms of succession to rebut the complaint that I have reconstructed, and, once again, he would face the challenge of showing that the notion of succession used in his treatment of the transfinite is sufficiently similar to the paradigms in which he would anchor the reference of '① follows all the members of the series ②.'

Quite evidently, I have not given a detailed historical reconstruction of the way in which Cantor's extension of mathematical language generated perplexity among his contemporaries and how he was able to dissolve that perplexity. What I have tried to show is that my approach to conceptual change allows us to see how the mathematicians of Cantor's time might have seen his work as conceptually confused; how, nonetheless, Cantor could use the existing mathematical language to refer to transfinite numbers; and, finally, how he could argue for replacement of those concepts of number and succession on which opposition to his specifications is based. We may note, in passing, that Cantor's papers in fact employ the strategies I have attributed to him. The introduction of transfinite ordinals is linked to the theory of infinite point sets and to a transfinite arithmetic.[25]

Let me now consider a last example, which will reinforce the points that have just been made. Mathematicians of the late sixteenth century began to use expressions for the square roots of negative numbers. Thus expressions like '$\sqrt{-1}$' (and cognate terms) became relatively common in writings on algebraic equations, and, later, in the early integral calculus. Now, since '$\sqrt{-1}$' is an abbreviation for the expression "the number whose product with itself is -1," an expression which is a syntactically well formed expression of the old language, we face a similar dilemma to that which we encountered in the case of Cantor's 'ω.' To what does '$\sqrt{-1}$' refer? Two hypotheses present themselves: first, '$\sqrt{-1}$' refers to i; second, '$\sqrt{-1}$' fails to refer. The first hypothesis has the advantage of making it clear how reference to complex numbers become possible. The language of mathematics always had the resources to refer to these numbers. But the hypothesis fails to explain the deep and longlasting suspicion of complex numbers and the strenuous efforts which were made to understand them. By contrast, the second hypothesis enables us to account for the resistance to complex numbers at the cost of making it mysterious how we ever came to be in a position to refer to them. '$\sqrt{-1}$' fails to refer, we might say, because, in the way in which 'number' was used at the time of the alleged introduction of complex numbers, there is no number whose product with itself is -1. The opposition to the numbers was so intense because mathematicians were all acquainted with a theorem to this effect.

Neither hypothesis is correct, but both have captured part of the story. One way to fix the referent of 'number' is to use the available paradigms—3, 1, -1, $\sqrt{2}$, π, and so forth—to restrict the referent to the reals. Given this mode of reference fixing, the theorem that there is no number whose product with itself is -1 is almost immediate. (Any number is positive, negative, or zero. The product of a positive number with itself is positive, the product of a negative number with itself is positive, the product of zero with itself is zero.) Given a different way of fixing the referent of 'number,' numbers are entities on which arithmetical operations can be performed. Here, from the point of view of medieval and renaissance mathematics, it is an open question whether one can find recognizable analogs of the paradigm operations which allow for the square of a "number" to be negative. In effect, Bombelli and the other mathematicians who allowed expressions of the form '$\sqrt{-\nu}$' to enter their calculations were fixing the referent of 'number' in this second way, and were referring to complex numbers. What needed to be done to show that the more restrictive mode of reference fixing should be dropped from the reference potential of 'number' was to allay fears that recognizable analogs of ordinary arithmetical operations could not be found. During the seventeenth and eighteenth centuries, algebraists, analysts, and geometers responded successfully to such fears. Gradual recognition of the parallels between complex arithmetic and real arithmetic led to repudiation of the more restrictive mode of reference fixing, so that the reference potential of '$\sqrt{-1}$' came to include only events in which i was identified as the referent.

In considering this example it is helpful to drop the stance of ontological neutrality which I have been adopting. One special feature of the concern about complex numbers was the felt need for a concrete interpretation of them. (Thus the metamathematical views of the practices of mathematicians up to the end of the eighteenth century contained a requirement that, for any kind of number, some statements about the numbers of that kind must admit of concrete construal.)[26] An important episode in the acceptance of complex numbers was the development, by Wessel, Argand, and Gauss, of a geometrical model of the numbers. We can obtain a clear view about what was being demanded and how the demand was satisfied if we adopt the picture of mathematical reality given in Chapter 6. Prior to the work of Bombelli and his successors, the referent of 'number' was fixed with respect to paradigms of number operations. Each of the paradigm number operations could be given a construal in concrete physical terms: natural number operations obtained their physical interpretation in the process of counting; real number operations found theirs in the process of measurement. Bombelli can be regarded as suggesting that there is a type of number operation which had not hitherto been recognized. To eliminate from the reference potential of 'number' the restrictive mode of fixing the reference to the familiar kinds of number operation, it was not sufficient to show that the new operations would submit to recognizably arithmetical treatment. Proponents of complex numbers had ultimately to argue that the new operations shared with the original paradigms a susceptibility to construal in physical terms. The geometrical models of complex numbers answered to this need, construing complex addition in terms of the operation of vector displacement and complex multiplication in terms of the operation of rotation.

In general, of course, I want to suggest that all the examples of conceptual change in mathematics should be understood by integrating the central idea of shifting reference potentials with my picture of mathematical reality as constituted by the operations of an ideal subject. It should be easy to see how the integration is to be accomplished. At any stage in the history of mathematics, mathematical language will contain expressions referring to or qualifying the operations of the ideal subject. These expressions may have their reference fixed through paradigms of such operations or through descriptive characterizations. They may even have a heterogeneous reference potential. In modifying the reference potentials, mathematicians attempt to achieve a more adequate theory of the ideal activity of the constructive subject. Thus, to translate the point of the examples of transfinite and complex numbers, modes of fixing the referents of mathematical expressions which unnecessarily restrict that activity come to be abandoned.

NOTES

1. The view I shall present appears to accord with the central ideas of such thinkers as Carnap, Hempel, and Feigl. Since these thinkers do not consider the question of providing a philosophical reconstruction of the historical development of natural sciences, it is no surprise that their writings contain no explicit endorsement of the view.

2. It should be clear from this characterization of them that T-statements are not necessarily couched in a special ("theoretical") vocabulary. The distinction I am drawing here is that between the alleged foundations of scientific knowledge and the theoretical superstructure erected upon them. The latter includes what are sometimes

called "empirical laws" as well as the principles which are expressed in the technical language of theories.

3. The *loci classici* of the attacks are W.V. Quine, "Two Dogmas of Empiricism" (sections 5 and 6), and W. Sellars, "Empiricism and the Philosophy of Mind." For earlier doubts about the observational foundations of scientific knowledge, see Karl Popper, *The Logic of Scientific Discovery*, chapter 5 (especially p. 111), and, for a clear recent presentation of the major criticism, Michael Williams, *Groundless Belief*.

4. See, for example, T.S. Kuhn, *The Structure of Scientific Revolutions*; P.K. Feyerabend, "Explanation, Reduction and Empiricism," "Problems of Empiricism," *Against Method*, and *Science in a Free Society*; N.R. Hanson, *Patterns of Discovery*; S. Toulmin, *Human Understanding*.

5. *The Structure of Scientific Revolutions*, pp. 150–59.

6. In particular, this interpretation of Kuhn's work is advanced by Dudley Shapere, Israel Scheffler, and Carl Kordig. See Dudley Shapere, "Meaning and Scientific Change"; Israel Scheffler, *Science and Subjectivity*; Carl Kordig, *The Justification of Scientific Change*.

7. *The Structure of Scientific Revolutions*, chapters 3–5.

8. The type of view presented here has some kinship with that advanced by R.L. Wilder in his *Evolution of Mathematical Concepts*. Wilder is one of the few people to have considered seriously the question of mathematical change, and, though he modestly disclaims all intentions to philosophize, I think that his work is more relevant to philosophical understanding of *mathematics* than many of the books and papers to which philosophers of mathematics give their attention. Some of Wilder's ideas are extended further in Michael Crowe's "Ten 'Laws' Concerning the History of Mathematics." I hope that the account I shall advance in this and the ensuing chapters will provide a general framework within which the suggestive observations of Crowe and Wilder can be embedded.

9. This conception of revolutionary debates stems from the works of the writers cited in note 4—particularly Kuhn and Feyerabend.

10. This remark needs a little qualification. Excellent work on Greek mathematics and pre-Greek mathematics has been done by Heath, Neugebauer, and others. But, with the exception of a few insightful essays by Philip Jourdain and Ernest Nagel, the history of mathematics from the seventeenth century on has been much less sophisticated than the general history of science until quite recently.

11. Here, and in what follows, I ignore the issues raised by the apparent "conventionality" of geometry as a theory of physical space. For classic discussion of these issues, see H. Reichenbach, *The Phillosophy of Space and Time*. Excellent recent treatments are available in L. Sklar, *Space, Time and Space-Time*, chapter 1, and C. Glymour, "The Epistemology of Geometry."

12. See T.S. Kuhn, "Mathematical versus Experimental Traditions in the Development of Physical Science," especially p. 37.

13. Historically, this position has taken the development of non-Euclidean geometry as its primary example. For a fine discussion of the merits and shortcomings of the position, see Michael Resnik, *Frege and the Philosophy of Mathematics*, chapter 3.

14. This applies not only to the work of Kuhn but also to others. For Kuhn, a revolution consists in a clash between rival paradigms, not rival theories, and "normal science" is always governed by a single paradigm, even though, during periods

of normal science, the field may employ a succession of theories. Similar conceptions can be found in the writings of Toulmin, Laudan, and Imre Lakatos.

15. Kuhn's conception of paradigm (or "disciplinary matrix" as he now prefers to call it) is well known for the difficulty of analysing it. (See Margaret Masterman, "The Nature of a Paradigm," and Kuhn, "Second Thoughts on Paradigms.")

16. Moreover, the two theses I have distinguished here are themselves intertwined with passages in which Kuhn suggests a subjectivism about science, which has excited some readers and received most of the attention of his critics. (See the works cited in note 6.) I think it is worth pointing out that, when he is interpreted in the way I favor, Kuhn's view is not inevitably subjectivist. It is one thing to say that some of the components of scientific practice involve judgments of value, and quite another to say that such judgments are arbitrary. It would be compatible with the position I have ascribed to Kuhn to propose that the value judgments which scientific communities make about the merits of various kinds of theories, explanations, problem-solutions, and so on are rationally explicable. Moreover, in some cases, the rational explanation of these judgments could trace them to reflection upon the elements of prior practices.

17. For further discussion of the rationale of this type of transition, see Chapter 9, especially Section IV.

18. This is the term favored by Kuhn and Feyerabend. In what follows, I shall adopt, without argument, a fairly straightforward reading of their claims about incommensurability. However, I want to note explicitly that there are remarks in the writings both of Kuhn and of Feyerabend which suggest that all they wish to maintain is the type of innocuous incommensurability that my account will ultimately allow.

19. Here, and in subsequent discussions, my use of the phlogiston theory example draws on material I have presented in more detail in "Theories, Theorists and Theoretical Change."

20. See Saul Kripke, *Naming and Necessity*; Hilary Putnam, "Meaning and Reference," "Explanation and Reference"; Keith Donnellan, "Proper Names and Identifying Descriptions," "Speaking of Nothing."

21. Hence I believe that the program of operationalism should not be dismissed as completely wrongheaded. There are contexts in which the ultimate aims of science are best served by requiring that an "operational definition" (better: a descriptive fixing of the referent of a token) should be given. That is not, of course, to assert that all contexts are of this type, or even that a majority of them are.

22. An excellent account of the dispute is provided in Ivor Grattan-Guinness, *The Development of the Foundations of Analysis from Euler to Riemann*, chapter 1.

23. See Cantor, *Gesammelte Abhandlungen*, p. 195. Cantor later defined the symbols for transfinite ordinals differently, but these later definitions rested on a new analysis of the concept of number. The later definitions can also be understood by applying my approach to conceptual change.

24. For further discussion of this example, see Section IV of Chapter 9.

25. See J. Dauben, *Georg Cantor*, chapters 3–5.

26. The presence of this requirement also helps us to understand the opposition to negative numbers, apparent even in Descartes. (See Part III of the *Géométrie.*)

Computers and Mathematical Practice: A Case Study

THOMAS TYMOCZKO

The Four-Color Problem and Its Philosophical Significance

Computers have been intruding upon mathematics for several decades. In the 1950s, Wang programmed a computer to prove many elementary theorems of *Principia Mathematica.* The mathematician Hans Zazzenhaus was using computers to discover conjectures by testing the hypotheses on many cases. When each instance of a conjecture turned out to be true, Zazzenhaus would attempt a traditional proof of the conjecture. In 1969 Davis and Cerutti programmed a computer to produce proofs in elementary geometry and it 'found' an unusual proof of an old theorem. A few mathematical topics were relegated entirely to 'computer mathematics', such as the search for the largest known prime or the longest decimal expansion of pi.

Nevertheless, the mathematical legitimacy of computer use remained an open and contested question. Many mathematicians denied that computers could figure in proofs 'in the strict sense of proof'. Recall that Thom was openly critical of computer proofs in his essay earlier in the anthology. The mathematicians Whitney and Tutte actually proved the negation of a certain computer based result and only afterwards learned that the original program was in error. They warned mathematicians against shifting the burden of proof from a few pages of closely reasoned text to a computer.[1]

The suspicion of computer proofs makes most sense in a foundational milieu where mathematical proofs are expected to be a priori constructions which guarantee their conclusions. The canonical method of checking such proofs, reading them over, and verifying that each inference is correct simply does not apply to interesting computer proofs. Hard copies of such proofs might be practically unobtainable due to the amount of computer time required to print them out. Even if obtained, the hard copies might fill several library rooms and so would be useless to mathematicians.

So what evidence could there be that such a computer result was correct? Well, we could run the program several times on several machines and verify that the

Reprinted, with permission, from The Journal of Philosophy, Vol. 76, No. 2, February 1979, pp. 57–83.

same result is obtained each time. Perhaps our efforts could be analogized to the replication of key experiments in natural science. Moreover, we could construct different programs, run them, and obtain the same result. This would be like scientists conducting variations of an original experiment. Finally, we could consider the general approach behind the computer program in order to assess the reliability of the latter. This is like scientists evaluating the design of an experiment.

Quite obviously, all such evidence is quasi-empirical and not at all like the a priori constructions to which foundationalists restrict mathematical proofs. It is not surprising that some foundationalists refuse to admit computer proofs to normal mathematics on the grounds that it would change the fundamental character of mathematics. Nor is it surprising that quasi-empiricists admit computer proofs as normal mathematics on the grounds that normal mathematics was quasi-empirical all along. However, this debate could remain purely speculative, or philosophical, as long as computer proofs did not enter mainstream mathematics.

The practical setting of this debate was dramatically changed in 1976 when Appel, Haken, and Koch offered what was accepted as a proof of the Four-Color Theorem. The Four-Color Conjecture—that four colors suffice to color every map—was a longstanding conjecture well known to every mathematician. It was clearly in the mainstream of mathematics. However, Appel, Haken, and Koch's proof was essentially dependent on computer use. Excise all mention of computers, and there is an unbridged gap in the proof. Thus the debate about computer proofs was shifted from the realm of speculation to that of actual practice. The *theoretical* question of the legitimacy of computer proofs became tied to the *practical* question of whether mathematicians had in fact solved the Four-Color Conjecture.

The following essay describes the computer proof of the Four-Color Theorem and traces out its philosophical significance. The central argument of the paper is that acceptance of such computer proofs forces us to adopt a quasi-empirical account of mathematics. This essay has engendered some discussion among both mathematicians and philosophers. Much of the criticism focuses on the author's claim that "the 4CT is the first mathematical proposition to be known a posteriori." Some of the critics admit that the 4CT is known a posteriori but argue that mathematics was quasi-empirical all along and had always admitted empirical elements.[2] Other critics deny that the 4CT is known only a posteriori and try to interpret computer proofs to be consistent with the doctrine that mathematical knowledge is a priori.

There is considerable variation among the a priori interpretations of computer proofs. One suggestion is that computer proofs can be converted to demonstrative proofs by adding a new axiom.[3] Unfortunately the relevant axiom is left unspecified. Another proposal is that the computer just *is* a mathematician and *it* knows the result it has deductively proved.[4] Unfortunately, the computer has at best proved a lemma, B, while we humans have proved the conditional, 'If B then 4CT'. We cannot account for the 4CT simply by admitting computers into the American Mathematical Society.

One critic attempted to discount the philosophical relevance of computer proofs with the explanation that their introduction is 'no more significant' than was the introduction of written proofs into mathematics in the far distant past.[5] This is absurd as a counter to an argument for the importance of computer proofs in the philosophy of mathematics. Writing completely changed the practice of mathematics. If computer proofs are only half as significant, they will change mathematics far more than we can even envisage.

Other apriorists prefer more linguistic solutions. For example, pre-computer mathematics is redescribed in terms of programs, algorithms, and implementing devices; and then it is noted that computers fit right into this description.[6] Of course this can be done, but what does it show: that computer proofs are a prori? or that classical mathematics was quasi-empirical? In desperation, perhaps, one critic simply redefined 'a priori' to include computer proofs and other experiments![7] Well yes, but if you redefine 'horses' to fall under 'wishes', then beggars would ride. Under current definitions, however, beggars don't ride, nor are computer proofs a priori.

Despite the proliferation of a priori alternatives, I continue to find the quasi-empirical interpretation of computer proofs to be the more plausible. I continue to count the 4CT as known only a posteriori on the basis of experimental and corrigible evidence. However, I would concede that it is not the first theorem known only a posteriori, and that mathematics was quasi-empirical before computer proofs. On the other hand, the very variety of a priori interpretations of computer proofs does strengthen the central claim of this essay, that such proofs pose an important challenge to the philosophy of mathematics. I would only stress that this philosophical question can not be answered apart from a pressing mathematical question. Since not everything that claims to be a computer proof can be accepted as valid, what are the mathematical criteria for acceptable computer proofs?

NOTES

1. H. Whitney and W.T. Tutte in "Kempe Chains and the Four Colour Problem," *Studies in Graph Theory, Part II,* Mathematical Association of America (1975), 378–380.

2. Advocates of the quasi-empirical interpretation include Davis and Hersh, Kitcher, and sometimes E.R. Swart in his discussion, "The Philosophical Implications of the Four-Color Problem," *American Mathematical Monthly,* 87 (1980), 697–707.

3. See Margarita Levin, "On Tymoczko's Arguments for Mathematical Empiricism," *Philosophical Studies,* 39 (1981), 81.

4. Israel Krakowski, "The Four-Color Problem Reconsidered," *Philosophical Studies,* 38 (1980), 91–96.

5. Levin, op. cit., 86. Her concluding two sentences are worth quoting in full. "It [computer proof] is a step comparable to that taken long ago when a mathematical notion was introduced and men were no longer limited to counting on their fingers. The use of computers marks no epistemological revolution in mathematical method."

6. M. Detlefsen and M. Luker, "The Four-Color Theorem and Mathematical Proof," *Journal of Philosophy,* 77 (1980), 808.

7. Swart, op. cit., 698.

• • • • •

The old four-color problem was a problem of mathematics for over a century. Mathematicians appear to have solved it to their satisfaction, but their solution raises a problem for philosophy which we might call the *new four-color problem.*

The old four-color problem was whether every map on the plane or sphere can be colored with no more than four colors in such a way that neighboring regions are never colored alike. This problem is so simple to state that even a child can understand it. Nevertheless, the four-color problem resisted attempts by mathematicians for more than one hundred years. From very early on it was proved that five colors suffice to color a map, but no map was ever found that required more than four colors. In fact some mathematicians thought that four colors were not sufficient and were working on methods to produce a counterexample when Kenneth Appel and Wolfgang Haken, assisted by John Koch, published a proof that four colors suffice.[1] Their proof has been accepted by most mathematicians, and the old four-color problem has given way in mathematics to the new four-color theorem (4CT).

The purpose of these remarks is to raise the question of whether the 4CT is really a theorem. This investigation should be purely philosophical, since the mathematical question can be regarded as definitively solved. It is not my aim to interfere with the rights of mathematicians to determine what is and what is not a theorem. I will suggest, however, that, if we accept the 4CT as a theorem, we are committed to changing the sense of 'theorem', or, more to the point, to changing the sense of the underlying concept of "proof." So, by raising the question of whether the 4CT has really been proved, I will be trying to elucidate the concept of proof and not attempting an evaluation of the mathematical work of Appel and Haken.

What reason is there for saying that the 4CT is not really a theorem or that mathematicians have not really produced a proof of it? Just this: no mathematician has seen a proof of the 4CT, nor has any seen a proof that it has a proof. Moreover, it is very unlikely that any mathematician will ever see a proof of the 4CT.

What reason is there, then, to accept the 4CT as proved? Mathematicians know that it has a proof according to the most rigorous standards of formal proof—a computer told them! Modern high-speed computers were used to verify some crucial steps in an otherwise mathematically acceptable argument for the 4CT, and other computers were used to verify the work of the first.

Thus, the answer to whether the 4CT has been proved turns on an account of the role of computers in mathematics. Even the most natural account leads to serious philosophical problems. According to that account, such use of computers in mathematics, as in the 4CT, introduces empirical experiments into mathematics. Whether or not we choose to regard the 4CT as proved, we must admit that the current proof is no traditional proof, no a priori deduction of a statement from premises. It is a traditional proof with a lacuna, or gap, which is filled by the results of a well-thought-out experiment. This makes the 4CT the first mathematical proposition to be known a posteriori and raises again for philosophy the problem of distinguishing mathematics from the natural sciences.

The plan of the argument is as follows. The paper begins with a preliminary analysis of the concept of 'proof' in order to extract certain features that will be useful to us later. Then the work of Appel, Haken, and Koch is described. The most natural interpretation of this work, I will argue, is that computer-assisted proofs introduce experimental methods into pure mathematics. This fact has serious implications not only for the philosophy of mathematics, but for philosophy in general, and we will examine some of these implications.

I

What is a proof? In this section three major characteristics of proofs will be considered:

(a) Proofs are convincing.
(b) Proofs are surveyable.
(c) Proofs are formalizable.

(a) Proofs are convincing. This fact is key to understanding mathematics as a human activity. It is because proofs are convincing to an arbitrary mathematician that they can play their role as arbiter of judgment in the mathematical community. On a very stark and skeptical position, such as is sometimes suggested in Wittgenstein's *Remarks on the Foundations of Mathematics,* this is all that there is to proofs: they are convincing to mathematicians. This is to be taken as a brute fact, something for which no explanation can be given and none is necessary. Most philosophers are unhappy with this position and instead feel that there must be some deeper characterization of mathematical proofs which explains, at least to some extent, why they are convincing. That proofs are surveyable and that they are formalizable are two such characterizations.

(b) Proofs are surveyable. Proofs are the guarantees of mathematical knowledge and so they must be comprehended by mathematicians. A proof is a construction that can be looked over, reviewed, verified by a rational agent. We often say that a proof must be perspicuous, or capable of being checked by hand. It is an exhibition, a derivation of the conclusion, and it needs nothing outside of itself to be convincing. The mathematician *surveys* the proof in its entirety and thereby comes to *know* the conclusion. Here is an example of a proof, attributed to the young Gauss, which helps to convey the idea of surveyability. It is a proof that the sum of the first one hundred positive numbers is 5050. Write down those numbers in two rows of fifty columns as shown:

1	2	3	4	. . .	49	50
100	99	98	97	. . .	52	51

Observe that the sum of the two numbers in each column is 101 and that there are 50 columns. Conclude that the sum of the first one hundred positive numbers is 5050.

We now know that $1 + 2 \ldots + 99 + 100 = 5050$. We have surveyed the proof in its entirety and become convinced. If someone actually attempted to add the numbers by hand and arrived at the sum 5048, we would say that he added wrong. The construction that we surveyed leaves no room for doubt. So it is with all mathematical proofs; to say that they can be surveyed is to say that they can be definitively checked by members of the mathematical community. Of course, some surveyable proofs are very long. They might take months for even a trained mathematician to review and work out—an example is Walter Feit and John G. Thompson's famous proof that all groups of odd order are solvable.[2]

Genius in mathematics lies in the discovery of new proofs, not in the verification of old ones. In a sense, the concept of surveyability provides for the democratization of mathematics by making proofs accessible to any competent mathematician. A teacher of mine, a very good mathematician but no genius, once remarked that there were only a few proofs that he couldn't understand, but that there were none that he could not follow.

Surveyability is an important subjective feature of mathematical proofs which relates the proofs to the mathematicians, the subjects of mathematical investigations. It is in the context of surveyability that the idea of 'lemma' fits. Mathematicians organize a proof into lemmas to make it more perspicuous. The proof relates the mathematical known to the mathematical knower, and the surveyability of the proof enables it to be comprehended by the pure power of the intellect—surveyed by the mind's eye, as it were. Because of surveyability, mathematical theorems are credited by some philosophers with a kind of certainty unobtainable in the other sciences. Mathematical theorems are known a priori.

(c) Proofs are formalizable. A proof, as defined in logic, is a finite sequence of formulas of a formal theory satisfying certain conditions. It is a deduction of the conclusion from the axioms of the theory by means of the axioms and rules of logic. Most mathematicians and philosophers believe that any acceptable proof can be formalized. We can always find an appropriate formal language and theory in which the informal proof can be embedded and "filled out" into a rigorous formal proof.

Formal proofs carry with them a certain objectivity. That a proof is formalizable, that the formal proofs have the structural properties that they do, explains in part why proofs are convincing to mathematicians.

We've noted three features of proofs: that they are convincing, surveyable, and formalizable. The first is a feature centered in the anthropology of mathematics, the second is the epistemology of mathematics, and the third in the logic of mathematics. The latter two are the deep features. It is because proofs are surveyable and formalizable that they are convincing to rational agents.

Surveyability and formalizability can be seen as two sides of the same coin. Formalizability idealizes surveyability, analyzes it into finite reiterations of surveyable patterns. Certainly when the two criteria work together, mathematicians do not hesitate to accept or reject a purported proof. Nevertheless the two ideas spring from such different sources that we can wonder whether they will always work together. Can there be surveyable proofs that are not formalizable or formal proofs that cannot be surveyed?

Are all surveyable proofs formalizable? Most mathematicians and philosophers would assent, but not all. Some intuitionists deny that the actual proof constructions of mathematics can be completely captured by formal systems.[3] Intuitionism aside, however, it is well known that no single theory is sufficient to formalize every proof. Given any sufficiently rich theory, we can find a surveyable proof of a statement of that theory which has no formal proof. Such a statement can be a Gödel statement which, when properly interpreted, says that it has no formal proof. Of course the surveyable proof can be formalized in a new and more powerful formal theory; but that theory, in turn, will yield new surveyable proofs that it cannot formalize.

At best, formalizability is a local characteristic of proofs, not a global one. There is not one system in which any proof can be formalized; but rather, given any proof, there is some appropriate formal system in which it can be formalized. The point that formalizability is a local and not a global phenomenon is made by René Thom where he notes the general significance of this distinction for the philosophy of mathematics.[4] However since our concern will not be with surveyable proofs that cannot be formalized, let us turn to the second question.

Are all formalizable proofs surveyable? Consider first the simpler question: Are all formal proofs surveyable? Here the answer is an easy no. We know that there must exist formal proofs that cannot be surveyed by mathematicians if only because the proofs are too long or involve formulas that are too long. Here "too long" can be taken to mean "can't be read over by a mathematician in a human lifetime." So it is logically possible that mathematicians could come across a statement with no surveyable proof but with a formalized proof.

However, if we stop to think abut this situation, it appears unlikely that this logical possibility can ever be realized. How is a mathematician to know that a statement has a formal proof? On the one hand, the mathematician might actually survey or look over the formal proof and check it for correctness. On the other hand, the mathematician can derive the existence of the required formal proof, in effect, by presenting a surveyable proof that the formal proof exists. This sort of thing is standard practice in proof theory, where we find, for example, general surveyable arguments that any proof in, say, elementary arithmetic can be formalized in Zermelo-Fraenkel set theory. Hence it begins to appear that, in practice, at least, mathematicians come to know formal proofs only through the mediation of surveyable proofs. Either the formal proofs are simple enough to be surveyed themselves and verified to be proofs, or their existence is established by means of informal surveyable arguments.

It is not really surprising that we should come to know the existence of specific formal proofs only through some more primitive concept of proof, surveyable proof. After all, in the last analysis, formal proofs are abstract mathematical objects. They can be represented by sets of natural numbers, Gödel numbers, without any loss of information. To state that there is a formal proof of a formula is very much like stating that there is a number with a certain property; and how are we to come to know the latter statement except by a proof?

In summary, although formal proofs outrun surveyable proofs, it is not at all obvious that mathematicians could come across formal proofs and recognize them as such without being able to survey them.

Nevertheless, it is the contention of this paper that the current proof of the 4CT does drive a wedge between the criteria of surveyability and formalizability. In fact, there is no surveyable proof, no proof in the traditional sense, of the 4CT, nor is there likely to be one. Still Appel, Haken, and Koch's work provides mathematically convincing grounds for the 4CT. What can be surveyed, what is presented in their published work, is like a mathematical proof where a key lemma is justified by an appeal to the results of certain computer runs or, as we might say "by computer." This appeal to computer, whether we count it as strictly a part of a proof or as a part of some explicitly non-proof-theoretic component of mathematical knowledge, is ultimately a report on a successful experiment. It helps establish the 4CT (actually, the existence of a formal proof of the 4CT) on grounds that are in part empirical.

The idea that a particular proposition of pure mathematics can be established, indeed must be established, by appealing to empirical evidence is quite surprising. It entails that many commonly held beliefs about mathematics must be abandoned or modified. Consider:[5]

1. All mathematical theorems are known a priori.
2. Mathematics, as opposed to natural science, has no empirical content.
3. Mathematics, as opposed to natural science, relies only on proofs, whereas natural science makes use of experiments.
4. Mathematical theorems are certain to a degree that no theorem of natural science can match.

In order to assess such claims, let us quickly review the proof of the 4CT.

II

Sooner or later any discussion of the 4CT must begin talking of graphs in place of maps, so we might as well begin at once.[6] We can think of a *planar graph* as a finite collection of points in the plane, called *vertices,* which are joined to each other by lines, called *edges,* such that no edges meet except at vertices. The number of edges meeting at any vertex is called the *degree* of the vertex, and vertices joined by an edge are said to be *neighboring,* or adjacent. A graph is *4-colorable* if every vertex can be colored by one of four colors in such a way that neighboring vertices never receive the same color.

If every planar graph can be 4-colored, then every planar map can be. This is because every map determines a graph, its *dual graph,* as follows: place one vertex (capital city) in each region (country) of the map and join the capitals of neighboring regions by an edge (road) that crosses their common border. Obviously, the resulting graph is 4-colorable if and only if the original map is.

Next we restrict our attention to graphs in a standard form. We can delete any parallel edges, edges joining two vertices already joined by another edge, without affecting 4-colorability. Graphs without parallel edges or loops are called *simple graphs.* Moreover, we can add edges by a process of triangulation. Given any region or polygon of the *graph* that is bounded by four or more edges, there will be at least two non-adjacent vertices on the boundary. We can join such vertices by a new edge across the region which does not intersect any other edge (except at the vertices). Continuing in this way, we can completely triangulate a graph until all regions have three sides. Since triangulation can only make 4-coloring more difficult because it restricts the possible colorings of a graph, it suffices to prove the 4CT for triangulated graphs.

Now any planar triangulation has only finitely many vertices; so the way to prove that all such graphs can be 4-colored is by induction on the number v of vertices. In case $v \leq 4$, the triangulation can be 4-colored. So we assume as induction hypothesis that any planar triangulation G' with n or fewer vertices if 4-colorable. We wish to show that, if G is a planar triangulation with $n + 1$ vertices, then G can be 4-colored.

There is a well-known formula relating the number of vertices a triangulation can have to the degrees of the individual vertices. If v_i is the number of vertices of degree i and if n is the maximum degree of any vertex in the triangulation, then Euler's formula states that

$$3v_3 + v_4 + v_5 + 0 \bullet v_6 - v_7 - 2v_8 - 3v_9 - \cdots - (m - 6)v_m = 12$$

At least one of v_3, v_4, v_5 must be nonzero; so any triangulated graph has a vertex with five or fewer edges. Incidentally, this fact suffices to prove, by induction, that any graph can be 6-colored. Look at the triangulation G and delete a vertex of degree 5 along with its edges. The resulting graph has one less vertex and, when triangulated, it can be 6-colored, by the induction hypothesis. However, the missing vertex has at most five neighbors, so one color will be left to color it.

To prove that any graph G can be 4-colored, we consider the following cases.

Case 1. G contains a vertex of degree 3; i.e., $v_3 \neq 0$.

Then, if we delete the vertex along with its adjacent edges, we get a graph with n vertices which can be 4-colored by assumption. Since the missing vertex has only three neighbors, it can be colored by the remaining color.

Case 2. $v_3 = 0$ but $v_4 \neq 0$; the graph G contains a vertex of degree 4.

Again, delete the vertex of minimal degree, call it v_0, and its adjoining edges, to obtain a smaller graph which is 4-colorable.

Subcase 2a. If the four neighbors of the missing vertex are colored by only three colors, then v_0 can be colored the remaining color.

Subcase 2b. The four neighbors of v_0 are each colored differently. This coloring cannot be extended to G directly, but must first be modified. Call the neighbors of v_0 v_1', v_2', v_3', v_4', and suppose that they are respectively colored, *a, b, c, d.* Look at the smaller graph G' $(G - v_0)$, and consider the subgraph of G' determined by all vertices colored *a* or *c* along with any edges connecting two such vertices. One of two alternatives must arise. Either there is an *a*–*c* chain of points and edges connecting v_1' to v_3', or there is not.

Subcase 2bi. If there is no such path between v_1 and v_3, we say that v_1 and v_3 belong to separate *a–c* components of G'. In this case reverse the colors in the *a–c* component containing v_3'. All vertices in this component formerly colored *a* are now colored *c*, and vice-versa. The resulting coloring is still a 4-coloring of G' since no neighboring vertices are colored the same, but the vertex v_3' is now colored *a*. The color *c* is not used to color any neighbor of v_0; so *c* can be used to color v_0.

Subcase 2bii. If there is such an *a–c* path connecting v_1' and v_3', then these vertices belong to the same *a–c* component of G', and reversing the colors won't help. However, in this case there cannot be a *b–d* path connecting v_2' and v_4', for any such path is blocked by the *a–c* path connecting v_1' and v_3'. Thus v_2' and v_4' belong to separate *b–d* components of G', and by reversing the colors in the *b–d* component containing v_4', we obtain a 4-coloring of G' in which v_4' and v_2' are both colored *b*, leaving *d* to color v_0.

In either case the 4-coloring of G' can be modified and extended to a 4-coloring of *G*. The argument used in subcase 2b is called a *Kempe chain argument.* Incidentally, this type of argument can be applied to a vertex of degree 5 to show that any graph can be 5-colored.

If *G* has a vertex of degree 3 or 4, then *G* is 4-colorable; so we may assume that $v_3 = 0 = v_4$, and thus we come to case 3.

Case 3. $v_5 \neq 0$, the minimum degree of any vertex in *G* is 5. In this case the simple proof breaks down; Kempe chain arguments do not suffice if we delete a single vertex of degree 5. Instead of deleting a single vertex, we must try to delete configurations, or systems of interconnected vertices. If we remove a configuration from a triangulation we are left with a graph with a "hole" in it. The vertices of the remaining graph which are adjacent to the hole form a circuit, or *ring* around the configuration. The size of the ring is determined by the number of vertices in it. A *configuration* can be more precisely defined as a subgraph with specifications of the number of vertices, vertex degrees, and the manner in which it is embedded in the original triangulation.

A configuration is *reducible* if the 4-coloring of any planar graph containing it is deducible from the 4-colorability of any graph with fewer vertices. Reducible configurations transmit 4-colorability upwards. Conversely, if *G* is a graph that *requires* five colors and if *G* contains the reducible configuration *C*, then the subgraph (*G–C*) requires five colors. By 1913, George Birkhoff had investigated the general methods of showing that a configuration was reducible.[7] In outline what must be proved is that every 4-coloring of the ring around a given configuration can either be extended to a 4-coloring of the configuration, or modified first by one or more Kempe interchanges and then extended, or modified by suitable identification of distinct vertices and then extended. A natural plan for attacking the four-color problem suggests itself. We can try to find a set of reducible configurations which is sufficiently large so that every triangulation contains a configuration from that set. Such an *unavoidable* set of configurations would enable us to complete the induction step in case 3. This plan runs into two related problems: the potential size of the unavoidable set and the potential size of the reducible configurations in it. As Haken observes, the amount of work required to prove that a configuration is reducible increases considerably with the ring size. For a ring of size 14, the number of possible colorations is $3^{14} + 3$ (about 2×10^5). In principle, each one of these colorations must be examined in showing that the configuration is reducible. On the other hand Edward F. Moore found a triangulation that does not contain any known reducible configuration of ring size less than 12. Thus, in order to find enough reducible configurations to fill out an unavoidable set, we will have to include some with large ring size.

In order then to establish case 3, we must find a finite list of reducible configurations such that every graph contains at least one configuration from the list. Building on some work of Heinrich Heesch, Appel and Haken developed a theory of discharging procedures any of which produces an unavoidable set of configurations, i.e., a set that no triangulation ($v_3 = v_4 = 0$) can avoid. Heesch had noticed that certain kinds of configurations were reduction obstacles in that they could not be reduced by known methods. In a preliminary study, Appel and Haken developed a discharging procedure that produced an unavoidable set of configurations which excluded two of the three major reduction obstacles of Heesch. This set the stage for the final assault on the four-color conjecture.

Appel and Haken began with a discharging algorithm and tested for reducibility the configurations in the resulting unavoidable set. Whenever a configuration in the list could not be shown reducible, the discharging algorithm was modified to produce a new unavoidable set that excluded the recalcitrant configuration although generally it included new configurations. The configurations of the new set were checked for reducibility, and so on. Although the discharging procedure and the reducibility checks on individual configurations went hand in hand, and computer work was in practice necessary to develop both, when they had finished, the work of Appel, Haken, and Koch fell nicely into two parts.

The authors could specify a discharging procedure and prove in a mathematically rigorous fashion that this procedure produced an unavoidable set U of 1834 configurations (in fact, only 1482 of these configurations are really necessary). Although computer work was used to develop the procedure and the resulting set U, once the set was produced it could be surveyed and is listed in figures 1 to 63 of Appel, Haken, and Koch. Moreover, one can give a surveyable proof that this set U is unavoidable (see the Discharging theorem and corollary in Appel, Haken, and Koch, 460).

However, to complete the proof of case 3, we need the lemma: Every configuration in U is reducible (actually, we need something a little stronger, but this version will suffice for our purposes. See Appel, Haken, and Koch on immersion reducibility). The proof of this lemma *cannot* be surveyed in detail. That these configurations are reducible is established by programming a computer to test for reducibility and running the program on the configurations in U. Since most of the configurations have large ring size (13 or 14), the use of computers to check reducibility is "unavoidable." Appel and Haken define a measure of complexity according to which the complexity of a proof of the D-reducibility of a 13-ring configuration will exceed 10^6 although other reductions (C-reducibility) of the same configuration might be of much less complexity (p. 487). In any case, no computer has printed out the complete proof of the reducibility lemma, nor would such a printout be of much use to human mathematicians. Over 1200 hours of computer time were required for the proof. Because of the complexity and time required, any proof of the reducibility lemma along its present lines must include an appeal to computer analysis. Thus it must presuppose the legitimacy of that appeal.

In its over-all outlines, the logic of the four-color proof is easy to see. It is a proof by induction which requires several cases. The first case is trivial, the second has several subcases, and the third has over a thousand subcases most of which cannot be handled except by high-speed computers. I would like to remove any impression that Appel and Haken's work is simply a "brute force" argument. To a certain extent, the appeal to computers might be regarded as "brute force," but it makes sense only when set in the context of a novel and sophisticated theory developed by the authors. However, establishing a theorem by introducing a novel and sophisticated theory is not in itself a novel mathematical procedure. The appeal to computers in order to ground key lemmas is.

To be sure, the use of computers in mathematics, even very sophisticated use, is not unfamiliar. We can cite programs for solving differential equations or the program of Hao Wang to prove theorems of propositional logic.[8] What makes the use of computers in the 4CT so dramatic is that it leads to a genuine extension of our knowledge of pure mathematics. It is not merely calculation, but yields a proof of a substantial new result.

Let us conclude this section with some general remarks on the complexity of the mathematical argument. Is the above proof of the 4CT, including computer work, the simplest or shortest proof of the 4CT? Might a surveyable proof be found some day?

Obviously some simplification is possible. Between the write-up of the proof and its publication it was found that 429 configurations could be eliminated from the set U. Further reduction could no doubt be achieved by modifying the discharging procedure. Nevertheless, it seems that any significant simplification of one part of the proof is likely to be matched with an increase in the complexity of another part of the proof. The current consensus among mathematicians is that the present proof is reasonably close to the simplest proof.[9] If this is so, then the appeal to computers would be essential to any mathematical justification of the 4CT.

Of course, no one can completely rule out the possibility that some mathematician will one day come up with a ten-page proof of the 4CT along lines currently unimaginable. (Although even here there are some grounds for skepticism; see Kainen and Saaty, 96.) Still, from a philosophical point of view such a discovery would have to be regarded as mere luck. The philosophical point at issue, obviously, is not simply the status of the 4CT, but the status of computer-assisted proofs in general. The work of Appel, Haken, Koch, and IBM 370-168 guarantees that the possibility of computer-assisted proofs is a real possibility.

III

The materials for our problem have been assembled. We have discussed some general features of proofs and some details of the proof of the 4CT. We can now ask whether the 4CT is really a theorem. Let us consider it with regard to the three characteristics of proofs.

(a) Is the proof of the 4CT convincing? Yes, most mathematicians have accepted the 4CT, and none, to my knowledge, has argued against it. Still, it should be noted that Appel and Haken themselves have recognized that there could be some resistance to their work, particularly from those mathematicians "educated before the development of high-speed computers" (Appel and Haken, 121). In any case, that an argument is convincing is not sufficient reason to accept it as a proof.

(b) Has the 4CT a surveyable proof? Here the answer is no. No mathematician has surveyed the proof in its entirety; no mathematician has surveyed the proof of the critical reducibility lemma. It has not been checked by mathematicians, step by step, as all other proofs have been checked. Indeed, it cannot be checked that way. Now Appel, Haken, and Koch *did* produce something that was surveyable in the sense that it could be looked over. Their work, as we have said, is very much like a surveyable proof with a lacuna where a key lemma is justified by nontraditional means—by computer. Incidentally, we must be wary of verbal entanglements here. Of course, if we call the appeal to computers a "new method of proof" in the strictest sense, then, trivially, the 4CT will have a surveyable proof. But the notion of proof itself will have shifted to accommodate the new method.

More serious is the objection that the appeal to computers is not a method of proof at all and that the idea that it is arises from a confusion between a proof and a description of a proof. Often mathematicians forgo a complete proof and make do with a description or a sketch of the proof sufficiently detailed for their purposes. In such descriptions, mathematicians may justify a lemma by reference to some already published work, by indicating the general method (e.g., "by diagonalizing") or by simply leaving the proof of the lemma as an exercise for the reader. Of course, these are not necessarily new methods of proof; in point of fact, they are more like shorthand, a brief way of indicating a proof. These devices belong to the description of the proof and not to the proof itself. The objection suggests that we regard Appel, Haken, and Koch's papers as descriptions of a proof (which they are) and try to assimilate the appeal to computers to the pragmatic shortcuts we've just noted.

The objection fails because there is a major difference between the cases. Traditionally any such abbreviation has been backed by a surveyable proof, even more, by a surveyed proof. Some mathematician and usually several mathematicians have surveyed the real thing and verified it. In principle this surveyable backing is available to any member of the mathematical community, either directly, as when the mathematicians can work it out for themselves, or indirectly, when they look it up in the archives, to use Wittgenstein's phrase.

But it is just this surveyable backing that is lacking in the 4CT! Mathematicians cannot work out the missing steps for themselves, not even in a lifetime of work; and it is nowhere recorded in the archives. What is recorded is the evidence that a computer once worked out the missing steps. So it would be a grave mistake to classify the appeal to computers as a theoretically dispensable convenience, like the appeal to published journal articles. Of course the appeal "by computer" does mark an abbreviation, and later we will consider it in more expanded form. The point at hand, however, is that surveyability is preserved in traditional descriptions of proofs, but not in the appeal to computers.

Let us consider a hypothetical example which provides a much better analogy to the appeal to computers. It is set in the mythical community of Martian mathematicians and concerns their discovery of the new method of proof "Simon says." Martian mathematics, we suppose, developed pretty much like Earth mathematics until the arrival on Mars of the mathematical genius Simon. Simon proved many new results by more or less traditional methods, but after a while began justifying new results with such phrases as "Proof is too long to include here, but I have verified it myself." At first Simon used this appeal only for lemmas, which, although crucial, were basically combinatorial in character. In his later work, however, the appeal began to spread to more abstract lemmas and even to theorems themselves. Oftentimes other Martian mathematicians could reconstruct Simon's results, in the sense of finding satisfactory proofs; but sometimes they could not. So great was the prestige of Simon, however, that the Martian mathematicians accepted his results; and they were incorporated into the body of Martian mathematics under the rubric "Simon says."

Is Martian mathematics, under Simon, a legitimate development of standard mathematics? I think not; I think it is something else masquerading under the name of mathematics. If this point is not immediately obvious, it can be made so by expanding on the Simon parable in any number of ways. For instance, imagine that Simon is a religious mystic and that among his religious teachings is the doctrine that the morally good Martian, when it frames the mathematical question justly, can always see the correct answer. In this case we cannot possibly treat the appeal "Simon says" in a purely mathematical context. What if Simon were a revered political leader like Chairman Mao? Under these circumstances we might have a hard time deciding where Martian mathematics left off and Martian political theory began. Still other variations on the Simon theme are possible. Suppose that other Martian mathematicians begin to realize that Simonized proofs are possible where the attempts at more traditional proofs fail, and they begin to use "Simon says" even when Simon didn't say! The appeal "Simon says" is an anomaly in mathematics; it is simply an appeal to authority and not a demonstration.

The point of the Simon parable is this: that the logic of the appeals "Simon says" and "by computer" are remarkably similar. There is no great formal difference between these claims: computers are, in the context of mathematical proofs, another kind of authority. If we choose to regard one appeal as bizarre and the other as legitimate, it can only be because we have some strong evidence for the reliability of the latter and none for the former. Computers are not simply authority, but warranted authority. Since we are inclined to accept the appeal to computers in the case of the 4CT and to reject the appeal to Simon in the hypothetical example, we must admit evidence for the reliability of computers into a philosophical account of computer-assisted proofs. The precise nature of this evidence will concern us later. For now it suffices to note that, whatever the evidence is, it cannot take the form of a traditional, surveyable proof. Otherwise Appel and Haken would have given that proof and dispensed with the appeal to computers altogether.

The conclusion is that the appeal to computers does introduce a new method into mathematics. The appeal is surveyable, but what it appeals to is not.

(c) Has the 4CT a formalizable proof? Most mathematicians would concur that there is a formal proof of the 4CT in an appropriate graph theory. We can describe the formal proof in some detail, actually exhibit sections of it, calculate the total length, and so on. Nevertheless, this belief in the formal proof cannot be used to legitimize the appeal to computers. Rather, we believe that the formal proof exists only because we accept the appeal to computers in the first place. It is important to get the order of justification correct. Some people might be tempted to accept the appeal to computers on the ground that it involves a harmless extension of human powers. On their view the computer merely traces out the steps of a complicated formal proof that is really out there. In fact, our only evidence for the existence of that formal proof presupposes the reliability of computers.

This point can be clarified by the Simon parable. Martian mathematicians could say that "Simon says" incorporates no new method of proof and say that any Martian proof was still formalizable. They could claim that all of Simon's work was formalizable, only they themselves couldn't always provide the formalization. This is much the same position we claim to be in with respect to the appeal to computers. The comparison makes clear that formalization comes in only after the fact. It cannot be used as the criterion for accepting computer-assisted proofs.

In summary, the proof of the 4CT, although much like a traditional proof, differs in certain key respects. It is convincing, and there is a formal proof. But no known proof of the 4CT is surveyable, and there is no known proof that a formal proof exists. The crucial difference between the 4-color proof and traditional proofs is that the 4-color proof requires the appeal to computers to fill the gap in an otherwise traditional proof. The work of the computer is itself not surveyable. However, there are very good grounds for believing that this computer work has certain characteristics, e.g., that it instantiated the pattern of a formal proof of the reducibility lemma. Let us consider these grounds.

What does the appeal to computers amount to? Remember, we are now considering the appeal in the context of justifying a mathematical result, not yet in the context of discovery. We have a given mathematical question:

Are the configurations in the unavoidable set *U* reducible? As part of the question, we are given procedures for testing configurations for reducibility. Second, we have a given machine with such and such characteristics. On the basis of our question and the machine's characteristics we construct a program of instruction for the machine. In this case the program is intended to "cause" the machine to "search" through the set *U*, testing each configuration for reducibility and reporting yes or no as the case may be. Finally we run this program on the computer and note the results. The appeal to computers, in the case of the 4CT, involves two claims: (1) that every configuration in *U* is reducible if a machine with such and such characteristics when programmed in such and such a way produces an affirmative result for each configuration, and (2) that such a machine so programmed did produce affirmative results for each configuration. The second claim is the report of a particular experiment. It has been experimentally established that a machine of type *T* when programmed by *P* will give output *O*.

But even the conditional conjunct is, at best, an empirical truth and not subject to traditional proof. Its trust depends on two interrelated factors, the reliability of the machine and the reliability of the program. The reliability of the machine is ultimately a matter for engineering and physics to assess. It is a sophisticated natural science that assures us that the computer "does what it's supposed to" in much the same way that it assures us that the electron microscope "does what it's supposed to." Of course, even if we grant that the machine does what it is supposed to—follow the program—there remains the question of whether the program does what *it* is supposed to. This question can be difficult to answer. The task of evaluating programs is a topic of computer science, but at present there are no general methods for accomplishing it at this level. Programs themselves are written in special "languages," and many of them can be quite complex. They can contain "bugs," or flaws that go unnoticed for a long time. The reliability of any appeal to computers must ultimately rest on such diffuse grounds as these.

In the case of the 4CT, most mathematicians feel that the reliability is sufficiently high to warrant a qualified acceptance of the theorem. In the first place, the problem was reducible to computer-manageable complexity. There is a very clear idea of what the computer is supposed to be doing—we have a good understanding of reduction techniques. Moreover, there is a great deal of accumulated evidence for the reliability of computers in such operations, and the work of the original computers was checked by other computers. Finally, there is good reason to believe that the theorem could not be reached by any other means. It is natural for mathematicians, at least for those educated after the development of high-speed computers and pocket calculators, to accept the truth of the 4CT. The reliability of the 4CT, however, is not of the same degree as that guaranteed by traditional proofs, for this reliability rests on the assessment of a complex set of empirical factors.

A digression on the reliability of computer-assisted proofs. No detailed estimate of this reliability, nor a general account of how such estimates should be made is offered here. Instead, let us try to probe our own subjective idea of computer reliability in mathematics by means of the following hypothetical examples.

In the case of the 4CT we understand the general shape of the computer proof. Would we be prepared to rely on computers even when we could not perceive the general shape of their work? Suppose that advances in computer science lead to the following circumstances. We can program a computer to initiate a search through various proof procedures, with subprograms to modify and combine procedures in appropriate circumstances, until it finds a proof of statement A. After a long time, the computer reports a proof of A, although we can't reconstruct the general shape of the proof beyond the bare minimum (e.g., by induction). Perhaps we could describe this hypothetical example by saying that the supercomputer found a human-assisted proof. Mathematicians served to aim the computer in a certain direction, to provide it with certain techniques, and it went on to find a cumbersome patchwork proof consisting of thousands of cases. Again, the question is whether mathematicians would have sufficient faith in the reliability of computers to accept this result.

The idea that a computer program can surprise its originators is not really very farfetched. The Appel-Haken program did surprise them.

> It was working out compound strategies based on all the tricks it had been taught, and the new approaches were often much cleverer than those we would have tried. In a sense the program was demonstrating superiority not only in the mechanical parts of the task but in some intellectual areas as well (Appel and Haken, 117).

Suppose some such supercomputer were set to work on the consistency of Peano arithmetic and it reported a proof of *inconsistency*, a proof which was so long and complex that no mathematician could understand it beyond the most general terms. Could we have sufficient faith in computers to accept this result, or would we say that the empirical evidence for their reliability is not enough? Would such a result justify a mathematician's claim to know that Peano arithmetic was inconsistent, and would such a mathematician have to abandon Peano arithmetic? These are bizarre questions, but they suggest that the reliability of computer-assisted proofs in mathematics, though easy to accept in the case of the 4CT, might some day be harder to swallow.

In conclusion, we have seen why it is reasonable to accept the 4CT even the crucial reducibility lemma. There is no surveyable proof of the lemma, but we know that there is a formal proof. Our knowledge of this is grounded, in part, in the results of a well-conceived computer experiment. A wedge has been driven between the two explanations of proof in terms of surveyability and formalizability. In addition, a new technique has been developed for establishing mathematical truths. It is largely a matter of notational convention whether we choose to describe the new technique—appeal to computers—as a method of proof or refuse to call it a proof and insist on describing it as an experiment. In the former case, we would count the 4CT as a bona fide theorem. In the latter case we would not count it a theorem in the strict sense but admit it as a new kind of mathematical knowledge. Mere choice of labels cannot mask the underlying reality, which is an unavoidable reliance on computer experiments to establish the 4CT. Let us now turn to the consequences of this fact for philosophy.

IV

The acceptance of the 4CT is significant for philosophy at a number of points. In the first place, it is relevant to philosophy in general, especially to the theory of knowledge. Obviously, it is relevant to the details of any philosophy of mathematics. Finally, it is relevant to some issues in the philosophy of science.

Mathematics has always been important to philosophical theorizing about knowledge and reason, of course, both because mathematics stands as one of the pinnacles of human reason and rational thought and because mathematical knowledge can appear so perplexing if not actually mysterious.

> The science of pure mathematics, in its modern developments, may claim to be the most original creation of the human spirit.[10]

> The apparent contrast between the indefinite flux of sense-impressions and the precise and timeless truths of mathematics has been among the earliest perplexities and problems not of the philosophy of mathematics only, but of philosophy in general.[11]

A widely shared assumption among philosophers is that there is a significant gulf between mathematics and mathematical knowledge on the one hand, and natural science and scientific knowledge on the other. Thoroughgoing empiricists have denied that this gulf exists and have tried to explain mathematical truth, for example as Mill did, as a very general type of empirical truth. Such explanations have not been very persuasive, and, in general, philosophy has assumed that the gulf between mathematics and natural science exists and has tried to characterize the different kinds of knowledge involved by some contrasting pair, e.g., a priori, a posteriori; innate, learned; formal, empirical; certain, dubitable; analytic, synthetic. Once established, these characterizations become philosophical tools that can be applied elsewhere in the theory of knowledge. Mathematical knowledge plays a role in establishing these characterizations by serving as a paradigm of one pole in the dichotomy. The proof of the 4CT, however, undercuts this role. Knowledge of the 4CT does not have any of the characteristics that the paradigm suggests. Let us examine the case of the a priori/a posteriori distinction; the other cases proceed along similar lines.

Traditionally, a priori truths are those truths which can be known independently of any experience and a posteriori truths are those which can be known only on the basis of particular experiences. An a priori truth might be immediately evident, stipulated by convention, or, most common, known by reason independently of any experience beyond pure thought. It is plausible to maintain that such theorems as the mini-theorem that the sum of the first one hundred positive numbers is 5050 are known by reason alone—we all know it and could demonstrate its truth if we desired. However, it is not plausible to maintain that the 4CT is known by reason alone.

By reason alone, we know that the reducibility lemma implies the 4CT; but our knowledge of the reducibility lemma does not take the form of a proof. Our knowledge rests on general empirical assumptions about the nature of computers and particular empirical assumptions about Appel and Haken's computer work. Moreover, it is unlikely that anyone could know the 4CT by reason alone. The only route to the 4CT that we can ever take appears to lead through computer experiments. Thus the 4CT is an a posteriori truth and not an a priori one; mathematicians, I suggest, will never know the 4CT by a priori means.[12]

It is with the claim that the 4CT is not a priori that I differ from the position suggested taken by Saul Kripke when he considers the example of a computer verification that some very large number is a prime.[13] Kripke argues that such a theorem would be known a posteriori for the same reasons that I give that the 4CT is known a posteriori. But he leaves open the question of whether his theorem can be known a priori. I have argued that the 4CT cannot be known a priori by us.

The 4CT is a substantial piece of pure mathematics which can be known by mathematicians only a posteriori. Our knowledge must be qualified by the uncertainty of our instruments, computer and program. There surely are truths from electrical engineering about current flow through switching networks which have a higher degree of certainty than the 4CT. The demonstration of the 4CT includes not only symbol manipulation, but the manipulation of sophisticated experimental equipment as well: the four-color problem is not a formal question. In fact, the argument for the 4CT is very like an argument in theoretical physics where a long argument can suggest a key experiment which is carried out and used to complete the argument.

This is a bit of a puzzle. In the first place, it blurs the intuitive distinction between mathematics and natural science which we began with. In the second place, we are left with the question of how to explain the role of experiment in pure mathematics. It is easy to see how experiments play role in the arguments of physical theory. The physical theory can predict phenomena of space-time which equipment can be designed to register. Are we to say that the computer registered a phenomenon of mathematical space? If not, then how else are we to explain the role of experiment in mathematics? Such puzzles are one aspect of what I have called "the new four-color problem." I will not attempt any solutions to the puzzles here, but simply note these puzzles as among the consequences of the 4CT.

Not every way of characterizing the difference between mathematics and natural science falls to the 4CT. Following Kripke, we can argue that all mathematical truths, even the 4CT, are necessary, or true in all possible worlds. The 4CT, we might say, records an essential property of planar maps. (The truths of natural science, on the other hand, might be counted as contingent, or true in our world but false in some possible world.) In this case the 4CT would be an important example of an a posteriori necessary truth and, a fortiori, a counterexample to the claim that all known necessary truths are known a priori.

The new four-color problem then might serve as a stimulus to general philosophy to rethink the commonly accepted relations among knowledge, reason, and experience. Nevertheless, the most significant impact of the 4CT in philosophy obviously will concern the details of our philosophy of mathematics.

Accepting the 4CT forces us to modify our concept of proof. We can modify it by admitting a new method (computer experiment) of establishing mathematical results in addition to proofs. Or we can modify it by allowing proof to include computer-assisted proofs. I prefer the latter terminology. Either way, the details of this new method can have a substantial impact on the way mathematics is done.

This points to one of the most exciting aspects of Appel, Haken, and Koch's work, but one we have not touched on yet. So far we have been concerned with the 4CT only in the context of its justification: given the purported proof, does it prove the theorem? We have not treated it in the context of discovery. Any conclusions based only on discovery would have invited the Fregean retort that what matters to philosophy is justification and not genesis. It is time to widen our perspective; for there is much of interest about the discovery of the 4CT both to mathematics and to philosophy.

How does one decide to attempt a computer experiment in mathematics? Even where questions of the form $P(n)$ are decidable and we have the techniques to program a computer to check the instances, we cannot simply run the computer as long as it will go, hoping that it finds, say, that $(\exists x)P(x)$ before the computer reaches its limits. There must be some reason to expect that the computer will stop with an answer within a reasonable time. In the case of the 4CT we can ask why anyone thought that an unavoidable set of reducible configurations each of ring size less than or equal to 14 could be found. From the outside, 14 looks no more probable as a bound than 20 or 50 or even 100. Yet, if the minimum ring size were 20 or more, the required proof experiment could not be conducted at present! From the other direction, we know because of Moore's map that we must include configurations whose ring size is at least 12. Perhaps Moore would discover a map requiring the minimum ring size to be 20. Why did Appel and Haken think that a computer experiment could work?

What happened was that they developed a sophisticated probabilistic argument, not a proof, that the ring size could be restricted to 17 or less, and that the restriction to 14 was a good bet. They provided an argument that invested statements of the form "There is an unavoidable set of reducible configurations each of which has a ring size less than or equal to n" with a probability derived from the ratio of the number of vertices in the configuration to the ring size n (Haken, 202). With $n = 14$, the statement was very likely. Together with this probabilistic argument was an argument that the required techniques could be programmed into a computer. Koch did much of the work on the programming, and in their earlier paper Appel and Haken had showed that there was an unavoidable set of geographically good configurations of manageable size. These two arguments made it feasible to conduct the experiment.

The first type of argument is especially interesting. It is a new kind of argument endowing mathematical statements with a probability. This probability cannot be accounted for in ontological terms according to which any statement is true, or false, in all possible worlds. Having modified the concept of proof to include computer-assisted proofs, we might want to modify it again to include the kind of probabilistic argument required to set up a computer experiment. In practice this would amount to permitting mathematicians to make such arguments as part of their mathematical work. That is, it might be counted as a significant mathematical step if someone were to argue that a certain statement is very likely to be true, while leaving it to someone else to design and run the actual computer experiment. We must take this possibility much more seriously after the work of Appel and Haken, who established that such probabilistic arguments can have an important function in mathematics.

On the other hand, such probabilistic arguments inevitably contain the possibility of error; they can go wrong in a way strict proofs cannot.

> To use the computer as an essential tool in their proofs, mathematicians will be forced to give up hope of verifying proofs by hand, just as scientific observations made with a microscope or telescope do not admit direct tactile confirmation. By the same token, however, computer-assisted mathematical proof can reach a much larger range of phenomena. There is a price for this sort of knowledge. It cannot be absolute. But the loss of innocence has always entailed a relativistic world view; there is no progress without risk of error (Kainen and Saaty, 98).

These shifts in the concept of proof initiated by the 4CT force us to reevaluate the role of formal proofs in the philosophy of mathematics. Of course such shifts cast no doubt whatever on the legitimacy of formal proof theory as a branch of mathematical logic. Formal proofs, as idealized abstraction, still figure in our account of the 4CT. Nevertheless, after the 4CT, formal proofs cannot continue to serve the philosophy of mathematics as the sole paradigm of mathematical activity. Philosophers and mathematicians have already noted the limitations of the formal paradigm, but the 4CT aggravates these limitations to the point of a problem.[14] The old idea that a proof is a thought-experiment suggests itself here. There is not such an apparent gulf between thought-experiments and computer-experiments as there is between formal proofs and experiments. On the other hand, there is not such a gulf between thought-experiments in mathematics and thought-experiments in physics either.

The primary impact of the new four-color problem in the philosophy of mathematics is on the concept of proof. We have discussed some of the consequences here.[15]

The relevance of the new four-color problem to the philosophy of science is largely a reworking of the earlier consequences. It is especially relevant to that branch of the philosophy of science which looks upon science as diachronic, or developing over time. In particular, it is relevant to the concept of paradigm outlined by Thomas Kuhn.[16] Paradigms, according to

Kuhn, are scientific achievements that some scientific community accepts as supplying a foundation for its further practice. To qualify as a paradigm, the achievement must be both "sufficiently unprecedented to attract an enduring group of adherents away from competing modes of scientific activity" and "sufficiently open-ended to leave all sorts of problems for the redefined group of practitioners to resolve" (10). The concept of paradigms plays an important role in Kuhn's explanation of the development of science. It is natural to wonder whether the methodology leading to the 4CT can serve as a paradigm in mathematics: Kainen and Saaty have suggested that it will. "In fact, the Appel-Haken methodology suggests a new paradigm for mathematics. This paradigm includes the traditional elements of intuition and standard logic, as well as heuristic and probabilistic techniques combined with the high order computational abilities of a modern computer" (96).

Looking at the 4CT from the viewpoint of paradigms and thereby placing it in a historical perspective can be very illuminating. I suggest that if a "similar" proof had been developed twenty-five years earlier, it would not have achieved the widespread acceptance that the 4CT has now. The hypothetical early result would probably have been ignored, possibly even attacked (one thinks of the early reaction to the work of Frege and of Cantor). A necessary condition for the acceptance of a computer-assisted proof is wide familiarity on the part of mathematicians with sophisticated computers. Now that every mathematician has a pocket calculator and every mathematics department has a computer specialist, that familiarity obtains. The mathematicial world was ready to recognize the Appel-Haken methodology as legitimate mathematics.

Before we can satisfactorily describe the 4CT in terms of paradigms, however, there are two obstacles that must be overcome. The concept of paradigm has been developed primarily for the natural sciences with some extensions to the social sciences. We would first have to extend the notion of paradigm to mathematics, both by example and by explanation of the nature of mathematical paradigms.[17] Many philosophers would resist the extension of paradigms to mathematics, of course. In the current philosophy of mathematics, mathematics is viewed solely as a synchronic or timeless structure. Against this position it might be argued that it is simply working out of another paradigm of mathematics, the formal paradigm provided by Cantor, Frege, Russell, and Hilbert. The controversy will be decided, in part, by whether the paradigm model of mathematics can provide a more satisfactory account of achievements like the 4CT than can the formal model.

A second difficulty in extending the notion of paradigm to mathematics is historical. Paradigms are defined in terms of their past performance; they are achievements that had a major effect on the development of their fields. It is one thing to characterize an achievement as a paradigm on the basis of the historical record. It is quite another to predict that a recent achievement will function as a paradigm on the basis of the limited data currently available. It is clear that claims of the second kind must be much more tentative. However, if any such claims succeed, they are likely to provide much more information to the metatheory of paradigms than is provided by the simple classification based on the historical record. Although there are obstacles to treating the 4CT as providing a new paradigm for mathematics, any attempts to solve these problems can be important exercises in the philosophy of science.

Mathematicians have solved their four-color problem, but there is a new four-color problem that has arisen for philosophy. I have tried to explain what this problem is and how it arises. I have argued for it philosophical significance by noting some of the consequences that our acceptance of the 4CT has for the theory of knowledge, the philosophy of mathematics, and the philosophy of science.

ACKNOWLEDGMENTS

I would like to thank Michael Albertson, Joan Hutchinson, and William Marsh for reading a draft of this paper and for some helpful discussions on a number of points.

NOTES

1. "Every Planar Map Is Four Colorable," *Illinois Journal of Mathematics,* XXI, 84 (September 1977): 429–567. Part I, on Discharging, is by Appel and Haken; part II, on Reducibility, was done in conjunction with Koch. Parenthetical page references to Appel, Haken, and Koch, will be to this article.

2. "Solvability of Groups of Odd Order," *Pacific Journal of Mathematics,* XIII (1963): 775–1029. It is important to realize that, despite its exceptional length, this proof was surveyed from start to finish by mathematicians including Feit, Thompson, and perhaps several dozen leading group theorists.

3. See, for example, Arend Heyting, *Intuitionism* (Amsterdam: North-Holland, 1966), ch. I.

4. "Modern Mathematics: An Educational and Philosophical Error?" *American Scientist,* LIX, 6 (November/December 1971): 695–699.

5. To be sure, not all philosophers hold these beliefs, but they are common enough to warrant criticism. Some philosophers have argued against them, notably Imre Lakatos in *Proofs and Refutations* (New York: Cambridge: 1976) and Hilary Putnam in *Mathematics, Matter and Method* (New York: Cambridge, 1975). Putnam, in particular, explicitly rejects the traditional view of mathematics as an absolutely a priori discipline set apart from natural science. He suggests replacing it with the view of mathematics as *quasi-empirical.* The present paper provides additional support for the thesis that mathematics is quasi-empirical.

6. For a simple account of the proof, see Appel and Haken, "The Solution of the Four Color Map Problem," *Scientific American,* CXXXVII, 8 (October 1977): 108–121. (Parenthetical page references to Appel and Haken are to this article; similarly for the authors cited below.) More detailed summaries can be found in Haken, "An Attempt to Understand the Four Color Problem" and F. Bernhart, "A Digest of the Four Color Theorem," both published in the *Journal of Graph Theory,* I (1977): 193–206 and 207–225, respectively. P. Kainen and T. Saaty provide an account of the theorem along with the required basis in graph theory in *The Four Color Problem: Assaults and Conquest* (New York: McGraw Hill, 1977). The definitive statement of the proof appears in Appel, Haken, and Koch, op. cit.

7. "The Reducibility of Maps," *American Journal of Mathematics*, XXXV (1913): 114–128.

8. "Toward Mechanical Mathematics" in K. Sayre and F. Cooson, eds., *The Modeling of the Mind* (Notre Dame, Ind.: University Press, 1963), pp. 91–120. J. Weizenbaum, *Computer Power and Human Reason* (San Francisco: W.H. Freeman, 1976), pp. 230/I.

9. Appel, Haken, and Koch, part I, sec. 5; Bernhart, p. 224.

10. A.N. Whitehead, *Science and the Modern World* (New York: New American Library, 1959), p. 25.

11. S. Körner, *The Philosophy of Mathematics* (New York: Harper, 1960), p. 9.

12. See the qualifications expressed on page 254 of this paper, at the end of sec. II.

13. "Naming and Necessity," in D. Davidson and G. Harman, eds., *Semantics of Natural Language* (Boston: Reidel, 1972), p. 261.

14. See, for example, Lakatos, op. cit.

15. For another approach that focuses on the idea of "difficult proof" and its relation to incompleteness results, see Haken, op. cit.

16. *The Structure of Scientific Revolutions* (Chicago: University Press, 1962).

17. Much material useful for this enterprise can be found in the works of Lakatos and in Raymond Wilder, *Evolution of Mathematical Concepts* (New York: Wiley, 1968).

RICHARD DE MILLO, RICHARD LIPTON, ALAN PERLIS

Social Processes and Proofs of Theorems and Programs

De Millo, Lipton and Perlis approach the topic of computers and mathematics from a very different direction than the previous essay. Their immediate topic is the developing discipline of program verification. The often espoused aim of that discipline is to develop general techniques for proving programs, that is, for giving mathematical proofs that particular programs are correct, or incorrect. Hence, philosophical conceptions of what mathematics is can shape conceptions of what program verification should be. According to the present authors, many, if not most, exponents of program verification adopt a foundational, especially a formalist account of mathematics.

These authors, in contrast, adopt a quasi-empirical account of mathematics although they do not label it as such. Instead they do describe mathematical proof in terms of general features of mathematical practice, a description that owes much to Lakatos. Their account, though brief, is quite suggestive and has occasioned considerable comment among mathematicians. De Millo, Lipton, and Perlis proceed to use their quasi-empirical account of mathematics to argue for an alternative approach to program verification. Their suggestion is that program verification is more like engineering and less like mathematical logic than is usually supposed. The fundamental aim of program verification, according to these authors, should be to make programs more reliable rather than to prove that programs are (absolutely) correct or incorrect.

The motivating insight of the essay is that proofs—the actual proofs that appear in mathematical practice—must be convincing; otherwise they wouldn't be recognized. It is hardly a new insight. In 1739, Hume wrote that

> There is no Algebraist nor Mathematician so expert in his science, as to place entire confidence in any truth immediately upon his discovery of it, or regard it as any thing, but a mere probability. Every time he runs over his proofs, his confidence encreases; but still more by the approbation of his friends; and is rais'd to its utmost perfection by the universal assent and applauses of the learned world.[1]

From Communications of the ACM, Vol. 22, No. 5, May 1979, pp. 271-280.

Despite its apparent obviousness, this social aspect of proofs is often dismissed as philosophically irrelevant. It is objected that almost anything could count as convincing in the right set of circumstances—just imagine suitable reinforcements, propaganda, prejudice, and so on. In reply, the present authors argue that conviction in mathematics is obtained by a highly evolved set of processes with very little arbitrariness about them. These general features of mathematical practice winnow out bad proofs. They include an initial series of checks on publications, which still manage to issue in roughly 200,000 theorems per year, some false and most eminently forgettable. After that series, another complex set of processes are applied to select useful theorems, attractive theorems, or at least memorable theorems.

Such processes are an integral part of mathematical practice and are familiar to every mathematician. Of course they don't appear in the idealized accounts of practice that foundationalists accept. Moreover, the social processes are arranged so as to confer a very high degree of probability to any proofs that survive all the stages. In fact, we can argue that they yield proofs that are actually *more* reliable than formal proofs strictly conceived. Any formal proof is invalid if even one single step is illegitimate. Since strict formal proofs are quite long and lacking in perspicuity, the potential for error can be quite large. In addition, even a rigorously correct formal proof must presuppose the consistency of the overarching formal system for the truth of its conclusion (Frege's Bane). Once again, even a slight error in the system can invalidate all proofs contained in it. On the other hand, good informal proofs, those meeting the criteria set forth by De Millo, Lipton, and Perlis, are very 'resilient' and well suited to surviving various kinds of errors.

Having recognized 'convincingness' as an essential feature of mathematical proofs, the authors go on to criticize the naive goal of proving programs. Even if suitable formal proofs of programs existed in theory, it is argued, they could not possibly serve to convince anyone of the correctness of the programs in question. Perhaps the merits of this conclusion are best left to computer scientists to decide, but the conception of mathematics that motivates it has a claim on all readers of this volume.

NOTE

1. Hume, *A Treatise of Human Nature*, Oxford University Press, Oxford (1964), 180–181.

• • • • •

> I should like to ask the same question that Descartes asked. You are proposing to give a precise definition of logical correctness which is to be the same as my vague intuitive feeling for logical correctness. How do you intend to show that they are the same?
> . . . The average mathematician should not forget that intuition is the final authority.
>
> J. BARKLEY ROSSER

Many people have argued that computer programming should strive to become more like mathematics. Maybe so, but not in the way they seem to think. The aim of program verification, an attempt to make programming more mathematics-like, is to increase dramatically one's confidence in the correct functioning of a piece of software, and the device that verifiers use to achieve this goal is a long chain of formal, deductive logic. In mathematics, the aim is to increase one's confidence in the correctness of a theorem, and it's true that one of the devices mathematicians *could* in theory use to achieve this goal is a long chain of formal logic. But in fact they don't. What they use is a proof, a very different animal. Nor does the proof settle the matter; contrary to what its name suggests, a proof is only one step in the direction of confidence. We believe that, in the end, it is a social process that determines whether mathematicians feel confident about a theorem—and we believe that, because no comparable social process can take place among program verifiers, program verification is bound to fail. We can't see how it's going to be able to affect anyone's confidence about programs.

Outsiders see mathematics as a cold, formal, logical, mechanical, monolithic process of sheer intellection; we argue that insofar as it is successful, mathematics is a social, informal, intuitive, organic, human process, a community project. Within the mathematical community, the view of mathematics as logical and formal was elaborated by Bertrand Russell and David Hilbert in the first years of this century. They saw mathematics as proceeding in principle from axioms or hypotheses to theorems by steps, each step easily justifiable from its predecessors by a strict rule of transformation, the rules of transformation being few and fixed. The *Principia Mathematica* was the crowning achievement of the formalists. It was also the deathblow for the formalist view. There is no contradiction here: Russell did succeed in showing that ordinary working proofs can be reduced to formal, symbolic deductions. But he failed, in three enormous, taxing volumes, to get beyond the elementary facts of arithmetic. He showed what can be done in principle and what cannot be done in practice. If the mathematical process were really one of strict, logical progression, we would still be counting on our fingers.

BELIEVING THEOREMS AND PROOFS

> Indeed every mathematician knows that a proof has not been "understood" if one has done nothing more than verify step by step the correctness of the deductions of which it is composed and has not tried to gain a clear insight into the ideas which have led to the construction of this particular chain of deductions in preference to every other one.
>
> N. BOURBAKI

> Agree with me if I seem to speak the truth.
>
> SOCRATES

Stanislaw Ulam estimates that mathematicians publish 200,000 theorems every year [20]. A number of these are subsequently contradicted or otherwise disallowed, others are thrown into doubt, and most are ignored. Only a tiny fraction come to be understood and believed by any sizable group of mathematicians.

The theorems that get ignored or discredited are seldom the work of crackpots or incompetents. In 1879, Kempe [11] published a proof of the four-color conjecture that stood for eleven years before Heawood [8] uncovered a fatal flaw in the reasoning. The first collaboration between Hardy and Littlewood resulted in a paper they delivered at the June 1911 meeting of the London Mathematical Society; the paper was never published because they subsequently discovered that their proof was wrong [4]. Cauchy, Lamé, and Kummer all thought at one time or another that they had proved Fermat's Last Theorem [3]. In 1945, Rademacher thought he had solved the Riemann Hypothesis; his results not only circulated in the mathematical world but were announced in *Time* magazine [3].

Recently we found the following group of footnotes appended to a brief historical sketch of some independence results in set theory [10]:

(1) The result of Problem 11 contradicts the results announced by Levy [1963b]. Unfortunately, the construction presented there cannot be completed.

(2) The transfer to *ZF* was also claimed by Marek [1966] but the outlined method appears to be unsatisfactory and has not been published.

(3) A contradicting result was announced and later withdrawn by Truss [1970].

(4) The example in Problem 22 is a counterexample to another condition of Mostowski, who conjectured its sufficiency and singled out this example as a test case.

(5) The independence result contradicts the claim of Felgner [1969] that the Cofinality Principle implies the Axiom of Choice. An error has been found by Morris (see Felgner's corrections to [1969]).

The author has no axe to grind; he has probably never even heard of the current controversy in programming; and it is clearly no part of his concern to hold his friends and colleagues up to scorn. There is simply no way to describe the history of mathematical ideas without describing the successive social processes at work in proofs. The point is not that mathematicians make mistakes; that goes without saying. The point is that mathematicians' errors are corrected, not by formal symbolic logic, but by other mathematicians.

Just increasing the number of mathematicians working on a given problem does not necessarily insure believable proofs. Recently, two independent groups of topologists, one American, the other Japanese, independently announced results concerning the same kind of topological object, a thing called a homotopy group. The results turned out to be contradictory, and since both proofs involved complex symbolic and numerical calculation, it was not at all evident who had goofed. But the stakes were sufficiently high to justify pressing the issue, so the Japanese and American proofs were exchanged. Obviously, each group was highly motivated to discover an error in the other's proof; obviously, one proof or the other was incorrect. But neither the Japanese nor the American proof could be discredited. Subsequently, a third group of researchers obtained yet another proof, this time supporting the American result. The weight of the evidence now being against their proof, the Japanese have retired to consider the matter further.

There are actually two morals to this story. First, a proof does not in itself significantly raise our confidence in the probable truth of the theorem it purports to prove. Indeed, for the theorem about the homotopy group, the horribleness of all the proffered proofs suggests that the theorem itself requires rethinking. A second point to be made is that proofs consisting entirely of calculations are not necessarily correct.

Even simplicity, clarity, and ease provide no guarantee that a proof is correct. The history of attempts to prove the Parallel Postulate is a particularly rich source of lovely, trim proofs that turned out to be false. From Ptolemy to Legendre (who tried time and time again), the greatest geometricians of every age kept ramming their heads against Euclid's fifth postulate. What's worse, even though we now know that the postulate is indemonstrable, many of the faulty proofs are still so beguiling that in Heath's definitive commentary on Euclid [7] they are not allowed to stand alone; Heath marks them up with italics, footnotes, and explanatory marginalia, lest some young mathematician, thumbing through the volume, be misled.

The idea that a proof can, at best, only probably express truth makes an interesting connection with a recent mathematical controversy. In a recent issue of *Science* [12], Gina Bari Kolata suggested that the apparently secure notion of mathematical proof may be due for revision. Here the central question is not "How do theorems get believed?" but "What is it that we believe when we believe a theorem?" There are two relevant views, which can be roughly labeled classical and probabilistic.

The classicists say that when one believes mathematical statement A, one believes that in *principle* there is a correct, formal, valid, step by step, syntactically checkable deduction leading to A in a suitable logical calculus such as Zermelo-Fraenkel set theory or Peano arithmetic, a deduction of A à la the *Principia*, a deduction that completely formalizes the truth of A in the binary, Aristotelian notion of truth: "A proposition is true if it says of what is, that it is, and if it says of what is not, that it is not." This formal chain of reasoning is by no means the same thing as an everyday, ordinary mathematical proof. The classical view does not require that an ordinary proof be accompanied by its formal counterpart; on the contrary, there are mathematically sound reasons for allowing the gods to formalize most of our arguments. One theoretician estimates, for instance, that a formal demonstraiton of one of Ramanujan's conjectures assuming set theory and elementary analysis would take about two thousand pages; the length of a deduction from first principles is nearly inconceivable [14]. But the classicist believes that the formalization is in principle a possibility and that the truth it expresses is binary, either so or not so.

The probabilists argue that since any very long proof can at best be viewed as only probably correct, why not state theorems probabilistically and give probablistic proofs? The probabilistic proof may have the dual advantage of being technically easier than the classical, bivalent one, and may allow mathematicians to isolate the critical ideas that give rise to uncertainty in traditional, binary proofs. This process may even lead to a more plausible classical proof. An illustration of the probabilist approach is Michael Rabin's algorithm for testing probable primality [17]. For very large integers

N, all of the classical techniques for determining whether N is composite become unworkable. Using even the most clever programming, the calculations required to determine whether numbers larger than 10^{10^4} are prime require staggering amounts of computing time. Rabin's insight was that if you are willing to settle for a very good probability that N is prime (or not prime), then you can get it within a reasonable amount of time—and with vanishingly small probability of error.

In view of these uncertainties over what constitutes an acceptable proof, which is after all a fairly basic element of the mathematical process, how is it that mathematics has survived and been so successful? If proofs bear little resemblance to formal deductive reasoning, if they can stand for generations and then fall, if they can contain flaws that defy detection, if they can express only the probability of truth within certain error bounds—if they are, in fact, not able to *prove* theorems in the sense of guaranteeing them beyond probability and, if necessary, beyond insight, well, then, how does mathematics work? How does it succeed in developing theorems that are significant and that compel belief?

First of all, the proof of a theorem is a message. A proof is not a beautiful abstract object with an independent existence. No mathematician grasps a proof, sits back, and sighs happily at the knowledge that he can now be certain of the truth of his theorem. He runs out into the hall and looks for someone to listen to it. He bursts into a colleague's office and commandeers the blackboard. He throws aside his scheduled topic and regales a seminar with his new idea. He drags his graduate students away from their dissertations to listen. He gets onto the phone and tells his colleagues in Texas and Toronto. In its first incarnation, a proof is a spoken message, or at most a sketch on a chalkboard or a paper napkin.

That spoken stage is the first filter for a proof. If it generates no excitement or belief among his friends, the wise mathematician reconsiders it. But if they find it tolerably interesting and believable, he writes it up. After it has circulated in draft for a while, if it still seems plausible, he does a polished version and submits it for publication. If the referees also find it attractive and convincing, it gets published so that it can be read by a wider audience. If enough members of that larger audience believe it and like it, then after a suitable cooling-off period the reviewing publications take a more leisurely look, to see whether the proof is really as pleasing as it first appeared and whether, on calm consideration, they really believe it.

And what happens to a proof when it is believed? The most immediate process is probably an internalization of the result. That is, the mathematician who reads and believes a proof will attempt to paraphrase it, to put it in his own terms, to fit it into his own personal view of mathematical knowledge. No two mathematicians are likely to internalize a mathematical concept in exactly the same way, so this process leads usually to multiple versions of the same theorem, each reinforcing belief, each adding to the feeling of the mathematical community that the original statement is likely to be true. Gauss, for example, obtained at least half a dozen independent proofs of his "law of quadratic reciprocity"; to date over fifty proofs of this law are known. Imre Lakatos gives, in his *Proofs and Refutations* [13], historically accurate discussions of the transformations that several famous theorems underwent from initial conception to general acceptance. Lakatos demonstrates that Euler's formula $V - E + F = 2$ was reformulated again and again for almost two hundred years after its first statement, until it finally reached its current stable form. The most compelling transformation that can take place is generalization. If, by the same social process that works on the original theorem, the generalized theorem comes to be believed, then the original statement gains greatly in plausibility.

A believable theorem gets used. It may appear as a lemma in larger proofs; if it does not lead to contradictions, then we are all the more inclined to believe it. Or engineers may use it by plugging physical values into it. We have fairly high confidence in classical stress equations because we see bridges that stand; we have some confidence in the basic theorems of fluid mechanics because we see airplanes that fly.

Believable results sometimes make contact with other areas of mathematics—important ones invariably do. The successful transfer of a theorem or a proof technique from one branch of mathematics to another increases our feeling of confidence in it. In 1964, for example, Paul Cohen used a technique called forcing to prove a theorem in set theory [2]; at that time, his notions were so radical that the proof was hardly understood. But subsequently other investigators interpreted the notion of forcing in an algebraic context, connected it with more familiar ideas in logic, generalized the concepts, and found the generalizations useful. All of these connections (along with the other normal social processes that lead to acceptance) made the idea of forcing a good deal more compelling, and today forcing is routinely studied by graduate students in set theory.

After enough internalization, enough transformation, enough generalization, enough use, and enough connection, the mathematical community eventually decides that the central concepts in the original theorem, now perhaps greatly changed, have an ultimate stability. If the various proofs feel right and the results are examined from enough angles, then the truth of the theorem is eventually considered to be established. The theorem is thought to be true in the classical sense—that is, in the sense that it *could* be demonstrated by formal, deductive logic, although for almost all theorems no such deduction ever took place or ever will.

THE ROLE OF SIMPLICITY

> For what is clear and easily comprehended attracts; the complicated repels.
>
> DAVID HILBERT

> Sometimes one has to say difficult things, but one ought to say them as simply as one knows how.
>
> G.H. HARDY

As a rule, the most important mathematical problems are clean and easy to state. An important theorem is much more likely to take form A than form B.

A: Every ----- is a -----.
B: If ----- and ----- and ----- and ----- and ----- except for special cases
a) -----
b) -----
c) -----,

then unless
i) ----- or
ii) ----- or
iii) -----,
every ----- that satisfies ----- is a -----.

The problems that have most fascinated and tormented and delighted mathematicians over the centuries have been the simplest ones to state. Einstein held that the maturity of a scientific theory could be judged by how well it could be explained to the man on the street. The four-color theorem rests on such slender foundations that it can be stated with complete precision to a child. If the child has learned his multiplication tables, he can understand the problem of the location and distribution of the prime numbers. And the deep fascination of the problem of defining the concept of "number" might turn him into a mathematician.

The correlation between importance and simplicity is no accident. Simple, attractive theorems are the ones most likely to be heard, read, internalized, and used. Mathematicians use simplicity as the first test for a proof. Only if it looks interesting at first glance will they consider it in detail. Mathematicians are not altruistic masochists. On the contrary, the history of mathematics is one long search for ease and pleasure and elegance—in the realm of symbols, of course.

Even if they didn't want to, mathematicians would have to use the criterion of simplicity; it is a psychological impossibility to choose any but the simplest and most attractive of 200,000 candidates for one's attention. If there are important, fundamental concepts in mathematics that are not simple, mathematicians will probably never discover them.

Messy, ugly mathematical propositions that apply only to paltry classes of structures, idiosyncratic propositions, propositions that rely on inordinately expensive mathematical machinery, propositions that require five blackboards or a roll of paper towels to sketch—these are unlikely ever to be assimilated into the body of mathematics. And yet it is only by such assimilation that proofs gain believability. The proof by itself is nothing; only when it has been subjected to the social processes of the mathematical community does it become believable.

In this paper, we have tended to stress simplicity above all else because that is the first filter for any proof. But we do not wish to paint ourselves and our fellow mathematicians as philistines or brutes. Once an idea has met the criterion of simplicity, other standards help determine its place among the ideas that make mathematicians gaze off abstractedly into the distance. Yuri Manin [14] has put it best: A good proof is one that makes us wiser.

DISBELIEVING VERIFICATIONS

> On the contrary, I find nothing in logistic for the discoverer but shackles. It does not help us at all in the direction of conciseness, far from it; and if it requires twenty-seven equations to establish that 1 is a number, how many will it require to demonstrate a real theorem?
>
> HENRI POINCARÉ

> One of the chief duties of the mathematician in acting as an advisor to scientists . . . is to discourage them from expecting too much from mathematics.
>
> NORBERT WEINER

Mathematical proofs increase our confidence in the truth of mathematical statements only after they have been subjected to the social mechanisms of the mathematical community. These same mechanisms doom the so-called proofs of software, the long formal verifications that correspond, not to the working mathematical proof, but to the imaginary logical structure that the mathematician conjures up to describe his feeling of belief. Verifications are not messages; a person who ran out into the hall to communicate his latest verification would rapidly find himself a social pariah. Verifications cannot really be read; a reader can flay himself through one of the shorter ones by dint of heroic effort, but that's not reading. Being unreadable and—literally—unspeakable, verifications cannot be internalized, transformed, generalized, used, connected to other disciplines, and eventually incorporated into a community consciousness. They cannot acquire credibility gradually, as a mathematical theorem does; one either believes them blindly, as a pure act of faith, or not at all.

At this point, some adherents of verification admit that the analogy to mathematics fails. having argued that A, programming, resembles B, mathematics, and having subsequently learned that B is nothing like what they imagined, they wish to argue instead that A is like B′, their mythical version of B. We then find ourselves in the peculiar position of putting across the arugment that was originally theirs, asserting that yes, indeed, A does resemble B; our argument, however, matches the terms up differently from theirs. (See Figures 1 and 2.)

Mathematics	*Programming*
theorem . . .	program
proof . . .	verification

FIG. 1. The verifiers' original analogy.

Mathematics		*Programming*
theorem	. . .	specification
proof	. . .	program
imaginary formal demonstration	. . .	verification

Fig. 2. Our analogy.

Verifiers who wish to abandon the simile and substitute B′ should as an aid to understanding abandon the language of B as well—in partiuclar, it would help if they did not call their verifications "proofs." As for ourselves, we will continue to argue that programming is like mathematics, and that the same social processes that work in mathematical proofs doom verifications.

There is a fundamental logical objection to verification, an objection on its own ground of formalistic rigor. Since the requirement for a program is informal and the program is formal, there must be a transition, and the transition itself must necessarily be informal. We have been distressed to learn that this proposition, which seems self-evident to us, is controversial. So we should emphasize that as antiformalists, we would not object to verification on these grounds; we only wonder how this inherently informal step fits into the formalist view. Have the adherents of verification lost sight of the informal origins of the formal objects they deal with? Is it their assertion that their formalizations are somehow incontrovertible? We must confess our confusion and dismay.

Then there is another logical difficulty, nearly as basic, and by no means so hair-splitting as the one above: The formal demonstration that a program is consistent with its specifications has value only if the specifications and the program are independently derived. In the toy-program atmosphere of experimental verification, this criterion is easily met. But in real life, if during the design process a program fails, it is changed, and the changes are based on knowledge of its specifications; or the specifications are changed, and those changes are based on knowledge of the program gained through the failure. In either case, the requirement of having independent criteria to check against each other is no longer met. Again, we hope that no one would suggest that programs and specifications should not be repeatedly modified during the design process. That would be a position of incredible poverty—the sort of poverty that does, we fear, result from infatuation with formal logic.

Back in the real world, the kinds of input/output specifications that accompany production software are seldom simple. They tend to be long and complex and peculiar. To cite an extreme case, computing the payroll for the French National Railroad requires more than 3,000 pay rates (one uphill, one downhill, and so on). The specifications for any reasonable compiler or operating system fill volumes—and no one believes that they are complete. There are even some cases of black-box code, numerical algorithms that can be shown to work in the sense that they are used to build real airplanes or drill real oil wells, but work for no reason that anyone knows; the input assertions for these algorithms are not even formulable, let alone formalizable. To take just one example, an important algorithm with the rather jaunty name of Reverse Cuthill-McKee was known for years to be far better than plain Cuthill-McKee, known empirically, in laboratory tests and field trials and in production. Only recently, however, has its superiority been theoretically demonstrable [6], and even then only with the usual informal mathematical proof, not with a formal deduction. During all of the years when Reverse Cuthill-McKee was unproved, even though it automatically made any program in which it appeared unverifiable, programmers perversely went on using it.

It might be countered that while real-life specifications are lengthy and complicated, they are not deep. Their verifications are, in fact, nothing more than extremely long chains of substitutions to be checked with the aid of simple algebraic identities.

All we can say in response to this is: Precisely. Verifications are long and involved but shallow; that's what's wrong with them. The verification of even a puny program can run into dozens of pages, and there's not a light moment or a spark of wit on any of those pages. Nobody is going to run into a friend's office with a program verification. Nobody is going to sketch a verification out on a paper napkin. Nobody is going to buttonhole a colleague into listening to a verification. Nobody is ever going to read it. One can feel one's eyes glaze over at the very thought.

It has been suggested that very high level languages, which can deal directly with a broad range of mathematical objects or functional languages, which it is said can be concisely axiomatized, might be used to insure that a verification would be interesting and therefore responsive to a social process like the social process of mathematics.

In theory this idea sounds hopeful; in practice, it doesn't work out. For example, the following verification condition arises in the proof of a fast Fourier transform written in MADCAP, a very high level language [18]:

If $S \in \{1, -1\}$, $b = \exp(2\pi i S/N)$, r is an integer, $N = 2^r$,

(1) $C = \{2j: 0 \leq j < N/4\}$ and

(2) $a = < a_r: a_r = b^{r \bmod (N/2)}, 0 \leq r < N/2 >$ and

(3) $A = \{j: j \bmod N < N/2, 0 \leq j < N\}$ and

(4) $A^* = \{j: 0 \leq j < N\} - A$ and

(5) $F = < f_r: f_r = \sum_{k_i \in R_n} k\,(b^{k_1 [r/2^{r-1}] \bmod N}),\ R_r = \{j: (j - r) \bmod (N/2) = 0\} >$ and $k \leq r$

then

(1) $A \cap (A + 2^{r-k-1}) = \{x: x \bmod 2^{r-k} < 2^{r-k-1}, 0 \leq x < N\}$

(2) $< \alpha_c \quad \alpha_c > = < \alpha_r: \alpha_r = b^{r2^k \bmod (N/2)}, 0 \leq r < N/2 >$

(3) $< (F_{A \cap (A+2^{r-k-1})} + F_{\{j: 0 \leq j < N\} - A \cap (A+2^{r-k-1})}) \ (< \alpha_c \quad \alpha_c >$

$*(F_{A \cap (A+2^{r-k-1})} + F_{\{j: 0 \leq j < N\} - A \cap (A+2^{r-k-1})})) >$

$= < f_r: f_r = \sum_{k_1 \in R_r} k_1 (b^{[r/2^{r-k-1}] j \bmod N}),$

$R_r = \{j: (j - r) \bmod 2^{r-k-1} = 0\} >$

$$(4) \quad < \rhd (F_A + F_{A*}) \rhd a^*(F_A - F_{A*}) > \; = \; < f_r \colon f_r = \sum_{k_1 \epsilon R_r} k_1 (b^{k_1 [r/2^{r-1}] \mathrm{mod} N}), \quad R_r = \{j \colon (j - r) \mathrm{mod}(N/2) = 0\} >$$

This is not what we would call pleasant reading.

Some verifiers will concede that verification is simply unworkable for the vast majority of programs but argue that for a few crucial applications the agony is worthwhile. They point to air-traffic control, missile systems, and the exploration of space as areas in which the risks are so high that any expenditure of time and effort can be justified.

Even if this were so, we would still insist that verification renounce its claim on all other areas of programming; to teach students in introductory programming courses how to do verification, for instance, ought to be as far-fetched as teaching students in introductory biology how to do open-heart surgery. But the stakes do not affect our belief in the basic impossibility of verifying any system large enough and flexible enough to do any real-world task. No matter how high the payoff, no one will ever be able to force himself to read the incredibly long, tedious verifications of real-life systems, and unless they can be read, understood, and refined, the verifications are worthless.

Now, it might be argued that all these references to readability and internalization are irrelevant, that the aim of verification is eventually to construct an automatic verifying system.

Unfortunately there is a wealth of evidence that fully automated verifying systems are out of the question. The lower bounds on the length of formal demonstrations for mathematical theorems are immense [19], and there is no reason to believe that such demonstrations for programs would be any shorter or cleaner—quite the contrary. In fact, even the strong adherents of program verification do not take seriously the possibility of totally automated verifiers. Ralph London, a proponent of verification, speaks of an out-to-lunch system, one that could be left unsupervised to grind out verifications; but he doubts that such a system can be built to work with reasonable reliability. One group, despairing of automation in the foreseeable future, has proposed that verifications should be performed by teams of "grunt mathematicians," low level mathematical teams who will check verification conditions. The sensibilities of people who could make such a proposal seem odd, but they do serve to indicate how remote the possibility of automated verification must be.

Suppose, however, that an automatic verifier could somehow be built. Suppose further that programmers did somehow come to have faith in its verifications. In the absence of any real-world basis for such belief, it would have to be blind faith, but no matter. Suppose that the philosopher's stone had been found, that lead could be changed to gold, and that programmers were convinced of the merits of feeding their programs into the gaping jaws of a verifier. It seems to us that the scenario envisioned by the proponents of verification goes something like this: The programmer inserts his 300-line input/output package into the verifier. Several hours later, he returns. There is his 20,000-line verification and the message "VERIFIED."

There is a tendency, as we begin to feel that a structure is logically, provably right, to remove from it whatever redundancies we originally built in because of lack of understanding. Taken to its extreme, this tendency brings on the so-called Titanic effect; when failure does occur, it is massive and uncontrolled. To put it another way, the severity with which a system fails is directly proportional to the intensity of the designer's belief that it cannot fail. Programs designed to be clean and tidy merely so that they can be verified will be particularly susceptible to the Titanic effect. Already we see signs of this phenomenon. In their notes on Euclid [16], a language designed for program verification, several of the foremost verification adherents say, "Because we expect all Euclid programs to be verified, we have not made special provisions for exception handling . . . Runtime software errors should not occur in verified programs." Errors should not occur? Shades of the ship that shouldn't be sunk.

So, having for the moment suspended all rational disbelief, let us suppose that the programmer gets the message "VERIFIED." And let us suppose further that the message does not result from a failure on the part of the verifying system. What does the programmer know? He knows that his program is formally, logically, provably, certifiably correct. He does not know, however, to what extent it is reliable, dependable, trustworthy, safe; he does not know within what limits it will work; he does not know what happens when it exceeds those limits. And yet he has that mystical stamp of approval: "VERIFIED." We can almost see the iceberg looming in the background over the unsinkable ship.

Luckily, there is little reason to fear such a future. Picture the same programmer returning to find the same 20,000 lines. What message would he really find, supposing that an automatic verifier could really be built? Of course, the message would be "NOT VERIFIED." The programmer would make a change, feed the program in again, return again. "NOT VERIFIED." Again he would make a change, again he would feed the program to the verifier, again "NOT VERIFIED." A program is a human artifact; a real-life program is a complex human artifact; and any human artifact of sufficient size and complexity is imperfect. The message will never read "VERIFIED."

THE ROLE OF CONTINUITY

> We may say, roughly, that a mathematical idea is "significant" if it can be connected, in a natural and illuminating way, with a large complex of other mathematical ideas.
>
> G.H. HARDY

The only really fetching defense ever offered for verification is the scaling-up argument. As best we can reproduce it, here is how it goes:

(1) Verification is now in its infancy. At the moment, the largest tasks it can handle are verifications of algorithms like FIND and model programs like GCD. It will in time be able to tackle more and more complicated algorithms and trickier and trickier model programs. These verifications are comparable to mathematical proofs. They are read. They generate the same kinds of in-

terest and excitement that theorems do. They are subject to the ordinary social processes that work on mathematical reasoning, or on reasoning in any other discipline, for that matter.

(2) Big production systems are made up of nothing more than algorithms and model programs. Once verified, algorithms and model programs can make up large, workaday production systems, and the (admittedly unreadable) verification of a big system will be the sum of the many small, attractive, interesting verifications of its components.

With (1) we have no quarrel. Actually, algorithms were proved and the proofs read and discussed and assimilated long before the invention of computers—and with a striking lack of formal machinery. Our guess is that the study of algorithms and model programs will develop like any other mathematical activity, chiefly by informal, social mechanisms, very little if at all by formal mechanisms.

It is with (2) that we have our fundamental disagreement. We argue that there is no continuity between the world of FIND or GCD and the world of production software, billing systems that write real bills, scheduling systems that schedule real events, ticketing systems that issue real tickets. And we argue that the world of production software is itself discontinuous.

No programmer would agree that large production systems are composed of nothing more than algorithms and small programs. Patches, ad hoc constructions, bandaids and tourniquets, bells and whistles, glue, spit and polish, signature code, blood-sweat-and-tears, and, of course, the kitchen sink—the colorful jargon of the practicing programmer seems to be saying something about the nature of the structures he works with; maybe theoreticians ought to be listening to him. It has been estimated that more than half the code in any real production system consists of user interfaces and error messages—ad hoc, informal structures that are by definition unverifiable. Even the verifiers themselves sometimes seem to realize the unverifiable nature of most real software. C.A.R. Hoare has been quoted [9] as saying, "In many applications, algorithm plays almost no role, and certainly presents almost no problem." (We wish we could report that he thereupon threw up his hands and abandoned verification, but no such luck.)

Or look at the difference between the world of GCD and the world of production software in another way: The specifications for algorithms are concise and tidy, while the specifications for real-world systems are immense, frequently of the same order of magnitude as the systems themselves. The specifications for algorithms are highly stable, stable over decades or even centuries; the specifications for real systems vary daily or hourly (as any programmer can testify). The specifications for algorithms are exportable, general; the specifications for real systems are idiosyncratic and ad hoc. These are not differences in degree. They are differences in kind. Babysitting for a sleeping child for one hour does not scale up to raising a family of ten—the problems are essentially, fundamentally different.

And within the world of real production software there is no continuity either. The scaling-up argument seems to be based on the fuzzy notion that the world of programming is like the world of Newtonian physics—made up of smooth, continuous functions. But, in fact, programs are jagged and full of holes and caverns. Every programmer knows that altering a line or sometimes even a bit can utterly destroy a program or mutilate it in ways that we do not understand and cannot predict. And yet at other times fairly substantial changes seem to alter nothing; the folklore is filled with stories of pranks and acts of vandalism that frustrated the perpetrators by remaining forever undetected.

There is a classic science-fiction story about a time traveler who goes back to the primeval jungles to watch dinosaurs and then returns to find his own time altered almost beyond recognition. Politics, architecture, language—even the plants and animals seem wrong, distorted. Only when he removes his time-travel suit does he understand what has happened. On the heel of his boot, carried away from the past and therefore unable to perform its function in the evolution of the world, is crushed the wing of a butterfly. Every programmer knows the sensation: A trivial, minute change wreaks havoc in a massive system. Until we know more about programming, we had better for all practical purposes think of systems as composed, not of sturdy structures like algorithms and smaller programs, but of butterflies' wings.

The discontinuous nature of programming sounds the death knell for verification. A sufficiently fanatical researcher might be willing to devote two or three years to verifying a significant piece of software if he could be assured that the software would remain stable. But real-life programs need to be maintained and modified. There is no reason to believe that verifying a modified program is any easier than verifying the original the first time around. There is no reason to believe that a big verification can be the sum of many small verifications. There is no reason to believe that a verification can transfer to any other program—not even to a program only one single line different from the original.

And it is this discontinuity that obviates the possibility of refining verifications by the sorts of social processes that refine mathematical proofs. The lone fanatic might construct his own verification, but he would never have any reason to read anyone else's, nor would anyone else ever be willing to read his. No community could develop. Even the most zealous verifier could be induced to read a verification only if he thought he might be able to use or borrow or swipe something from it. Nothing could force him to read someone else's verification once he had grasped the point that no verification bears any necessary connection to any other verification.

BELIEVING SOFTWARE

> The program itself is the only complete description of what the program will do.
>
> P.J. Davis

Since computers can write symbols and move them about with negligible expenditure of energy, it is tempting to leap to the conclusion that anything is possible in the symbolic realm. But reality does not yield so easily; physics does not suddenly break down. It is no more possible to construct symbolic structures without using resources than it is to construct material structures without using them. For even the most trivial mathematical theories, there are simple statements whose formal demonstrations would be impossibly long. Albert Meyer's outstanding lecture on the history of such research [15] concludes with a striking interpretation of how hard it may be to deduce even fairly simple mathematical statements. Suppose that we encode logical formulas as binary strings and set out to build a computer that will decide the truth of a simple set of formulas of length, say, at most a thousand bits. Suppose that we even allow ourselves the luxury of a technology that will produce proton-size electronic components connected by infinitely thin wires. Even so, the computer we design must densely fill the entire observable universe. This precise observation about the length of formal deductions agrees with our intuition about the amount of detail embedded in ordinary, workaday mathematical proofs. We often use "Let us assume, without loss of generality . . . " or "Therefore, by renumbering, if necessary . . . " to replace enormous amounts of formal detail. To insist on the formal detail would be a silly waste of resources. Both symbolic and material structures must be engineered with a very cautious eye. Resources are limited; time is limited; energy is limited. Not even the computer can change the finite nature of the universe.

We assume that these constraints have prevented the adherents of verification from offering what might be fairly convincing evidence in support of their methods. The lack at this late date of even a single verification of a working system has sometimes been attributed to the youth of the field. The verifiers argue, for instance, that they are only now beginning to understand loop invariants. At first blush, this sounds like another variant of the scaling-up argument. But in fact there are large classes of real-life systems with virtually no loops—they scarcely ever occur in commercial programming applications. And yet there has never been a verification of, say, a Cobol system that prints real checks; lacking even one makes it seem doubtful that there could at some time in the future be many. Resources, and time, and energy are just as limited for verifiers as they are for all the rest of us.

We must therefore come to grips with two problems that have occupied engineers for many generations: First, people must plunge into activities that they do not understand. Second, people cannot create perfect mechanisms.

How then do engineers manage to create reliable structures? First, they use social processes very like the social processes of mathematics to achieve successive approximations at understanding. Second, they have a mature and realistic view of what "reliable" means; in particular, the one thing it never means is "perfect." There is no way to deduce logically that bridges stand, or that airplanes fly, or that power stations deliver electricity. True, no bridges would fall, no airplanes would crash, no electrical systems black out if engineers would first demonstrate their perfection before building them—true because they would never be built at all.

The analogy in programming is any functioning, useful, real-world system. Take for instance an organi-chemical synthesizer called SYNCHEM [5]. For this program, the criterion of reliability is particularly straightforward—if it synthesizes a chemical, it works; if it doesn't, it doesn't work. No amount of correctness could ever hope to improve on this standard; indeed, it is not at all clear how one could even begin to formalize such a standard in a way that would lend itself to verification. But it is a useful and continuing enterprise to try to increase the number of chemicals the program can synthesize.

It is nothing but symbol chauvinism that makes computer scientists think that our structures are so much more important than material structures that (a) they should be perfect, and (b) the energy necessary to make them perfect should be expended. We argue rather that (a) they cannot be perfect, and (b) energy should not be wasted in the futile attempt to make them perfect. It is no accident that the probabilistic view of mathematical truth is closely allied to the engineering notion of reliability. Perhaps we should make a sharp distinction between program reliability and program perfection—and concentrate our efforts on reliability.

The desire to make programs correct is constructive and valuable. But the monolithic view of verification is blind to the benefits that could result from accepting a standard of correctness like the standard of correctness for real mathematical proofs, or a standard of reliability like the standard for real engineering structures. The quest for workability within economic limits, the willingness to channel innovation by recycling successful design, the trust in the functioning of a community of peers—all the mechanisms that make engineering and mathematics really work are obscured in the fruitless search for perfect verifiability.

What elements could contribute to making programming more like engineering and mathematics? One mechanism that can be exploited is the creation of general structures whose specific instances become more reliable as the reliability of the general structure increases.[1] This notion has appeared in several incarnations, of which Knuth's insistence on creating and understanding generally useful algorithms is one of the most important and encouraging. Baker's team-programming methodology [1] is an explicit attempt to expose software to social processes. If reusability becomes a criterion for effective design, a wider and wider community will examine the most common programming tools.

The concept of verifiable software has been with us too long to be easily displaced. For the practice of programming, however, verifiability must not be allowed to overshadow reliability. Scientists should not confuse mathematical models with reality—and verification is nothing but a model of believability. Verifiability is not and cannot be a dominating concern in software design. Economics, deadlines, cost-benefit ratios, personal and group style, the limits of acceptable error—all these carry immensely much more weight in design than verifiability or nonverifiability.

So far, there has been little philosophical discussion of making software reliable rather than verifiable. If verification adherents could redefine their efforts and reorient themselves to this goal, or if another view of software could arise that would draw on the social processes of mathematics and the modest expectations of engineering, the interests of real-life programming and theoretical computer science might both be better served.

Even if, for some reason that we are not now able to understand, we should be proved wholly wrong and the verifiers wholly right, this is not the moment to restrict research on programming. We know too little now to sense what directions will be most fruitful. If our reasoning convinces no one, if verification still seems an avenue worth exploring, so be it; we three can only try to argue against verification, not blast it off the face of the earth. But we implore our friends and colleagues not to narrow their vision to this one view no matter how promising it may seem. Let it not be the only view, the only avenue. Jacob Bronowski has an important insight about a time in the history of another discipline that may be similar to our own time in the development of computing: "A science which orders its thought too early is stifled . . . The hope of the medieval alchemists that the elements might be changed was not as fanciful as we once thought. But it was merely damaging to a chemistry which did not yet understand the composition of water and common salt."

ACKNOWLEDGMENTS

We especially wish to thank those who gave us public forums—the 4th POPL program committee for giving us our first chance; Bob Taylor and Jim Morris for letting us express our views in a discussion at Zerox PARC; L. Zadeh and Larry Rowe for doing the same at the Computer Science Department of the University of California at Berkeley; Marvin Dennicoff and Peter Wegner for allowing us to address the DOD conference on research directions in software technology.

We also wish to thank Larry Landweber for allowing us to visit for a summer the University of Wisconsin at Madison. The environment and the support of Ben Noble and his staff at the Mathematics Research Center was instrumental in letting us work effectively.

The seeds of these ideas were formed out of discussions held at the DOD Conference on Software Technology in 1976 at Durham, North Carolina. We wish to thank in particular J.R. Suttle, who organized this conference and has been of continuing encouragement in our work.

We also wish to thank our many friends who have discussed these issues with us. They include: Al Aho, Jon Barwise, Manuel Blum, Tim Budd, Lucio Chiaraviglio, Philip Davis, Peter Denning, Bernie Elspas, Mike Fischer, Ralph Griswold, Leo Guibas, David Hansen, Mike Harrison, Steve Johnson, Jerome Kiesler, Kenneth Kunen, Nancy Lynch, Albert Meyer, Barkley Rosser, Fred Sayward, Tim Standish, Larry Travis, Tony Wasserman and Ann Yasuhara.

We also wish to thank both Bob Grafton and Marvin Dennicoff of ONR for their comments and encouragement.

Only those who have seen earlier drafts of this paper can appreciate the contribution made by our editor, Mary-Claire van Leunen. Were it the custom in computer science to list a credit line "As told to . . . ," that might be a better description of the service she performed.

NOTE

1. This process has recently come to be called "abstraction," but we feel that for a variety of reasons "abstraction" is a bad term. It is easily confused with the totally dif-

ferent notion of abstraction in mathematics, and often what has passed for abstraction in the computer science literature is simply the removal of implementation details.

REFERENCES

[1] Baker, F.T. Chief programmer team management of production programming. *IBM Syst. J. 11*, 1 (1972), 56–73.

[2] Cohen, P.J. The independence of the continuum hypothesis. Proc. Nat. Acad. Sci., USA. Part I, vol. 50 (1963), pp. 1143–1148; Part II, vol. 51 (1964), pp. 105–110.

[3] Davis, P.J. Fidelity in mathematical discourse: Is one and one really two? *The Amer. Math. Monthly 79*, 3 (1972), 252–263.

[4] Bateman, P., and Diamond, H. John E. Littlewood (1885–1977): An informal obituary. *The Math. Intelligencer 1*, 1 (1978), 28–33.

[5] Gelerenter, H., et al. The discovery of organic synthetic roots by computer. *Topics in Current Chemistry 41*, Springer-Verlag, 1973, pp. 113–150.

[6] George, J. Alan. Computer Implementation of the Finite Element Method. Ph.D. Th., Stanford U., Stanford, Calif., 1971.

[7] Heath, Thomas L. *The Thirteen Books of Euclid's Elements*. Dover, New York, 1956, pp. 204–219.

[8] Heawood, P.J. Map colouring theorems. *Quarterly J. Math., Oxford Series 24* (1890), 322–339.

[9] Hoare, C.A.R. Quoted in *Software Management*, C. McGowan and R. McHenry, Eds.; to appear in *Research Directions in Software Technology*, M.I.T. Press, Cambridge, Mass., 1978.

[10] Jech, Thomas J. *The Axiom of Choice*. North-Holland Pub. Co., Amsterdam, 1973, p. 118.

[11] Kempe, A.B. On the geographical problem of the four colors. *Amer. J. Math. 2* (1879), 193–200.

[12] Kolata, G. Bari. Mathematical proof: The genesis of reasonable doubt. *Science 192* (1976), 989–990.

[13] Lakatos, Imre. *Proofs and Refutations: The Logic of Mathematical Discovery*. Cambridge University Press, England, 1976.

[14] Manin, Yu. I. *A Course in Mathematical Logic*. Springer-Verlag, 1977, pp. 48–51.

[15] Meyer, A. The inherent computational complexity of theories of ordered sets: A brief survey. Int. Cong. of Mathematicians, Aug. 1974.

[16] Popek, G., et al. Notes on the design of Euclid, Proc. Conf. Language Design for Reliable Software, SIGPLAN Notices (ACM) *12*, 3 (1977), pp. 11–18.

[17] Rabin, M.O. Probabilistic algorithms. In *Algorithms and Complexity: New Directions and Recent Results*, J.F. Traub, Ed., Academic Press, New York, 1976, pp. 21–40.

[18] Schwartz, J. On programming. Courant Rep., New York U., New York, 1973.

[19] Stockmeyer, L. The complexity of decision problems in automata theory and logic. Ph.D. Th., M.I.T., Cambridge, Mass., 1974.

[20] Ulam, S.M. *Adventures of a Mathematician*. Scribner's, New York, 1976, p. 288.

GREGORY CHAITIN

Information-Theoretic Computational Complexity *and* Gödel's Theorem and Information

The following two papers by Chaitin draw together many of the themes of this anthology. In these essays Chaitin blends standard mathematical logic with a computer-oriented information theory to obtain a new version of Gödel's fundamental result. This investigation, he argues, clarifies the significance of Gödel's incompleteness theorem, showing that it is not an isolated paradox but a natural consequence of the constraints imposed by information theory. "From the point of view of information theory . . . [Gödel's theorem] seems simply to suggest that in order to progress, mathematicians, like investigators in other sciences, must search for new axioms."[1]

The second essay, "Gödel's Theorem and Information," is the more general of the two and makes the argument for what I've called 'quasi-empiricism'. Chaitin compares mathematics to physics and suggests that mathematicians should adopt a more flexible attitude toward new axioms and methods of proof. "Perhaps number theory should be pursued more openly in the spirit of experimental science!" Early on in this anthology, Putnam had argued for a similar reading of Gödel's theorem. In the intervening essays, we have been exploring mathematical practice, informal proofs and the continuum between mathematics and science. We are now in a much better position to put flesh on the bones of the Chaitin-Putnam proposal.

What is distinctive about Chaitin's argument is his technical variation on Gödel's theorem. The first essay, "Information-Theoretic computational Complexity," provides the necessary technical background to his arguments in a reasonably accessible fashion. For a more detailed exposition of the results, the reader is referred to Chaitin's "Information-Theoretic Limitations of Formal Systems".[2] In the remainder of this introduction, I'll try to provide some philosophical background to Chaitin's work by developing an analogy. Chaitin's theorem stands to Berry's paradox in much the same relation that Gödel's theorem stands to the liar paradox (also known as Tarski's paradox). Let's begin with the two better-known elements of the analogy.

The liar paradox concerns the following sentence.

(S1) This sentence is not *true.*

If S1 is true, then what it asserts must be the case, so it is false. Yet if S1 is not true, then it asserts what is the case, so S1 is true. Tarski proved that every component of the paradox could be formalized in arithmetic, save one—a predicate "is true" of sentences satisfying the condition: 'S' is true <=> S, for every sentence S. Tarski resolved the paradox by concluding that sufficiently rich languages cannot formalize the concept of truth for their sentences.[3]

Earlier Godel had skirted paradox by considering the following sentence.

(S2) This sentence is not *provable.*

In contrast to truth, provability can be formalized, at least when it is relativized to provability within a particular formal system. Thus S2, unlike S1, has a formal analogue in arithmetic. Let us consider the status of this formal analogue. If S2 were true, then it would be unprovable and the underlying formal system would be incomplete. There would be arithmetical truths not provable in it. Next suppose that S2 yields a false statement of arithmetic. Then it would be provable and its negation, which asserts that S2 is provable, would be both true and provable! A proof of S2 ("This sentence is not provable") would demonstrate that not-S2 (That is, S2 *is* provable)! So the underlying formal system would be actually inconsistent. Notice that there is no paradox here. Instead we have a demonstration of the fundamental limits to any formal proof procedure: either it is inconsistent or it is incomplete.

Now let us turn to Berry's paradox. It concerns the phrase P1.

(P1) the least number not denoted by a phrase with fewer than fourteen words

Given a fixed and finite vocabulary, there can be only a finite number of phrases with fewer than fourteen words. Consequently only finitely many numbers can be denoted by such phrases and so there is a least number, n, not so denoted. P1 seems to pick this number out, yet P1 has only thirteen words so it cannot denote n. As in the case of the liar paradox, we can formalize each component of Berry's paradox in arithmetic save one; the relation of denotation between terms and numbers. So like the liar paradox, Berry's paradox is avoided by denying that sufficiently rich languages can formalize the concept of denotation for their terms. According to one traditional distinction, both paradoxes are semantic paradoxes, not logical paradoxes, and so they cause trouble for linguistics, but not for mathematics.[4]

Chaitin and others skirt Berry's paradox by considering an analogous phrase, P2.

(P2) the least number not computed by a program of complexity less than n

(In order to smooth out the analogy I have departed from Chaitin somewhat by continuing to talk of numbers where he talks of binary strings, but I hope that the gist of his idea is preserved.) Chaitin argues that relative to certain natural background assumptions, this phrase can be formalized in arithmetic and actually determines a computer program for searching out such a number. Let us say that a number is random relative to n if it isn't computed by any program of complexity less than n. Even if we choose n to be very large, say 10 to the 100th power, we can still prove that (infinitely) many numbers must be random. Nevertheless, the search procedure corresponding to P2 can not produce a single example of a random number since that program can be shown to have complexity much less than 10 to the 100th power. We cannot discover a number of complexity greater than n by any procedure of complexity less than n.

Berry's paradox is avoided by denying that a key concept in it, denotation, can be formalized. A major part of Chaitin's work is devoted to showing that the concepts relevant to his phrase can be formalized. Thus, he proves that the resulting program does not halt with a correct output. The conclusion he draws is that "If we use the methods of reasoning accepted by Hilbert, there is an upper bound to the complexity that it is possible to prove that a particular string [of 0's and 1's] has." Actually the moral is more general: insofar as we precisely and consistently specify the methods of reasoning permitted, we determine an upper bound to the complexity of our results. (This upper bound is the information-theoretic limit imposed by Gödel's theorem.) To put the matter the other way around, if mathematicians wish to prove more complex results, they will have to continually introduce new axioms or new methods. Hence, progress in mathematics would appear to be much more like progress in the natural sciences than hitherto expected.

Chaitin concludes his presentation by comparing the roles of complexity in mathematics and in science.

NOTES

1. "Randomness and Mathematical Proof," *Scientific American,* 232 (May 1975), 52.

2. "Information-Theoretic Limitations of Formal Systems," *Journal of the ACM,* 21 (1977), 403–424.

3. Of course Tarski did give a formally correct definition of truth for sentences in a language relative to a model. The point is that there is no predicate $T(x)$ *in the language* which is true of all and only the true sentences in the language (relative to a given model).

4. This distinction was first made by F.P. Ramsey in 1925. See his collected papers, *The Foundations of Mathematics,* Littlefield, Adams and Co., Patterson, New Jersey (1960), 20–21.

• • • • •

Information-Theoretic Computational Complexity

This field's fundamental concept is the complexity of a binary string, that is, a string of bits, of zeros and ones. The complexity of a binary string is the minimum quantity of information needed to define the string. For example, the string of length n consisting entirely of ones is of complexity approximately $\log_2 n$, because only $\log_2 n$ bits of information are required to specify n in binary notation.

However, this is rather vague. Exactly what is meant by the definition of a string? To make this idea precise a computer is used. One says that a string defines another when the first string gives instructions for constructing the second string. In other words, one string defines another when it is a program for a computer to calculate the second string. The fact that a string of n ones is of complexity approximately $\log_2 n$ can now be translated more correctly into the following. There is a program $\log_2 n + c$ bits long that calculates the string of n ones. The program performs a loop for printing ones n times. A fixed number c of bits are needed to program the loop, and $\log_2 n$ bits more for specifying n in binary notation.

Exactly how are the computer and the concept of information combined to define the complexity of a binary string? A computer is considered to take one binary string and perhaps eventually produce another. The first string is the program that has been given to the machine. The second string is the output of this program; it is what this program calculates. Now consider a given string that is to be calculated. How much information must be given to the machine to do this? That is to say, what is the length in bits of the shortest program for calculating the string? This is its complexity.

It can be objected that this is not a precise definition of the complexity of a string, inasmuch as it depends on the computer that one is using. Moreover, a definition should not be based on a machine, but rather on a model that does not have the physical limitations of real computers.

Here we will not define the computer used in the definition of complexity. However, this can indeed be done with all the precision of which mathematics is capable. Since 1936 it has been known how to define an idealized computer with unlimited memory. This was done in a very intuitive way by Turing and also by Post, and there are elegant definitions based on other principles [2]. The theory of recursive functions (or computability theory) has grown up around the questions of what is computable and what is not.

Thus it is not difficult to define a computer mathematically. What remains to be analyzed is which definition should be adopted, inasmuch as some computers are easier to program than others. A decade ago Solomonoff solved this problem [7]. He constructed a definition of a computer whose programs are not much longer than those of any other computer. More exactly, Solomonoff's machine simulates running a program on another computer, when it is given a description of that computer together with its program.

Thus it is clear that the complexity of a string is a mathematical concept, even though here we have not given a precise definition. Furthermore, it is a very natural concept, easy to understand for those who have worked with computers. Recapitulating, the complexity of a binary string is the information needed to define it, that is to say, the number of bits of information that must be given to a computer in order to calculate it, or in other words, the size in bits of the shortest program for calculating it. It is understood that a certain mathematical definition of an idealized computer is being used, but it is not given here, because as a first approximation it is sufficient to think of the length in bits of a program for a typical computer in use today.

Now we would like to consider the most important properties of the complexity of a string. First of all, the complexity of a string of length n is less than $n + c$, because any string of length n can be calculated by putting it directly into a program as a table. This requires n bits, to which must be added c bits of instructions for printing the table. In other words, if nothing better occurs to us, the string itself can be used as its definition, and this requires only a few more bits than its length.

Thus the complexity of each string of length n is less than $n + c$. Moreover, the complexity of the great majority of strings of length n is approximately n, and very few strings of length n are of complexity much less than n. The reason is simply that there are much fewer programs of length appreciably less than n than strings of length n. More exactly, there are 2^n strings of length n, and less than 2^{n-k} programs of length less than $n - k$. Thus the number of strings of length n and complexity less than $n - k$ decreases exponentially as k increases.

These considerations have revealed the basic fact that the great majority of strings of length n are of complexity very close to n. Therefore, if one generates a binary string of length n by tossing a fair coin n times and noting whether each toss gives head or tail, it is highly probable that the complexity of this string will be very close to n. In 1965 Kolmogorov proposed calling random those strings of length n whose complexity is approximately n [8]. We made the same proposal independently [9]. It can be shown that a string that is random in this sense has the statistical properties that one would expect. For example, zeros and ones appear in such strings with relative frequencies that tend to one-half as the length of the strings increases.

Consequently, the great majority of strings of length n are random, that is, need programs of approximately length n, that is to say, are of complexity approximately n. What happens if one wishes to show that a particular string is random? What if one wishes to prove that the complexity of a certain string is almost equal to its length? What if one wishes to exhibit a specific example of a string of length n and complexity close to n, and assure oneself by means of a proof that there is no shorter program for calculating this string?

It should be pointed out that this question can occur quite naturally to a programmer with a competitive spirit and a mathematical way of thinking. At the beginning of the sixties we attended a course at Columbia University in New York. Each time the professor gave an exercise to be programmed, the students tried to see who could write the shortest program. Even though several times it seemed very difficult to improve upon the best program that had been discovered, we did not fool ourselves. We realized that in order to be sure, for example, that the shortest program for the IBM 650 that prints the prime numbers has, say, 28 instructions, it would be necessary to prove it, not merely to continue for a long time unsuccessfully trying to discover a program with less than 28 instructions. We could never even sketch a first approach to a proof.

It turns out that it was not our fault that we did not find a proof, because we faced a fundamental limitation. One confronts a very basic difficulty when one tries to prove that a string is random, when one attempts to establish a lower bound on its complexity. We will try to suggest why this problem arises by means of a famous paradox, that of Berry [1, p. 153].

Consider the smallest positive integer that cannot be defined by an English phrase with less than 1 000 000 000 characters. Supposedly the shortest definition of this number has 1 000 000 000 or more characters. However, we defined this number by a phrase much less than 1 000 000 000 characters in length when we described it as "the smallest positive integer that cannot be defined by an English phrase with less than 1 000 000 000 characters!"

What relationship is there between this and proving that a string is complex, that its shortest program needs more than n bits? Consider the first string that can be proven to be of complexity greater than 1 000 000 000. Here once more we face a paradox similar to that of Berry, because this description leads to a program with much less than 1 000 000 000 bits that calculates a string supposedly of complexity greater than 1 000 000 000. Why is there a short program for calculating "the first string that can be proven to be of complexity greater than 1 000 000 000?"

The answer depends on the concept of a formal axiom system, whose importance was emphasized by Hilbert [1]. Hilbert proposed that mathematics be made as exact and precise as possible. In order to avoid arguments between mathematicians about the validity of proofs he set down explicitly the methods of reasoning used in mathematics. In fact, he invented an artificial language with rules of grammar and spelling that have no exceptions. He proposed that this language be used to eliminate the ambiguities and uncertainties inherent in any natural langauge. The specifications are so precise and exact that checking if a proof written in this artificial language is correct is completely mechanical. We would say today that it is so clear whether a proof is valid or not that this can be checked by a computer.

Hilbert hoped that this way mathematics would attain the greatest possible objectivity and exactness. Hilbert said that there can no longer be any doubt about proofs. The deductive method should be completely clear.

Suppose that proofs are written in the language that Hilbert constructed, and in accordance with his rules concerning the accepted methods of reasoning. We claim that a computer can be programmed to print all the theorems that can be proven. It is an endless program that every now and then writes on the printer a theorem. Furthermore, no theorem is omitted. Each will eventually be printed, if one is very patient and waits long enough.

How is this possible? The program works in the following manner. The language invented by Hilbert has an alphabet with finitely many signs or characters. First the program generates the strings of characters in this alphabet that are one character in length. It checks if one of these strings satisfies the completely mechanical rules for a correct proof and prints all the theorems whose proofs it has found. Then the program generates all the possible proofs that are two characters in length, and examines each of them to determine if it is valid. The program then examines all possible proofs of length three, of length four, and so on. If a theorem can be proven, the program will eventually find a proof for it in this way, and then print it.

Consider again "the first string that can be proven to be of complexity greater than 1 000 000 000." To find this string one generates all the theorems until one finds the first theorem that states that a particular string is of complexity greater than 1 000 000 000. Moreover, the program for finding this string is short, because it need only have the number 1 000 000 000 written in binary notation $\log_2$ 1 000 000 000 bits, and a routine of fixed length c that examines all possible proofs until it finds one that a specific string is of complexity greater than 1 000 000 000.

In fact, we see that there is a program $\log_2 n + c$ bits long that calculates the first string that can be proven to be of complexity greater than n. Here we have Berry's paradox again, because this program of length $\log_2 n + c$ calculates something that supposedly cannot be calculated by a program of length less than or equal to n. Also, $\log_2 n + c$ is much less than n for all sufficiently great values of n, because the logarithm increases very slowly.

What can the meaning of this paradox be? In the case of Berry's original paradox, one cannot arrive at a meaningful conclusion, inasmuch as one is dealing with vague concepts such as an English phrase's defining a positive integer. However our version of the paradox deals with exact concepts that have been defined mathematically. Therefore, it cannot really be a contradiction. It would be absurd for a string not to have a program of length less than or equal to n for calculating it, and at the same time to have such a program. Thus we arrive at the interesting conclusion that such a string cannot exist. For all sufficiently great values of n, one cannot talk about "the first string that can be proven to be of complexity greater than n," because this string cannot exist. In other words, for all sufficiently great values of n, it cannot be proven that a particular string is of complexity greater than n. If one uses the methods of reasoning accepted by Hilbert, there is an upper bound to the complexity that it is possible to prove that a particular string has.

This is the surprising result that we wished to obtain. Most strings of length n are of complexity approximately n, and a string generated by tossing a coin will almost certainly have this property. Nevertheless, one cannot exhibit individual examples of arbitrarily complex strings using methods of reasoning accepted by Hilbert. The lower bounds on the complexity of specific strings that can be established are limited, and we will never be mathematically certain that a particular string is very complex, even though most strings are random.[1]

In 1931 Gödel questioned Hilbert's ideas in a similar way [1], [2]. Hilbert had proposed specifying once and for all exactly what is accepted as a proof, but Gödel explained that no matter what Hilbert specified so precisely, there would always be true statements about the integers that the methods of reasoning accepted by Hilbert would be incapable of proving. This mathematical result has been considered to be of great philosophical importance. Von Neumann commented that the intellectual shock provoked by the crisis in the foundations of mathematics was equaled only by two other scientific events in this century: the theory of relativity and quantum theory [4].

We have combined ideas from information theory and computability theory in order to define the complexity of a binary string, and have then used this concept to give a definition of a random string and to show that a formal axiom system enables one to prove that a random string is indeed random in only finitely many cases.

Now we would like to examine some other possible applications of this viewpoint. In particular, we would like to suggest that the concept of the complexity of a string and the fundamental methodological problems of science are intimately related. We will also suggest that this concept may be of theoretical value in biology.

Solomonoff [7] and the author [9] proposed that the concept of complexity might make it possible to precisely formulate the situation that a scientist faces when he has made observations and wishes to understand them and make predictions. In order to do this the scientist searches for a theory that is in agreement with all his observations. We consider his observations to be represented by a binary string, and a theory to be a program that calculates this string. Scientists consider the simplest theory to be the best one, and that if a theory is too "ad hoc," it is useless. How can we formulate these intuitions about the scientific method in a precise fashion? The simplicity of a theory is inversely proportional to the length of the program that constitutes it. That is to say, the best program for understanding or predicting observations is the shortest one that reproduces what the scientist has observed up to that moment. Also, if the program has the same number of bits as the observations, then it is useless, because it is too "ad hoc." If a string of observations only has theories that are programs with the same length as the string of observations, then the observations are random, and can neither be comprehended nor predicted. They are what they are, and that is all; the scientist cannot have a theory in the proper sense of the concept; he can only show someone else what he observed and say "it was this."

In summary, the value of a scientific theory is that it enables one to compress many observations into a few theoretical hypotheses. There is a theory only when the string of observations is not random, that is to say, when its complexity is appreciably less than its length in bits. In this case the scientist can communicate his observations to a colleague much more economically than by just transmitting the string of observations. He does this by sending his colleague the program that is his theory, and this program must have much fewer bits than the original string of observations.

It is also possible to make a similar analysis of the deductive method, that is to say, of formal axiom systems. This is accomplished by analyzing more carefully the new version of Berry's paradox that was presented. Here we only sketch the three basic results that are obtained in this manner.[2]

(1) In a formal system with n bits of axioms it is impossible to prove that a particular binary string is of complexity greater than $n + c$.

(2) Contrariwise, there are formal systems with $n + c$ bits of axioms in which it is possible to determine each string of complexity less than n and the complexity of each of these strings, and it is also possible to exhibit each string of complexity greater than or equal to n, but without being able to know by how much the complexity of each of these strings exceeds n.

(3) Unfortunately, any formal system in which it is possible to determine each string of complexity less than n has either one grave problem or

another. Either it has few bits of axioms and needs incredibly long proofs, or it has short proofs but an incredibly great number of bits of axioms. We say "incredibly" because these quantities increase more quickly than any computable function of n.

It is necessary to clarify the relationship between this and the preceding analysis of the scientific method. There are less than 2^n strings of complexity less than n, but some of them are incredibly long. If one wishes to communicate all of them to someone else, there are two alternatives. The first is to directly show all of them to him. In this case one will have to send him an incredibly long message because some of these strings are incredibly long. The other alternative is to send him a very short message consisting of n bits of axioms from which he can deduce which strings are of complexity less than n. Although the message is very short in this case, he will have to spend an incredibly long time to deduce from these axioms the strings of complexity less than n. This is analogous to the dilemma of a scientist who must choose between directly publishing his observations, or publishing a theory that explains them, but requires very extended calculations in order to do this.

Finally, we would like to suggest that the concept of complexity may possibly be of theoretical value in biology.

At the end of his life von Neumann tried to lay the foundation for a mathematics of biological phenomena. His first effort in this direction was his work *Theory of Games and Economic Behavior*, in which he analyzes what is a rational way to behave in situations in which there are conflicting interests [3]. *The Computer and the Brain*, his notes for a lecture series, was published shortly after his death [5]. This book discusses the differences and similarities between the computer and the brain, as a first step to a theory of how the brain functions. A decade later his work *Theory of Self-Reproducing Automata* appeared, in which von Neumann constructs an artificial universe and within it a computer that is capable of reproducing itself [6]. But von Neumann points out that the problem of formulating a mathematical theory of the evolution of life in this abstract setting remains to be solved; and to express mathematically the evolution of the complexity of organisms, one must first define complexity precisely.[3] We submit that "organism" must also be defined, and have tried elsewhere to suggest how this might perhaps be done [10].

We believe that the concept of complexity that has been presented here may be the tool that von Neumann felt is needed. It is by no means accidental that biological phenomena are considered to be extremely complex. Consider how a human being analyzes what he sees, or uses natural languages to communicate. We cannot carry out these tasks by computer because they are as yet too complex for us–the programs would be too long.[4]

APPENDIX

In this Appendix we try to give a more detailed idea of how the results concerning formal axiom systems that were stated are established.[5]

Two basic mathematical concepts that are employed are the concepts of a recursive function and a partial recursive function. A function is recursive if there is an algorithm for calculating its value when one is given the value of its arguments, in other words, if there is a Turing machine for doing this. If it is possible that this algorithm never terminates and the function is thus undefined for some values of its arguments, then the function is called partial recursive.[6]

In what follows we are concerned with computations involving binary strings. The binary strings are considered to be ordered in the following manner: Λ ,0,1,00,01,10,11,000,001,010, ... The natural number n is represented by the nth-binary string ($n = 0,1,2, \ldots$). The length of a binary string s is denoted $\lg(s)$. Thus if s is considered to be a natural number, then $\lg(s) = [\log_2(s + 1)]$. Here $[x]$ is the greatest integer $\leq x$.

Definition 1: *A computer* is a partial recursive function $C(p)$. Its argument p is a binary string. The value of $C(p)$ is the binary string output by the computer C when it is given the program p. If $C(p)$ is undefined, this means that running the program p on C produces an unending computation.

Definition 2: *The complexity* $I_c(s)$ of a binary string s is defined to be the length of the shortest program p that makes the computer C output s, i.e., $I_c(s) = \min_{C(p)=s} \lg(p)$. If no program makes C output s, then $I_c(s)$ is defined to be infinite.

Definition 3: A computer U is *universal* if for any computer C and any binary string s, $I_U(s) \leq I_C(s) + c$, where the constant c depends only on C.

It is easy to see that there are universal computers. For example, consider the computer U such that $U(0^i1p) = C_i(p)$, where C_i is the ith computer, i.e., a program for U consists of two parts: the left-hand part indicates which computer is to be simulated, and the right-hand part gives the program to be simulated. We now suppose that some particular universal computer U has been chosen as the standard one for measuring complexities, and shall henceforth write $I(s)$ instead of $I_U(s)$.

Definition 4: The *rules of inference* of a class of formal axiom systems is a recursive function $F(a,h)$ (a a binary string, h a natural number) with the property that $F(a,h) \subset F(a, h + 1)$. The value of $F(a,h)$ is the finite (possibly empty) set of theorems that can be proven from the axioms a by means of proofs $\leq h$ characters in length. $F(a) = \cup_h F(a,h)$ is the set of theorems that are consequences of the axioms a. The ordered pair $<F,a>$, which implies both the choice of rules of inference and axioms, is a particular formal axiom system.

This is a fairly abstract definition, but it retains all those features of formal axiom systems that we need. Note that although one may not be interested in some axioms (e.g., if they are false or incomprehensible), it is stipulated that $F(a,h)$ is always defined.

Theorem 1: a) There is a constant c such that $I(s) \leq \lg(s) + c$ for all binary strings s. b) There are less than 2^n binary strings of complexity less than n.

Proof of a): There is a computer C such that $C(p) = p$ for all programs p. Thus for all binary strings s, $I(s) \leq I_c(s) + c = \lg(s) + c$.

Proof of b): As there are less than 2^n *programs of length less than n*, there must be less than this number of binary strings of complexity less than n.

Q.E.D.

Thesis: A random binary string s is one having the property that $I(s) \approx \lg(s)$.

Theorem 2: Consider the rules of inference F. Suppose that a proposition of the form "$I(s) \geq n$" is in $F(a)$ only if it is true, i.e., only if $I(s) \geq n$. Then a proposition of the form "$I(s) \geq n$" is in $F(a)$ only if $n \leq \lg(a) + c$, where c is a constant that depends only on F.

Proof: Consider that binary string s_k having the shortest proof from the axioms a that it is of complexity $> \lg(a) + 2k$. We claim that $I(s_k) \leq \lg(a) + k + c'$, where c' depends only on F. Taking $k = c'$, we conclude that the binary string $s_{c'}$ with the shortest proof from the axioms a that it is of complexity $> \lg(a) + 2c'$ is, in fact, of complexity $\leq \lg(a) + 2c'$, which is impossible. It follows that s_k doesn't exist for $k = c'$, that is, no binary string can be proven from the axioms a to be of complexity $> \lg(a) + 2c'$. Thus the theorem is proved with $c = 2c'$.

It remains to verify the claim that $I(s_k) \leq \lg(a) + k + c'$. Consider the computer C that does the following when it is given the program $0^k 1a$. It calculates $F(a,h)$ for $h = 0,1,2,\ldots$ until it finds the first theorem in $F(a,h)$ of the form "$I(s) \geq n$" with $n > \lg(a) + 2k$. Finally C outputs the binary string s in the theorem it has found. Thus $C(0^k 1a)$ is equal to s_k, if s_k exists. It follows that $I(s_k) = I(C(*^k 1a)) \leq I_c(C(0^k 1a)) + c'' \leq \lg(0^k 1a) + c'' = \lg(a) + k + (c'' + 1) = \lg(a) + k + c'$. Q.E.D.

Definition 5: A_n is defined to be the kth binary string of length n, where k is the number of programs p of length $< n$ for which $U(p)$ is defined, i.e., A_n has n and this number k coded into it.

Theorem 3: There are rules of inference F^1 such that for all n, $F^1(A_n)$ is the union of the set of all true propositions of the form "$I(s) = k$" with $k < n$ and the set of all true propositions of the form "$I(s) \geq n$."

Proof: From A_n one knows n and for how many programs p of length $< n$ $U(p)$ is defined. One then simulates in parallel, running each program p of length $< n$ on U until one has determined the value of $U(p)$ in all those cases in which $U(p)$ is defined. Knowing the value of $U(p)$ for each p of length $< n$ for which $U(p)$ is defined, one easily determines each string of complexity $< n$ and its complexity. What's more, all other strings must be of complexity $\geq n$. This completes our sketch of how all true propositions of the form "$I(s) = k$" with $k < n$ and of the form "$I(s) \geq n$" can be deduced from the axiom A_n. Q.E.D.

Recall that we consider the nth binary string to be the natural number n.

Definition 6: The partial function $B(n)$ is defined to be the biggest natural number of complexity $\leq n$, i.e., $B(n) = \max_{I(k) \leq n} k = \max_{\lg(p) \leq n} U(p)$.

Theorem 4: Let f be a partial recursive function that carries natural numbers into natural numbers. Then $B(n) \geq f(n)$ for all sufficiently great values of n.

Proof: Consider the computer C such that $C(p) = f(p)$ for all p. $I(f(n)) \leq I_C(f(n)) + c \leq \lg(n) + c = [\log_2(n+1)] + c < n$ for all sufficiently great values of n. Thus $B(n) \geq f(n)$ for all sufficiently great values of n. Q.E.D.

Theorem 5: Consider the rules of inference F Let $F_n = \cup_a F(a,B(n))$, where the union is taken over all binary strings a of length $\leq B(n)$, i.e., F_n is the (finite) set of all theorems that can be deduced by means of proofs with not more than $B(n)$ characters from axioms with not more than $B(n)$ bits. Let s_n be the first binary string s not in any proposition of the form "$I(s) = k$" in F_n. Then $I(s_n) \leq n + c$, where the constant c depends only on F.

Proof: We claim that there is a computer C such that if $U(p) = B(n)$, then $C(p) = s_n$. As, by the definition of B, there is a p_0 of length $\leq n$ such that $U(p_0) = B(n)$, it follows that $I(s_n) \leq I_C(s_n) + c = c = I_C(C(p_0)) + c \leq \lg(p_0) + c \leq n + c$, which was to be proved.

It remains to verify the claim that there is a C such that if $U(p) = B(n)$, then $C(p) = s_n$. C works as follows. Given the program p, C first stimulates running the program p on U. Once C has determined $U(p)$, it calculates $F(a, U(p))$ for all binary strings a such that $\lg(a) \leq U(p)$, and forms the union of these $2^{U(p)+1} - 1$ different sets of propositions, which is F_n if $U(p) = B(n)$. Finally C outputs the first binary string s not in any proposition of the form "$I(s) = k$" in this set of propositions; s is s_n if $U(p) = B(n)$. Q.E.D.

Theorem 6: Consider the rules of inference F. If $F(a,h)$ includes all true propositions of the form "$I(s) = k$" with $k \leq n + c$, then either $\lg(a) > B(n)$ or $h > B(n)$. Here c is a constant that depends only on F.

Proof: This is an immediate consequence of Theorem 5. Q.E.D.

The following theorem gives an upper bound on the size of the proofs in the formal systems $<F^1, A_n>$ that were studied in Theorem 3, and also shows that the lower bound on the size of these proofs that is given by Theorem 6 cannot be essentially improved.

Theorem 7: There is a constant c such that for all n $F^1(A_n, B(n+c))$ includes all true propositions of the form "$I(s) = k$" with $k < n$.

Proof: We claim that there is a computer C such that for all n, $C(A_n) =$ the least natural number h such that $F^1(A_n, h)$ includes all true propositions of the form "$I(s) = k$" with $k < n$. Thus the complexity of this value of h is $\leq \lg(A_n) + c = n + c$, and $B(n+c)$ is $\geq$ this value of h, which was to be proved.

It remains to verify the claim. C works as follows when it is given the program A_n. First, it determines each binary string of complexity $<n$ and its complexity, in the manner described in the proof of Theorem 3. Then it calculates $F^1(A_n, h)$ for $h = 0,1,2, \ldots$ until all true propositions of the form "$I(s) = k$" with $k < n$ are included in $F^1(A_n, h)$. The final value of h is then output by C. Q.E.D.

NOTES

1. This is a particularly perverse example of Kac's comment [13, p. 18] that "as is often the case, it is much easier to prove that an overwhelming majority of objects

possess a certain property than to *exhibit* even one such object." The most familiar example of this is Shannon's proof of the coding theorem for a noisy channel; while it is shown that most coding schemes achieve close to the channel capacity, in practice it is difficult to implement a good coding scheme.

2. See the Appendix.

3. In an important paper [14], Eigen studies these questions from the point of view of thermodynamics and biochemistry.

4. Chandrasekaran and Reeker [15] discuss the relevance of complexity to artificial intelligence.

5. See [11], [12] for different approaches.

6. Full treatments of these concepts can be found in standard texts, e.g., Rogers [16].

REFERENCES

[1] J. van Heijenoort, Ed., *From Frege to Gödel: A source Book in Mathematical Logic*, 1879–1931. Cambridge, Mass.: Harvard Univ. Press, 1967.

[2] M. Davis, Ed., *The Undecidable—Basic Papers on Undecidable Propositions, Unsolvable Problems and Computable Functions.* Hewlett, N.Y.: Raven Press, 1965.

[3] J. von Neumann and O. Morgenstern, *Theory of Games and Economic Behavior.* Princeton, N.J.: Princeton Univ. Press, 1944.

[4] ——, "Method in the physical sciences," in *John von Neumann—Collected Works.* New York: Macmillan, 1963, vol. 6, no. 35.

[5] ——, *The Computer and the Brain.* New Haven, Conn.: Yale Univ. Press, 1958.

[6] ——, *Theory of Self-Reproducing Automata.* Urbana, Ill.: Univ. Illinois Press, 1966. (Edited and completed by A.W. Burks.)

[7] R.J. Solomonoff, "A formal theory of inductive inference," *Inform. Contr.*, vol. 7, pp. 1–22, Mar. 1964; also, pp. 224–254, June 1964.

[8] A.N. Kolmogorov, "Logical basis for information theory and probability theory," *IEEE Trans. Inform. Theory*, vol. IT-14, pp. 662–664, Sept. 1968.

[9] G.J. Chaitin, "On the difficulty of computations," *IEEE Trans. Inform. Theory*, vol. IT-16, pp. 5–9, Jan. 1970.

[10] ——, "To a mathematical definition of 'life'," *ACM SIGACT News*, no. 4, pp. 12–18, Jan. 1970.

[11] ——, "Computational complexity and Gödel's incompleteness theorem," (Abstract) *AMS Notices*, vol. 17, p. 672, June 1970; (Paper) *ACM SIGACT News*, no. 9, pp. 11–12, Apr. 1971.

[12] ——, "Information-theoretic limitations of formal systems," presented at the Courant Institute Computational Complexity Symp., N.Y., Oct. 1971. A revised version will appear in *J. Ass. Comput. Mach.*

[13] M. Kac, "Statistical independence in probability, analysis, and number theory," Carus Math. Mono., Mathematical Association of America, no. 12, 1959.

[14] M. Eigen, "Selforganization of matter and the evolution of biological macromolecules," *Die Naturwissenschaften*, vol. 58, pp. 465–523, Oct. 1971.

[15] B. Chandrasekaran and L.H. Reeker, "Artificial intelligence—a case for agnosticism," Ohio State University, Columbus, Ohio, Rep. OSU-CISRC-TR-72-9, Aug. 1972; also, *IEEE Trans. Syst., Man. Cybern.*, vol. SMC-4, pp. 88–94, Jan. 1974.

[16] H. Rogers, Jr., *Theory of Recursive Functions and Effective Computability.* New York: McGraw-Hill, 1967.

Gödel's Theorem and Information

1 INTRODUCTION

To set the stage, let us listen to Hermann Weyl (1946), as quoted by Eric Temple Bell (1951):

> We are less certain than ever about the ultimate foundations of (logic and) mathematics. Like everybody and everything in the world today, we have our "crisis." We have had it for nearly fifty years. Outwardly it does not seem to hamper our daily work, and yet I for one confess that it has had a considerable practical influence on my mathematical life: it directed my interests to fields I considered relatively "safe," and has been a constant drain on the enthusiasm and determination with which I pursued my research work. This experience is probably shared by other mathematicians who are not indifferent to what their scientific endeavors mean in the context of man's whole caring and knowing, suffering and creative existence in the world.

And these are the words of John von Neumann (1963):

> . . . there have been within the experience of people now living at least three serious crises . . . There have been two such crises in physics—namely, the conceptual soul-searching connected with the discovery of relativity and the conceptual difficulties connected with discoveries in quantum theory . . . The third crisis was in mathematics. It was a very serious conceptual crisis, dealing with rigor and the proper way to carry out a correct mathematical proof. In view of earlier notions of the absolute rigor of mathematics, it is surprising that such a thing could have happened, and even more surprising that it could have happened in these latter days when miracles are not supposed to take place. Yet it did happen.

At the time of its discovery, Kurt Gödel's incompleteness theorem was a great shock and caused much uncertainty and depression among mathematicians sensitive to foundational issues, since it seemed to pull the rug out from under mathematical certainty, objectivity, and rigor. Also, its proof was considered to be extremely difficult and recondite. With the passage of time the situation has been reversed. A great many different proofs of Gödel's theorem are now known, and the result is now considered easy to prove and almost obvious: It is equivalent to the unsolvability of the halting problem, or alternatively to the assertion that there is an r.e. (recursively enumerable) set that is not recursive. And it has had no lasting impact on the daily lives of mathematicians or on their working habits; no one loses sleep over it any more.

Gödel's original proof constructed a paradoxical assertion that is true but not provable within the usual formalizations of number theory. In contrast I would like to measure the power of a set of axioms and rules of inference. I would like to be able to say that if one has ten pounds of axioms and a

Reprinted with permission, from International Journal of Theoretical Physics, Vol. 21, No. 12, 1982, pp. 941–954.

twenty-pound theorem, then that theorem cannot be derived from those axioms. And I will argue that this approach to Gödel's theorem does suggest a change in the daily habits of mathematicians, and that Gödel's theorem cannot be shrugged away.

To be more specific, I will apply the viewpoint of thermodynamics and statistical mechanics to Gödel's theorem, and will use such concepts as probability, randomness, entropy, and information to study the incompleteness phenomenon and to attempt to evaluate how widespread it is. On the basis of this analysis, I will suggest that mathematics is perhaps more akin to physics than mathematicians have been willing to admit, and that perhaps a more flexible attitude with respect to adopting new axioms and methods of reasoning is the proper response to Gödel's theorem. Probabilistic proofs of primality via sampling (Chaitin and Schwartz, 1978) also suggest that the sources of mathematical truth are wider than usually thought. Perhaps number theory should be pursued more openly in the spirit of experimental science (Polya, 1959)!

I am indebted to John McCarthy and especially to Jacob Schwartz for making me realize that Gödel's theorem is not an obstacle to a practical AI (artificial intelligence) system based on formal logic. Such an AI would take the form of an intelligent proof checker. Gottfried Wilhelm Liebnitz and David Hilbert's dream that disputes could be settled with the words "Gentlemen, let us compute!" and that mathematics could be formalized, should still be a topic for active research. Even though mathematicians and logicians have erroneously dropped this train of thought dissuaded by Gödel's theorem, great advances have in fact been made "covertly," under the banner of computer science, LISP, and AI (Cole et al., 1981; Dewar et al., 1981; Levin, 1974; Wilf, 1982).

To speak in metaphors from Douglas Hofstadter (1979), we shall now stroll through an art gallery of proofs of Gödel's theorem, to the tune of Moussorgsky's pictures at an exhibition! Let us start with some traditional proofs (Davis, 1978; Hofstadter, 1979; Levin, 1974; Post, 1965).

2 TRADITIONAL PROOFS OF GÖDEL'S THEOREM

Gödel's original proof of the incompleteness theorem is based on the paradox of the liar: "This statement is false." He obtains a theorem instead of a paradox by changing this to: "This statement is unprovable." If this assertion is unprovable, then it is true, and the formalization of number theory in question is incomplete. If this assertion is provable, then it is false, and the formalization of number theory is inconsistent. The original proof was quite intricate, much like a long program in machine language. The famous technique of Gödel numbering statements was but one of the many ingenious ideas brought to bear by Gödel to construct a number-theoretic assertion which says of itself that it is unprovable.

Gödel's original proof applies to a particular formalization of number theory, and was to be followed by a paper showing that the same methods applied to a much broader class of formal axiomatic systems. The modern approach in fact applies to all formal axiomatic systems, a concept which could not even be defined when Gödel wrote his original paper, owing to the lack of a mathematical definition of effective procedure or computer algorithm. After Alan Turing succeeded in defining effective procedure by inventing a simple idealized computer now called the Turing machine (also done independently by Emil Post), it became possible to proceed in a more general fashion.

Hilbert's key requirement for a formal mathematical system was that there be an objective criterion for deciding if a proof written in the language of the system is valid or not. In other words, there must be an algorithm, a computer program, a Turing machine, for checking proofs. And the compact modern definition of formal axiomatic system is a recursively enumerable set of assertions is an immediate consequence if one uses the so-called British Museum algorithm. One applies the proof checker in turn to all possible proofs, and prints all the theorems, which of course would actually take astronomical amounts of time. By the way, in practice LISP is a very convenient programming language in which to write a simple proof checker (Levin, 1974).

Turing showed that the halting problem is unsolvable, that is, that there is no effective procedure or algorithm for deciding whether or not a program ever halts. Armed with the general definition of a formal axiomatic system as an r.e. set of assertions in a formal language, one can immediately deduce a version of Gödel's incompleteness theorem from Turing's theorem. I will sketch three different proofs of the unsolvability of the halting problem in a moment; first let me derive Gödel's theorem from it. The reasoning is simply that if it were always possible to prove whether or not particular programs halt, since the set of theorems is r.e., one could use this to solve the halting problem for any particular program by enumerating all theorems until the matter is settled. But this contradicts the unsolvability of the halting problem.

Here come three proofs that the halting problem is unsolvable. One proof considers that function $F(N)$ defined to be either one more than the value of the Nth computable function applied to the natural number N, or zero if this value is undefined because the Nth computer program does not halt on input N. F cannot be a computable function, for if program N calculated it, then one would have $F(N) = F(N) + 1$, which is impossible. But the only way that F can fail to be computable is because one cannot decide if the Nth program ever halts when given input N.

The proof I have just given is of course a variant of the diagonal method which Georg Cantor used to show that the real numbers are more numerous than the natural numbers (Courant and Robbins, 1941). Something much closer to Cantor's original technique can also be used to prove Turing's theorem. The argument runs along the lines of Bertrand Russell's paradox (Russell, 1967) of the set of all things that are not members of themselves. Consider programs for enumerating sets of natural numbers, and number these computer programs. Define a set of natural numbers consisting of the numbers of all programs which do not include their own number in their output set. This set of natural numbers cannot be recursively enumerable, for if it were listed by computer program N, one arrives at Russell's paradox of the barber in a small town who shaves all those and only those who do not shave themselves, and can neither shave himself nor avoid doing so. But the only way that this set can fail to be recursively enumerable is if it is impossible to decide whether or not a program ever outputs a specific natural number, and this is a variant of the halting problem.

For yet another proof of the unsolvability of the halting problem, consider programs which take no input and which either produce a single natural number as output or loop forever without ever producing an output. Think of these programs as being written in binary notation, instead of as natural numbers as before. I now define a so-called Busy Beaver function: *BB* of *N* is the largest natural number output by any program less than *N* bits in size. The original Busy Beaver function measured program size in terms of the number of states in a Turing machine instead of using the more correct information-theoretic measure, bits. It is easy to see that *BB* of *N* grows more quickly than any computable function, and is therefore not computable, which as before implies that the halting problem is unsolvable.

In a beautiful and easy to understand paper Post (1965) gave versions of Gödel's theorem based on his concepts of simple and creative r.e. sets. And he formulated the modern abstract form of Gödel's theorem, which is like a Japanese haiku: there is an r.e. set of natural numbers that is not recursive. This set has the property that there are programs for printing all the members of the set in some order, but not in ascending order. One can eventually realize that a natural number is a member of the set, but there is no algorithm for deciding if a given number is in the set or not. The set is r.e. but its complement is not. In fact, the set of (numbers of) halting programs is such a set. Now consider a particular formal axiomatic system in which one can talk about natural numbers and computer programs and such, and let *X* be any r.e. set whose complement is not r.e. It follows immediately that not all true assertions of the form "the natural number *N* is not in the set *X*" are theorems in the formal axiomatic system. In fact, if *X* is what Post called a simple r.e. set, then only finitely many of these assertions can be theorems.

These traditional proofs of Gödel's incompleteness theorem show that formal axiomatic systems are incomplete, but they do not suggest ways to measure the power of formal axiomatic systems, to rank their degree of completeness or incompleteness. Actually, Post's concept of a simple set contains the germ of the information-theoretic versions of Gödel's theorem that I will give later, but this is only visible in retrospect. One could somehow choose a particular simple r.e. set *X* and rank formal axiomatic systems according to how many different theorems of the form "*N* is not in *X*" are provable. Here are three other quantitative versions of Gödel's incompleteness theorem which do sort of fall within the scope of traditional methods.

Consider a particular formal axiomatic system in which it is possible to talk about total recursive functions (computable functions which have a natural number as value for each natural number input) and their running time computational complexity. It is possible to construct a total recursive function which grows more quickly than any function which is provably total recursive in the formal axiomatic system. It is also possible to construct a total recursive function which takes longer to compute than any provably total recursive function. That is to say, a computer program which produces a natural number output and then halts whenever it is given a natural number input, but this cannot be proved in the formal axiomatic system, because the program takes too long to produce its output.

It is also fun to use constructive transfinite ordinal numbers (Hofstadter, 1979) to measure the power of formal axiomatic systems. A constructive ordinal is one which can be obtained as the limit from below of a computable sequence of smaller constructive ordinals. One measures the power of a formal axiomatic system by the first constructive ordinal which cannot be proved to be a constructive ordinal within the system. This is like the paradox of the first unmentionable or indefinable ordinal number (Russell, 1967)!

Before turning to information-theoretic incompleteness theorems, I must first explain the basic concepts of algorithmic information theory (Chaitin, 1975b, 1977, 1982).

3 ALGORITHMIC INFORMATION THEORY

Algorithmic information theory focuses on individual objects rather than on the ensembles and probability distributions considered in Claude Shannon and Norbert Wiener's information theory. How many bits does it take to describe how to compute an individual object? In other words, what is the size in bits of the smallest program for calculating it? It is easy to see that since general-purpose computers (universal Turing machines) can simulate each other, the choice of computer as yardstick is not very important and really only corresponds to the choice of origin in a coordinate system.

The fundamental concepts of this new information theory are: algorithmic information content, joint information, relative information, mutual information, algorithmic randomness, and algorithmic independence. These are defined roughly as follows.

The algorithmic information content $I(X)$ of an individual object X is defined to be the size of the smallest program to calculate X. Programs must be self-delimiting so that subroutines can be combined by concatenating them. The joint information $I(X, Y)$ of two objects X and Y is defined to be the size of the smallest program to calculate X and Y simultaneously. The relative or conditional information content $I(X|Y)$ of X given Y is defined to be the size of the smallest program to calculate X from a minimal program for Y.

Note that the relative information content of an object is never greater than its absolute information content, for being given additional information can only help. Also, since subroutines can be concatenated, it follows that joint information is subadditive. That is to say, the joint information content is bounded from above by the sum of the individual information contents of the objects in question. The extent to which the joint information is less than this sum leads to the next fundamental concept, mutual information.

The mutual information content $I(X:Y)$ measures the commonality of X and Y: it is defined as the extent to which knowing X helps one to calculate Y, which is essentially the same as the extent to which knowing Y helps one to calculate X, which is also the same as the extent to which it is cheaper to calculate them together than separately. That is to say, $I(X:Y) = I(X) - I(X|Y) = I(Y) - I(Y|X) = I(X) + I(Y) - I(X,Y)$. Note that this implies that $I(X,Y) = I(X) + I(Y|X) = I(Y) + I(X|Y)$.

I can now define two very fundamental and philosophically significant notions: algorithmic randomness and algorithmic independence. These concepts are, I believe, quite close to the intuitive notions that go by the same name, namely, that an object is chaotic, typical, unnoteworthy, without structure, pattern, or distinguishing features, and is irreducible information, and that two objects have nothing in common and are unrelated.

Consider, for example, the set of all N-bit long bit strings. Most such strings S have $I(S)$ approximately equal to N plus $I(N)$, which is N plus the algorithmic information contained in the base-two numeral for N, which is equal to N plus order of log N. No N-bit long S has information content greater than this. A few have less information content; these are strings with a regular structure or pattern. Those strings S of a given size having greatest information content are said to be random or patternless or algorithmically incompressible. The cutoff between random and nonrandom is somewhere around $I(S)$ equal to N if the string S is N bits long.

Similarly, an infinite binary sequence such as the base-two expansion of pi is random if and only if all its initial segments are random, that is, if and only if there is a constant C such that no initial segment has information content less than C bits below its length. Of course, pi is the extreme opposite of a random string: it takes only $I(N)$ which is order of log N bits to calculate pi's first N bits. But the probability that an infinite sequence obtained by independent tosses of a fair coin is algorithmically random is unity.

Two strings are algorithmically independent if their mutual information is essentially zero, more precisely, if their mutual information is as small as possible. Consider, for example, two arbitrary strings X and Y each N bits in size. Usually, X and Y will be random to each other, excepting the fact that they have the same length, so that $I(X:Y)$ is approximately equal to $I(N)$. In other words, knowing one of them is no help in calculating the other, excepting that it tells one the other string's size.

To illustrate these ideas, let me give an information-theoretic proof that there are infinitely many prime numbers (Chaitin, 1979). Suppose on the contrary that there are only finitely many primes, in fact, K of them. Consider an algorithmically random natural number N. On the one hand, we know that $I(N)$ is equal to $\log_2 N$ + order of loglog N, since the base-two numeral for N is an algorithmically random ($\log_2 N$)-bit string. On the other hand, N can be calculated from the exponents in its prime factorization, and vice versa. Thus $I(N)$ is equal to the joint information of the K exponents in its prime factorization. By subadditivity, this joint information is bounded from above by the sum of the information contents of the K individual exponents. Each exponent is of order log N. The information content of each exponent is thus of order loglog N. Hence $I(N)$ is simultaneously equal to $\log_2 N + O(\text{loglog } N)$ and less than or equal to $KO(\text{loglog } N)$, which is impossible.

The concepts of algorithmic information theory are made to order for obtaining quantitative incompleteness theorems, and I will now give a number of information-theoretic proofs of Gödel's theorem (Chaitin, 1974a, 1974b, 1975a, 1977, 1982; Chaitin and Schwartz, 1978; Gardner, 1979).

4 INFORMATION-THEORETIC PROOFS OF GÖDEL'S THEOREM

I propose that we consider a formal axiomatic system to be a computer program for listing the set of theorems, and measure its size in bits. In other words, the measure of the size of a formal axiomatic system that I will use is quite crude. It is merely the amount of space it takes to specify a proof-checking algorithm and how to apply it to all possible proofs, which is roughly the amount of space it takes to be very precise about the alphabet, vocabulary, grammar, axioms, and rules of inference. This is roughly proportional to the number of pages it takes to present the formal axiomatic system in a textbook.

Here is the first information-theoretic incompleteness theorem. Consider an N-bit formal axiomatic system. There is a program of size N which does not halt, but one cannot prove this within the formal axiomatic system. On the other hand, N bits of axioms can permit one to deduce precisely which programs of size less than N halt and which ones do not. Here are two different N-bit axioms which do this. If God tells one how many different programs of size less than N halt, this can be expressed as an N-bit base-two numeral, and from it one could eventually deduce which of these programs halt and which do not. An alternative divine revelation would be knowing that program of size less than N which takes longest to halt. (In the current context, programs have all input contained within them.)

Another way to thwart an N-bit formal axiomatic system is to merely toss an unbiased coin slightly more than N times. It is almost certain that the resulting binary string will be algorithmically random, but it is not possible to prove this within the formal axiomatic system. If one believes the postulate of quantum mechanics that God plays dice with the universe (Albert Einstein did not), then physics provides a means to expose the limitations of formal axiomatic systems. In fact, within an N-bit formal axiomatic system it is not even possible to prove that a particular object has algorithmic information content greater than N, even though almost all (all but finitely many) objects have this property.

The proof of this closely resembles G.G. Berry's paradox of "the first natural number which cannot be named in less than a billion words," published by Russell at the turn of the century (Russell, 1967). The version of Berry's paradox that will do the trick is "that object having the shortest proof that its algorithmic information content is greater than a billion bits." More precisely, "that object having the shortest proof within the following formal axiomatic system that its algorithmic information content is greater than the information content of the formal axiomatic system: . . . ," where the dots are to be filled in with a complete description of the formal axiomatic system in question.

By the way, the fact that in a given formal axiomatic system one can only prove that finitely many specific strings are random, is closely related to

Post's notion of a simple r.e. set. Indeed, the set of nonrandom or compressible strings is a simple r.e. set. So Berry and Post had the germ of my incompleteness theorem!

In order to proceed, I must define a fascinating algorithmically random real number between zero and one, which I like to call omega (Chaitin, 1975b; Gardner, 1979). Omega is a suitable subject for worship by mystical cultists, for as Charles Bennett (Gardner, 1979) has argued persuasively, in a sense omega contains all constructive mathematical truth, and expresses it as concisely and compactly as possible. Knowing the numerical value of omega with N bits of precision, that is to say, knowing the first N bits of omega's base-two expansion, is another N-bit axiom that permits one to deduce precisely which programs of size less than N halt and which ones do not.

Omega is defined as the halting probability of whichever standard general-purpose computer has been chosen, if each bit of its program is produced by an independent toss of a fair coin. To Turing's theorem in recursive function theory that the halting problem is unsolvable, there corresponds in algorithmic information theory the theorem that the base-two expansion of omega is algorithmically random. Therefore it takes N bits of axioms to be able to prove what the first N bits of omega are, and these bits seem completely accidental like the products of a random physical process. One can therefore measure the power of a formal axiomatic system by how much of the numerical value of omega it is possible to deduce from its axioms. This is sort of like measuring the power of a formal axiomatic system in terms of the size in bits of the shortest program whose halting problem is undecidable within the formal axiomatic system.

It is possible to dress this incompleteness theorem involving omega so that no direct mention is made of halting probabilities, in fact, in rather straightforward number-theoretic terms making no mention of computer programs at all. Omega can be represented as the limit of a monotone increasing computable sequence of rational numbers. Its Nth bit is therefore the limit as T tends to infinity of a computable function of N and T. Thus the Nth bit of omega can be expressed in the form Exists X Forall Y (computable predicate of X, Y, and N). Complete chaos is only two quantifiers away from computability! Omega can also be expressed via a polynomial P in, say, one hundred variables, with integer coefficients and exponents (Davis et al., 1976): the Nth bit of omega is a 1 if and only if there are infinitely many natural numbers K such that the equation $P(N, K, X_1, \ldots, X_{98}) = 0$ has a solution in natural numbers.

Of course, omega has the very serious problem that it takes much too long to deduce theorems from it, and this is also the case with the other two axioms we considered. So the ideal, perfect mathematical axiom is in fact useless! One does not really want the most compact axiom for deducing a given set of assertions. Just as there is a trade-off between program size and running time, there is a trade-off between the number of bits of axioms one assumes and the size of proofs. Of course, random or irreducible truths cannot be compressed into axioms shorter than themselves. If, however, a set of assertions is not algorithmically independent, then it takes fewer bits of axioms to deduce them all than the sum of the number of bits of axioms it takes to deduce them separately, and this is desirable as long as the proofs do not get too long. This suggests a pragmatic attitude toward mathematical truth, somewhat more like that of physicists.

Ours has indeed been a long stroll through a gallery of incompleteness theorems. What is the conclusion or moral? It is time to make a final statement about the meaning of Gödel's theorem.

5 THE MEANING OF GÖDEL'S THEOREM

Information theory suggests that the Gödel phenomenon is natural and widespread, not pathological and unusual. Strangely enough, it does this via counting arguments, and without exhibiting individual assertions which are true but unprovable! Of course, it would help to have more proofs that particular interesting and natural true assertions are not demonstrable within fashionable formal axiomatic systems.

The real question is this: Is Gödel's theorem a mandate for revolution, anarchy, and license?! Can one give up after trying for two months to prove a theorem, and add it as a new axiom? This sounds ridiculous, but it is sort of what number theorists have done with Bernhard Riemann's zeta conjecture (Polya, 1959). Of course, two months is not enough. New axioms should be chosen with care, because of their usefulness and large amounts of evidence suggesting that they are correct, in the same careful manner, say, in practice in the physics community.

Gödel himself has espoused this view with remarkable vigor and clarity, in his discussion of whether Cantor's continuum hypothesis should be added to set theory as a new axiom (Gödel, 1964):

> . . . even disregarding the intrinsic necessity of some new axiom, and even in case it has no intrinsic necessity at all, a probable decision about its truth is possible also in another way, namely, inductively by studying its "success." Success here means fruitfulness in consequences, in particular in "verifiable" consequences, i.e., consequences demonstrable without the new axiom, whose proofs with the help of the new axiom, however, are considerably simpler and easier to discover, and make it possible to contract into one proof many different proofs. The axioms for the system of real numbers, rejected by intuitionists, have in this sense been verified to some extent, owing to the fact that analytical number theory frequently allows one to prove number-theoretical theorems which, in a more cumbersome way, can subsequently be verified by elementary methods. A much higher degree of verification than that, however, is conceivable. There might exist axioms so abundant in their verifiable consequences, shedding so much light upon a whole field, and yielding such powerful methods for solving problems (and even solving them constructively, as far as that is possible) that, no matter whether or not they are intrinsically necessary, they would have to be accepted at least in the same sense as any well-established physical theory.

Later in the same discussion Gödel refers to these ideas again:

> It was pointed out earlier . . . that, besides mathematical intuition, there exists another (though only probable) criterion of the truth of mathematical

> axioms, namely their fruitfulness in mathematics and, one may add, possibly also in physics . . . The simplest case of an application of the criterion under discussion arises when some . . . axiom has number-theoretical consequences verifiable by computation up to any given integer.

Gödel also expresses himself in no uncertain terms in a discussion of Russell's mathematical logic (Gödel, 1964):

> The analogy between mathematics and a natural science is enlarged upon by Russell also in another respect . . . axioms need not be evident in themselves, but rather their justification lies (exactly as in physics) in the fact that they make it possible for these "sense perceptions" to be deduced . . . I think that . . . this view has been largely justified by subsequent developments, and it is to be expected that it will be still more so in the future. It has turned out that solution of certain arithmetical problems requires the use of assumptions essentially transcending arithmetic . . . Furthermore it seems likely that for deciding certain questions of abstract set theory and even for certain related questions of the theory of real numbers new axioms based on some hitherto unknown idea will be necessary. Perhaps also the apparently unsurmountable difficulties which some other mathematical problems have been presenting for many years are due to the fact that the necessary axioms have not yet been found. Of course, under these circumstances mathematics may lose a good deal of its "absolute certainty;" but, under the influence of the modern criticism of the foundations, this has already happened to a large extent . . .

I end as I began, with a quotation from Weyl (1949): "A truly realistic mathematics should be conceived, in line with physics, as a branch of the theoretical construction of the one real world, and should adopt the same sober and cautious attitude toward hypothetic extensions of its foundations as is exhibited by physics."

6 DIRECTIONS FOR FUTURE RESEARCH

(a) Prove that a famous mathematical conjecture is unsolvable in the usual formalizations of number theory. Problem: if Pierre Fermat's "last theorem" is undecidable then it is true, so this is hard to do.

(b) Formalize all of college mathematics in a practical way. One wants to produce textbooks that can be run through a practical formal proof checker and that are not too much larger than the usual ones. LISP (Levin, 1974) and SETL (Dewar et al., 1981) might be good for this.

(c) Is algorithmic information theory relevant to physics, in particular, to thermodynamics and statistical mechanics? Explore the thermodynamics of computation (Bennett, 1982) and determine the ultimate physical limitations of computers.

(d) Is there a physical phenomenon that computes something noncomputable? Contrariwise, does Turing's thesis that anything computable can be computed by a Turing machine constrain the physical universe we are in?

(e) Develop measures of self-organization and formal proofs that life must evolve (Chaitin, 1979; Eigen and Winkler, 1981; von Neumann, 1966).

(f) Develop formal definitions of intelligence and measures of its various components; apply information theory and complexity theory to AI.

REFERENCES

Let me give a few pointers to the literature. The following are my previous publications on Gödel's theorem: Chaitin 1974a, 1974b, 1975a, 1977, 1982; Chaitin and Schwartz, 1978. Related publications by other authors include Davis, 1978; Gardner, 1979; Hofstadter, 1979; Levin, 1974; Post, 1965. For discussions of the epistemology of mathematics and science, see Einstein, 1944, 1954; Feynman, 1965; Gödel, 1964; Polya, 1959; von Neumann, 1956, 1963; Taub, 1961; Weyl, 1946, 1949.

Bell, E.T. (1951). *Mathematics, Queen and Servant of Science*, McGraw-Hill, New York.

Bennett, C.H. (1982). The thermodynamics of computation—a review, *International Journal of Theoretical Physics*, **21**, 905-940.

Chaitin, G.J. (1974a). Information-theoretic computational complexity, *IEEE Transactions on Information Theory*, **IT-20**, 10-15.

——— (1974b). Information-theoretic limitations of formal systems, *Journal of the ACM*, **21**, 403-424.

——— (1975a). Randomness and mathematical proof, *Scientific American*, **232** (5) (May 1975), 47-52. (Also published in the French, Japanese, and Italian editions of *Scientific American*.)

——— (1975b). A theory of program size formally identical to information theory, *Journal of the ACM*, **22**, 329-340.

——— (1977). Algorithmic information theory, *IBM Journal of Research and Development*,. **21**, 350-359, 496.

Chaitin, G.J., and Schwartz, J.T. (1978). A note on Monte Carlo primality tests and algorithmic information theory, *Communications on Pure and Applied Mathematics*, **31**, 521-527.

Chaitin, G.J. (1979). Toward a mathematical definition of 'life', in *The Maximum Entropy Formalism*, R.D. Levine and M. Tribus (eds.), MIT Press, Cambridge, Massachusetts, pp. 477-498.

Chaitin, G.J. (1982). Algorithmic information theory, *Encyclopedia of Statistical Sciences*, Vol. 1, Wiley, New York, pp. 38-41.

Cole, C.A., Wolfram, S., et al. (1981). *SMP: a symbolic manipulation program*, California Institute of Technology, Pasadena, California.

Courant, R., and Robbins, H. (1941). *What is Mathematics?*, Oxford University Press, London.

Davis, M., Matijasevic, Y., and Robinson, J. (1976). Hilbert's tenth problem. Diophantine equations: positive aspects of a negative solution, in *Mathematical Developments Arising from Hilbert Problems, Proceedings of Symposia in Pure Mathematics*, Vol. XXVII, American Mathematical Society, Providence, Rhode Island, pp. 323-378.

Davis, M. (1978). What is a computation?, in *Mathematics Today: Twelve Informal Essays*, L.A. Steen (ed.), Springer-Verlag, New York, pp. 241-267.

Dewar, R..B.K., Schonberg, E., and Schwartz, J.T. (1981). *Higher Level Programming: Introduction to the Use of the Set-Theoretic Programming Language SETL,* Courant Institute of Mathematical Sciences, New York University, New York.

Eigen, M., and Winkler, R. (1981). *Laws of the Game*, Knopf, New York.

Einstein, A. (1944). Remarks on Bertrand Russell's theory of knowledge, in *The Philosophy of Bertrand Russell*, P.A. Schilpp (ed.), Northwestern University, Evanston, Illinois, pp. 277-291.

——— (1954). *Ideas and Opinions*, Crown, New York, pp. 18-24.

Feynman, R. (1965). *The Character of Physical Law*, MIT Press, Cambridge, Massachusetts.

Gardner, M. (1979). The random number omega bids fair to hold the mysteries of the universe, Mathematical Games Dept., *Scientific American*, **241** (5) (November 1979), 20–34.

Gödel, K. (1964). Russell's mathematical logic, and What is Cantor's continuum problem?, in *Philosophy of Mathematics*, P. Benacerraf and H. Putnam (eds.), Prentice-Hall, Englewood Cliffs, New Jersey, pp. 211–232, 258–273.

Hofstadter, D.R. (1979). *Gödel, Escher, Bach: an Eternal Golden Braid*, Basic Books, New York.

Levin, M. (1974). *Mathematical Logic for Computer Scientists*, MIT Project MAC report MAC TR-131, Cambridge, Massachusetts.

Polya, G. (1959). Heuristic reasoning in the theory of numbers, *American Mathematical Monthly*, **66**, 375–384.

Post, E. (1965). Recursively enumerable sets of positive integers and their decision problems, in *The Undecidable: Basic Papers on Undecidable Propositions, Unsolvable Problems and Computable Functions*, M. Davis (ed.), Raven Press, Hewlett, New York, pp. 305–337.

Russell, B. (1967). Mathematical logic as based on the theory of types, in *From Frege to Gödel: A Source Book in Mathematical Logic, 1879–1931*, J. van Heijenoort (ed.), Harvard University Press, Cambridge, Massachusetts, pp. 150–182.

Taub, A.H. (ed.) (1961). *J. von Neumann—Collected works*, Vol. I, Pergamon Press, New York, pp. 1-9.

von Neumann, J. (1956). The mathematician, in *The World of Mathematics*, Vol. 4, J.R. Newman (ed.), Simon and Schuster, New York, pp. 2053–2063.

——— (1963). The role of mathematics in the sciences and in society, and Method in the physical sciences, in *J. von Neumann-Collected Works*, Vol. VI, A.H. Taub (ed.), McMillan, New York, pp. 477–498.

——— (1966). *Theory of Self-Reproducing Automata*, A.W. Burks (ed.), University of Illinois Press, Urbana, Illinois.

Weyl, H. (1946). Mathematics and logic, *American Mathematical Monthly*, **53**, 1–13.

——— (1949). *Philosophy of Mathematics and Natural Science*, Princeton University Press, Princeton, New Jersey.

Wilf, H.S. (1982). The disk with the college education, *American Mathematical Monthly*, **89**, 4–8.

Bibliography

This bibliography contains works referred to in this volume.

Abel, N. *Oeuvres Complètes*. 2 vols. New York, 1965.
Appel, K. and W. Haken. "The Solution of the Four Color Map Problem," *Scientific American,* **137** (8) (1977):108–121.
Appel, K., Haken, W. and K. Koch. "Every Planar Map is Four Colorable," *Illinois Journal of Mathematics,* **21** (84) (1977):429–567.
Ayer, A.J. *Languages, Truth and Logic*. London: Victor Gollancz, 1936.
Baker, F.T. "Chief Programmer Team Management of Production Programming," *IBM Systems Journal,* **11** (1972):56–73.
Ball, W.W.R. *A Short Account of the History of Mathematics*. London: Macmillan, 1888; 4th ed., 1908.
Bar-Hillel, Y. (ed.). *Essays on the Foundations of Mathematics*. Amsterdam: North-Holland, 1961.
——— . (ed.). *Logic, Methodology and Philosophy of Science,* Amsterdam: North-Holland, 1965.
Barwise, J. (ed.). *Handbook of Mathematical Logic*. Amsterdam: North-Holland, 1977.
Bateman, P. and H. Diamond. "John E. Littlewood (1885–1977): An Informal Obituary," *The Mathematical Intelligencer,* **1** (1978):28–33.
Bell, E.T. *The Development of Mathematics*. New York: McGraw-Hill, 2nd ed., 1945.
——— . *Mathematics, Queen and Servant of Science*. New York: McGraw-Hill, 1951.
Benacerraf, P. "What Numbers Could Not Be," *Philosophical Review,* **74** (1965): 47–73.
——— . "Mathematical Truth," *Journal of Philosophy,* **70** (1973):661–679.
Benacerraf, P. and H. Putnam. (eds.). *Philosophy of Mathematics: Selected Readings*. Englewood Cliffs: Prentice-Hall, 1964. Second Edition, Cambridge: Cambridge University Press, 1983.
Ben David, J. *The Scientist's Role in Society*. Englewood Cliffs: Prentice-Hall, 1971.
Bennett, C.H. "The Thermodynamics of Computation—A Review," *International Journal of Theoretical Physics,* **21** (1982):905–940.
Berkeley, G. *The Works of George Berkeley*. 4 vols. edited by A.A. Luce and T.E. Jessop, Edinburgh, 1948–1957.

Bernays, P. "Bemerkungen zur Grundlagenfrage," in Gonseth, 83–87.
——— . "Some Empirical Aspects of Mathematics," in P. Bernays and S. Dockx (eds.), *Information and Prediction in Science.* New York: Academic Press, 1965, 123–128.
Bernays, P. and D. Hilbert. *Grundlagen der Mathematik.* 2 vols. Berlin: Springer, 1939.
Bernhart, F. "A Digest of the Four Color Theorem," *Journal of Graph Theory,* **1** (1977):207–225.
Birkhoff, G. "The Reducibility of Maps," *American Journal of Mathematics,* **35** (1913):114–128.
Bishop, E. *Foundations of Constructive Analysis.* New York: McGraw-Hill, 1967.
——— . "Aspects of Constructivism," New Mexico State University, Las Cruces, 1972.
Bolzano, B. *Functionenlehre, Shriften, Band I.* Prague, 1930.
Boolos, G. "The Iterative Conception of Set," *Journal of Philosophy,* **68** (1971), 215–231.
Bourbaki, N. "The Architecture of Mathematics," *American Mathematical Monthly,* **57** (1950):221–232.
Boyer, C. *History of Analytic Geometry.* New York: Scripta Mathematica, 1956.
——— . *History of the Calculus and Its Conceptual Development.* New York: Dover, 1959.
Bridgeman, P. *The Logic of Modern Physics.* New York: Macmillan, 1927.
Brouwer, E.J. "Intuitionism and Formalism," in Benacerraf and Putnam, 66–77.
Bunge, M. *Intuition and Science.* Englewood Cliffs: Prentice-Hall, 1962.
Cajori, F. *A History of Mathematics.* New York: Macmillan, 1924.
——— . *A History of the Conceptions of Limits and Fluxions in Great Britain from Newton to Woodhouse.* Chicago: Open Court, 1931.
Cantor, G. *Gesammelte Abhandlungen.* E. Zermelo (ed.), Berlin: Springer, 1932.
Carnap, R. "Die Logizistische Grundlegung der Mathematik," *Erkenntnis,* **2** (1931): 91–105. Translation in Benacerraf and Putnam.
——— . "Beobachtungssprache und Theoretische Sprache," *Dialectica,* **12** (1958): 236–247.
Carnot, L.N.M. *Réflexions sur la Métaphysique du Calcul Infinitésimal.* Paris: Duprat, 1797.
Cauchy, A.L. "Recherches sur les Polyèdres," *Journal de l'Ecole Polytechnique,* **9** (1813):68–86.
——— . *Oeuvres Complètes.* Paris: Gauthier-Villars, 1897.
Cerutti, E. and P.J. Davis. "FORMAC Meets PAPPUS: Some Observations on Elementary Analytic Geometry by Computer," *American Mathematical Monthly,* **76** (1969):895–905.
Chaitin, G. "On the Difficulty of Computations," *IEEE Trans. Info. Theory,* IT-16 (1970):5–9.
——— . "Toward a Mathematical Definition of 'Life'," *ACM SIGACT NEWS,* **4** (1970):12–18.
——— . "Information-Theoretic Computational Complexity," *IEEE Transactions on Information Theory,* IT-20 (1974):10–15. Reprinted in this volume.
——— . "Information-Theoretic Limitations on Formal Systems," *Journal of the ACM,* **21** (1974):403–424.
——— . "Randomness and Mathematical Proof," *Scientific American,* **232** (5): (1975):47–52.
——— . "A Theory of Program Size Formally Identical to Information Theory," *Journal of the ACM,* **22** (1975):329–340.
——— . "Algorithmic Information Theory," *IBM Journal of Research and Development,* **21** (1977):350–359, 496.
——— . "Gödel's Theorem and Information," *International Journal of Theoretical Physics,* **21** (1982):941–954. Reprinted in this volume.

Chaitin, G. and J.T. Schwartz. "A Note on Monte Carlo Primality Tests and Logarithmic Information Theory," *Communications on Pure and Applied Mathematics,* **31** (1978):521-527.

Chihara, C. *Ontology and the Vicious Circle Principle.* Ithaca: Cornell University Press, 1973.

Church, A. "A Set of Postulates for the Foundation of Logic," *Annals of Mathematics,* 33 Second Series (1932):346-366.

——— . "The Present Situation in the Foundations of Mathematics," in Gonseth, 67-72.

Cohen, P.J. "The Independence of the Continuum Hypothesis," *Proceedings of the National Academy of Sciences,* Part 1, vol. 50 (1963):1143-1148, Part 2, vol. 51 (1964):105-110.

——— . "Comments on the Foundations of Set Theory," in Scott.

Cole, C.A., S. Wolfram et al. "SMP: A Symbolic Manipulation Program," Pasadena: California Institute of Technology, 1981.

Courant, R. and H. Robbins. *What is Mathematics?* London: Oxford University Press, 1941.

Crowe, M. "Ten 'Laws' Concerning Patterns of Change in the History of Mathematics," *Historia Mathematica,* **2** (1975):161-166.

Curry, H. *Outlines of Formalist Philosophy of Mathematics.* Amsterdam: North-Holland, 1958.

——— . *Foundations of Mathematical Logic.* New York: McGraw-Hill, 1963.

——— . "The Relation of Logic to Science," in P. Bernays and S. Dockx (eds.), *Information and Prediction in Science,* New York: Academic Press, 1965, 79-98.

D'Alembrt, J. "Reflexions sur les Suites et sur les Racines Imaginaires," *Opuscules Mathématiques.* vol. 5, Paris, 1768.

Dauben, J. *Georg Cantor.* Cambridge: Harvard University Press, 1979.

Davis, C. "Materialist Mathematics," in *Boston Studies in the Philosophy of Science,* **15** Boston: D. Reidel, 1974.

Davis, M. "What is Computation," in L.A. Steen (ed.), *Mathematics Today: Twelve Informal Essays,* New York: Springer-Verlag, 1978, 241-267.

Davis, M., Y. Matijasevic and J. Robinson. "Hilbert's Tenth Problem: Positive Aspects of a Negative Solution," in *Mathematical Developments Arising from Hilbert Problems, Proceedings of Symposia in Pure Mathematics,* Vol. 27, Providence: American Mathematical Society, 1976, 323-378.

Davis, P.J. "Fidelity in Mathematical Discourse," *American Mathematical Monthly,* **79** (1972):252-262. Reprinted in this volume.

——— . "Visual Geometry, Computer Graphics, and Theorems of Perceived Type," in *Influence of Computing on Mathematical Research and Education.* Proc. Symp. Appl. Math., 20, Providence: American Mathematical Society, 1974.

Davis, P.J. and R. Hersh, *The Mathematical Experience.* Boston: Birkhäuser, 1981.

Dedekind, R. *Essays on the Theory of Numbers.* New York: Dover, 1963.

deLong, H. *A Profile of Mathematical Logic.* Reading: Addison-Wesley, 1970.

DeMillo, R., R. Lipton and A. Perlis, "Social Processes and Proofs of Theorems and Programs," *Communications of the ACM,* **22** (1979):271-280. Reprinted in this volume.

Descartes. *Geometry.* Translation and facsimile reproduction of *La Géométrie* by D.E. Smith and M.L. Latham. New York: Dover, 1954.

Detlefsen, M. and M. Luker. "The Four-Color Theorem and Mathematical Proof," *Journal of Philosophy,* **77** (1980).

Dewar, R., E. Schonberg and J.T. Schwartz. "Higher Level Programming: Introduction to the Use of the Set-Theoretic Programming Language SETL," Courant Institute, New York University, New York: 1981.

Dieudonné, J. "The Work of Nicholas Bourbaki," *American Mathematical Monthly,* **77**, (1970):134-145.

——. "Modern Axiomatic Methods and the Foundations of Mathematics," in *Great Currents of Mathematical Thought*, Vol. 2 New York: Dover, 1971.

——."Should We Teach Modern Mathematics?," *American Scientist,* **77** (1973): 16–19.

Donnelan, K. "Proper Names and Identifying Descriptions," in D. Davidson and G. Harman (eds.), *Semantics of Natural Language,* Dordrecht: Reidel, 1972.

——. "Speaking of Nothing," *Philosophical Review,* **83** (1974):3-31.

Dresden, A. "Some Philosophical Aspects of Mathematics," *Bulletin of the American Mathematical Society,* **34** (1928):438–452.

Dummett, M. "The Philosophical Basis of Intuitionistic Logic," H.E. Rose and J.C. Sheperdson (eds.), *Logic Colloquium '73*, Amsterdam: North-Holland, 1975, 5-40.

——. *Elements of Intuitionism*. Oxford: Clarendon Press, 1977.

Eigen, M. "Selforganization of Matter and the Evolution of Biological Macromolecules," *Die Naturwissenschaften,* **58** (1971):465–523.

Eigen, M. and R. Winkler. *Laws of the Game*. New York: Knopf, 1981.

Eilenberg, S. and N. Steenrod. *Foundations of Algebraic Topology.* Princeton: Princeton University Press, 1952.

Einstein, A. "Remarks on Bertrand Russell's Theory of Knowledge," in P.A. Schilpp (ed.), *The Philosophy of Bertrand Russell*, Evanston: Northwestern University Press, 1944.

——. *Ideas and Opinions*. New York: Crown, 1954.

Euler, L. "Institutiones calculi integralis," 1768, *Opera Omnia*, Series I, vol. 11, Leipzig and Berlin: Teubner, 1911–1936.

——. "Introductio in analysin infinitorum," 1748, *Opera Omnia*, Series I, vols. 8–9.

Feferman, S. "Autonomous Transfinite Progressions and the Extent of Predicative Mathematics" in B. van Rootselaar and J.F. Staal (eds.), *Logic, Methodology and Philosophy of Science III,* Amsterdam: North-Holland, 1963, 121–135.

Feit, W. and J.G. Thompson. "Solvability of Groups of Odd Order," *Pacific Journal of Mathematics,* **13** (1963):775–1029.

Feyerabend, P. "Explanation, Reduction, and Empiricism," in H. Feigl and G. Maxwell (eds.), *Minnesota Studies in the Philosophy of Science,* vol. 3, Minneapolis: University of Minnesota Press, 1962.

——. "Problems of Empiricism," in R. Colodny (ed.), *Beyond the Edge of Certainty,* Englewood Cliffs: Prentice-Hall, 1965.

——. *Against Method*. London: Verso Books, 1975.

——. *Science in a Free Society*. London: New Left Books, 1978.

Feynman, R. *The Character of Physical Law*. Cambridge: MIT Press, 1965.

Fraenkel, A.A. *Zehn Vorlesungen über die Gundlegung der Mengenlehre*. Leipzig and Berlin: B.G. Teubner, 1927.

Fraenkel, A.A., Y. Bar-Hillel and A. Levy. *Foundations of Set Theory*. 2nd edition. Amsterdam: North-Holland, 1973.

Frege, G. *Begriffscrift*. Reprinted in van Heijenoort.

——. *The Foundations of Arithmetic*. Translation by J.L. Austin, Oxford: Blackwell, 1950.

——. *The Basic Laws of Arithmetic*. Translation by M.L. Furth, Berkeley: University of California Press, 1964.

Freudenthal, H. *Mathematics as an Educational Task*. Dordrecht: D. Reidel, 1973.

Gardner, M. "The Random Number Omega Bids Fair to Hold the Mysteries of the Universe," *Scientific American,* **241** (5) (1979):20–34.

Gelerenter, H. et al. "The Discovery of Organic Synthetic Roots by Computer," *Topics in Current Chemistry 41*, New York: Springer-Verlag, 1973, 113–150.

George, J.A., "Computer Implementation of the Finite Element Methods," Ph.D. Thesis, Stanford University, Stanford, Calif., 1971.

Gillispie, C.C. *Lazare Carnot Savant*. Princeton: Princeton University Press, 1971.

Glymour, C. "The Epistemology of Geometry," *Noûs,* **11** (1970):227–251.

Gödel, K. "Discussion zur Grundlegung der Mathematik," *Erkenntnis*, **2** (1931): 147-148.

———. "The Consistency of the Axiom of Choice and the Generalized Continuum Hypothesis," *Proceedings of the National Academy of Sciences*, **24** (1938): 556-567.

———. "Russell's Mathematical Logic," in P.A. Schilpp (ed.), *The Philosophy of Bertrand Russell*, Northwestern University Press, 1944, 121-153. Reprinted in Benacerraf and Putnam, 211-232.

———. "What is Cantor's Continuum Problem?" *American Mathematical Monthly*, **54** (1947):515-525. Revised and reprinted in Benacerraf and Putnam, 85-112.

Goldfarb, W. "The Unsolvability of the Gödel Class with Identity," *Journal of Symbolic Logic*, **49** (1984):1237-1252.

Gonseth, F. (ed.), *Philosophie Mathématique*, Paris: Hermann, 1939.

Goodman, N. "Mathematics as an Objective Science," *American Mathematical Monthly*, **86** (1979):540-551. Reprinted in this volume.

Garbiner, J.V. "Is Mathematical Truth Time-Dependent?," *American Mathematical Monthly*, **81** (1974):354-365. Reprinted in this volume.

Grattan-Guinness, I. *The Development of the Foundations of Analysis from Euler to Riemann*. Cambridge: MIT Press, 1970.

Gupta, A. "Truth and Paradox," *Journal of Philosophical Logic*, **11** (1982):1-60.

Hadamard, J. *The Psychology of Invention in the Mathematical Field*. Princeton: Princeton University Press, 1945.

Hall, A.R. *The Scientific Revolution, 1500-1800*. Boston: Beacon, 1966.

Hanson, N.R. *Patterns of Discovery*. Cambridge: Cambridge University Press, 1961.

Hardy, G.H. *A Mathematician's Apology*. Cambridge: Cambridge University Press, 1941.

Heath, T.L. *The Thirteen Books of Euclid's Elements*. New York: Dover, 1956.

Heawood, P.J. "Map Colouring Theorems," *Quarterly Journal of Mathematics, Oxford Series*, **24** (1890):322-339.

Heijenoort, J. van, *From Frege to Gödel*. Cambridge: Harvard University Press, 1967.

Hempel, C. "On the Nature of Mathematical Truth," in Benacerraf and Putnam, 366-381.

———. "Geometry and Empirical Science," *American Mathematical Monthly*, **52** (1945):7-17.

Herbrand, J. "Les Bases de la Logique Hibertienne," *Revue de la Métaphysique et de la Morale*, **37** (1930):243-255.

Hersh, R. "Some Proposals for Reviving the Philosophy of Mathematics," *Advances in Mathematics*, vol. 31 (1979):31-50. Reprinted in this volume.

———. "Introducing Imre Lakatos," *Mathematical Intelligencer*, **1** (1980).

Herzenberger, H. "Notes on Naive Semantics," *Journal of Philosophical Logic*, **11** (1982):61-102.

Heyting, A. *Intuitionism: An Introduction*. Amsterdam: North-Holland, 1966.

Hilbert, D. "Über das Unendliche," *Mathematische Annalen*, **95** (1925):161-190. Translated in Benacerraf and Putnam.

Hintikka, J. *The Philosophy of Mathematics*. Oxford: Oxford University Press, 1963.

Hofstadter, D. *Gödel, Escher and Bach: An Eternal Golden Braid*. New York: Basic Books, 1979.

Hooper, A. *Makers of Mathematics*. New York: Random House, 1984.

Hume, D. *A Treatise of Human Nature*. Oxford: Oxford University Press, 1964.

Isles, D. "On the Notion of Standard Non-Isomorphic Natural Number Series," *Constructive Mathematics: Proceedings, New Mexico, 1980*. Berlin: Springer-Verlag (1980):274-313.

Jech, T.J. *The Axiom of Choice*. Amsterdam: North-Holland, 1973.

Kac, M. "Statistical Independence in Probability, Analysis, and Number Theory," Carus Mathematical Monographs, Mathematical Association of America, 12, 1959.

Kainen, P. and T. Saaty. *The Four Color Problem: Assaults and Conquest*. New York: McGraw-Hill, 1977.

Kalmár, L. "An Argument against the Plausibility of Church's Thesis," in A. Heyting (ed.), *Constructivity in Mathematics*, Amsterdam: North-Holland, 1959, 72–80.

———. "Foundations of Mathematics—Whither Now?" in Lakatos, 1967, 187–194.

Kant, I. *Groundwork of the Metaphysic of Morals*. Translated by H.J. Paton, New York: Harper and Row, 1964.

Kemeny, J. "Undedidable Problems in Elementary Number Theory," *Mathematische Annalen,* **135** (1958):160–169.

Kempe, A.B. "On the Geographical Problem of the Four Colors," *American Journal of Mathematics,* **2** (1879):193–200.

Keyser, C.J. "Mathematics as a Culture Clue," *Scripta Mathematica,* **1** (1932–33):185–203.

Kitcher, P. "The Plight of the Platonist," *Noûs,* **12** (1978):119–136.

———. *The Nature of Mathematical Knowledge*. Oxford: Oxford University Press, 1983.

Kleene, S.C. "Recursive Predicates and Quantifiers," *Transactions of the American Mathematical Society,* **53** (1943):41–73.

———. *Introduction to Metamathematics*. Amsterdam: North-Holland, 1952.

Kleene, S.C. and J.B. Rosser. "The Inconsistency of Certain Formal Logics," *Annals of Mathematics,* **46** (1935):630–636.

Klein, F. *Vorlesunger über die Entwicklung der Mathematik im 19. Jahrhundert*. 1926. Reprinted New York: Chelsea, 1967.

Kline, M. *Mathematics in Western Culture*. New York: Oxford University Press, 1953.

———. *Mathematical Thought from Ancient to Modern Times*. New York: Oxford University Press, 1972.

———. *Mathematics: The Loss of Certainty*. New York: Oxford University Press, 1980.

Kneale, W.C. "The Necessity of Invention," *Proceedings of the British Academy,* **41** (1955):85–108.

Kolata, G.B. "Mathematical Proof: The Genesis of Reasonable Doubt," *Science,* **192** (1976):989–990.

Kolmogorov, A.N. "Logical Basis for Information Theory and Probability Theory," *IEEE Transactions in Information Theory*, IT-14, 1968:662–664.

Kordig, C. *The Justification of Scientific Change*. Dordrecht: Reidel, 1971.

Korner, S. *The Philosophy of Mathematics*. New York: Harper, 1960.

———. "On the Relevance of Post-Gödelian Mathematics to Philosophy," in Lakatos, 1967, 118–133.

Krakowski, I. "The Four-Color Problem Reconsidered," *Philosophical Studies,* **38** (1980):91–96.

Kreisel, G. "Informal Rigour and Completeness Proofs," in Lakatos, 1967, 138–171.

———. "Reply to Bar-Hillel," in Lakatos, 1967, 175–178.

———. "Comment on Mostowski," in Lakatos, 1967, 97–103.

———. "Hilbert's Program" in Benacerraf and Putnam, 157–180.

———. "The Formalist-Positivist Doctrine of Mathematical Precision in the Light of Experience," *L'Age de la Science,* **3** (1970):17–46.

Kripke, S. "Outline of a Theory of Truth," *Journal of Philosophy,* **72** (1975): 690–716.

———. *Naming and Necessity*. Cambridge: Harvard University Press, 1980.

———. *Wittgenstein on Rules and Private Language*. Cambridge: Harvard University Press, 1982.

Kroeber, A.L. *Anthropology*. rev. ed. New York: Harcourt Brace, 1948.

Kuhn, T. *The Structure of Scientific Revolutions*. Chicago: University of Chicago Press, 1962.

——— . *The Essential Tension.* Chicago: Chicago University Press, 1977.
——— . "Mathematical versus Experimental Traditions in the Development of Physical Science." In *Essential Tension.*
Lagrange, J.-L. *Oeuvres.* Paris: Gauthier-Villars, 1867-1892.
Lakatos, I. (ed.). *Problems in the Philosophy of Mathematics,* Amsterdam: North-Holland, 1967.
——— . *Proofs and Refutations.* edited by J. Worrall and G. Currie, Cambridge: Cambridge University Press, 1976.
——— . *Philosophical Papers,* 2 vols. Edited by J. Worrall and G. Currie, Cambridge: Cambridge University Press, 1978.
——— . "Infinite Regress and Foundations of Mathematics," in Lakatos, 1978(b).
——— . "A Renaissance of Empiricism in the Recent Philosophy of Mathematics?" in Lakatos, 1978(b) and this volume.
——— . "What Does a Mathematical Proof Prove?" in Lakatos, 1978(b) and this volume.
Lee, D.D. "A Primitive System of Values," *Philosophy of Science,* **7** (1940):355-378.
Lehman, H. *Introduction to the Philosophy of Mathematics.* Totowa: Rowman and Littlefield, 1979.
Levin, M. "Mathematical Logic for Computer Scientists," MIT Project MAC Report MAC TR-131, Cambridge, Mass. (1974).
Levin, M. "On Tymoczko's Argument for Mathematical Empiricism," *Philosophical Studies,* **39** (1981).
Levy, A. and R.M. Solovay, "Measurable Cardinals and the Continuum Hypothesis," *Israeli Journal of Mathematics,* **5** (1967):234-248.
L'Huilier, S. *Exposition élémentaire des Principes des Calculs Supérieurs* Berlin: Decker, 1787.
Linton, R. *The Study of Man.* New York: Appleton-Century, 1936.
Littlewood, J.E. *A Mathematician's Miscellany.* London: Methuen, 1953.
Lusin, N. "Sur les Ensembles Analytiques Nuls," *Fundamenta Mathematica,* **25** (1935):109-131.
Manin, Y. *A Course in Mathematical Logic.* New York: Springer-Verlag, 1977.
Martin, D.A. and R.M. Solovay. "Internal Cohen Extensions," *Annals of Mathematical Logic,* **2** (1970):143-178.
Masterman, M. "The Nature of a Paradigm," in I. Lakatos and A. Musgrave (eds.), *Criticism and the Growth of Knowledge,* Cambridge: Cambridge University Press, 1970.
Mehlberg, M. "The Present Situation in the Philosophy of Mathematics," in B.M. Kazemier and D. Vuysje (eds.), *Logic and Language,* Dordrecht: Reidel, 1962, 69-103.
Meyer, A. "The Inherent Computational Complexity of Theories of Ordered Sets: A Brief Survey," Int. Cong. of Mathematicians, 1974.
Mikami, Y. *The Development of Mathematics in China and Japan.* Leipzig: Drugulin, 1913.
Mill, J.S. *Inaugural Address,* delivered to the University of St. Andrews, Feb. 1, 1867. Boston: Littell and Gay.
Monk, J.D. "On the Foundations of Set Theory," *American Mathematical Monthly,* **77** (1970):703-711.
Moritz, M. *On Mathematics and Mathematicians.* New York: Dover, 1942.
Mostowski, A. "The Present State of Investigations on the Foundations of Mathematics," *Rozprawy Matematyczne,* **9** (1955).
Myhill, J. "Some Remarks on the Notion of Proof," *Journal of Philosophy,* **57** (1960):461-471.
Neumann, J. von, "The Mathematician," in R.B. Heywood (ed.), *The Works of the Mind,* Chicago: Chicago University Press, 1947, 180-196.
——— . *The Computer and the Brain.* New Haven: Yale University Press, 1958.
——— . "Method in the Physical Sciences," in Taub, vol. 6.

——— . *Theory of Self-Reproducing Automata.* A.W. Burks (ed.), Urbana: University of Illinois Press, 1966.

Neumann, J. von and O. Morgenstern. *Theory of Games and Economic Behavior.* Princeton: Princeton University Press, 1944.

Newton, I. *Mathematical Principles of Natural Philosophy.* Translated by Motte, revised by Cajori, Berkeley: University of California Press, 1946.

——— . "On the Analysis by Equations of an Infinite Number of Terms," 1669, in Whiteside.

——— . "Universal Arithmetic," 1707, in Whiteside.

Nidditch, P.H. *Introductory Formal Logic of Mathematics.* London: University Tutorial Press, 1954.

Paris, J. and L. Harrington. "A Mathematical Incompleteness in Peano Arithmetic," in Barwise, 1977, 1133–1142.

Parsons, C. "What is the Iterative Conception of Set?" *Logic, Foundations of Mathematics and Computability Theory*, Dordrecht: D. Reidel, 1977, 335–367.

Peano, G. *Opera Scelte.* Rome: 1957.

Piaget, J. *Genetic Epistemology.* New York: Columbia University Press, 1970.

Polya, G. *How To Solve It.* Princeton: Princeton University Press, 1945.

——— . *Induction and Analogy in Mathematics.* Princeton: Princeton University Press, 1954.

——— . *Patterns of Plausible Inference.* Princeton: Princeton University Press, 1954.

——— . "Heuristic Reasoning in the Theory of Numbers," *American Mathematical Monthly,* **66** (1959):375–384.

Popek, G. et al. "Notes on the Design of Euclid," Proc. Conf. Language Design for Reliable Software, *SIGPLAN Notices (ACM),* **12** (1977):11–18.

Popper, K. *Logik der Forschung.* Vienna: Springer, 1934.

——— . *The Logic of Scientific Discovery.* London: Hutchinson, 1959.

——— . *Objective Knowledge.* Oxford: Oxford University Press, 1972.

Post, E. "Recursively Enumerable Sets of Positive Integers and their Decision Problems," in M. Davis (ed.), *The Undecidable: Basic Papers on Undecidable Propositions, Unsolvable Problems and Computable Functions,* New York: Raven Press, 1965.

Putnam, H. *Philosophy of Logic.* New York: Harper and Row, 1971.

——— . *Philosophical Papers.* 2 vols. Cambridge: Cambridge University Press, 1975.

——— . "Mathematics Without Foundations," in Putnam, 1975(a).

——— . "What is Mathematical Truth," in Putnam, 1975(a) and this volume.

——— . "Explanation and Reference," in Putnam 1975(b).

——— . "Meaning and Reference," *Journal of Philosophy,* **70** (1973):699–711.

Quine, W.V.O. "Element and Number," *Journal of Symbolic Logic,* **6** (1941):135–149.

——— . "Review of Rosser," *Journal of Symbolic Logic,* **6** (1941):163.

——— . "Two Dogmas of Empiricism," *Philosophical Review,* **60** (1951).

——— . "On ω-inconsistency and a So-called Axiom of Infinity," *Journal of Symbolic Logic,* **18** (1953):119–124.

——— . "The Philosophical Bearing of Modern Logic," in R. Klibansky (ed.), *Philosophy in the Mid-Century,* volume 1, Firenze: La Nouva Italia, 1958.

——— . *Set Theory and Its Logic.* Cambridge: Harvard University Press, 1963.

——— . *Elementary Logic.* Revised edition. New York: Harper Torchbooks, 1965.

——— . *Philosophy of Logic.* Englewood Cliffs: Prentice-Hall, 1970.

Rabin, M.O. "Probabilistic Algorithms," in J.F. Traub (ed.), *Algorithms and Complexity: New Directions and Recent Results,* New York: Academic Press, 21–40.

Ramsey, F.P. *The Foundations of Mathematics* Patterson, New Jersey: Littlefield, Adams and Co., 1960.

Reichenbach, H. *The Philosophy of Space and Time.* New York: Dover, 1958.

Reiff, R. *Geschichte der unendliche Reinhen.* Tubingen, 1889.
Renyi, A. "On a New Axiomatic Theory of Probability," *Acta Mathematica Academiae Scientiarum Hungaricae,* **6** (1955):285-337.
Resnik, M. "Mathematical Knowledge and Pattern Cognition," *Canadian Journal of Philosophy,* **5** (1975):25-39.
Robinson, A. "From a Formalist's Point of View," *Dialectica,* **23** (1969):45-49.
——— . "Formalism 64" in Bar-Hillel, 228-246.
Rogers, H. *Theory of Recursive Functions and Effective Computability.* New York: McGraw-Hill, 1967.
Rosser, J.B. "Gödel's Theorems for Non-Constructive Logics," *Journal of Symbolic Logic,* **2** (1937):129-137.
——— . "The Independence of Quine's Axioms *200 and *201," *Journal of Symbolic Logic,* **6** (1941):96-97.
——— . *Logic for Mathematicians.* New York: McGraw-Hill, 1953.
Rosser, J.B. and H. Wang. "Non-Standard Models for Formal Logics," *Journal of Symbolic Logic,* **15** (1950):113-129.
Russell, B. "The Study of Mathematics," in *Philosophical Essays*, reprinted in *Mysticism and Logic*, London: Allen and Unwin, 1917, 48-58.
——— . *An Introduction to Mathematical Philosophy.* London: Allen and Unwin, 1919.
——— . "Logical Atomism," in J.H. Muirhead (ed.), *Contemporary British Philosophy: Personal Statements*, First Series, 357-383. Reprinted in R.C. Marsh (ed.), *Logic and Knowledge*, London: Allen and Unwin, 1956, 323-343.
——— . *My Philosophical Development.* London: Allen and Unwin, 1959.
——— . "Mathematical Logic as Based on the Theory of Types," in van Heijenoort.
Scheffler, I. *Science and Subjectivity.* Indianapolis: Bobbs-Merrill, 1967.
Schwartz, J. "On Programming," Courant Reports, New York University, New York, 1973.
Scott, D. (ed.). *Axiomatic Set Theory.* Proceedings in Pure Mathematics 13, Part 1, Providence: American Mathematical Society, 1971.
Sellars, W. "Empiricism and the Philosophy of Mind," in his *Science, Perception, and Reality*, London: Routledge and Kegan Paul, 1963.
Shapere, D. "Meaning and Scientific Change," in R. Colodny, *Mind and Cosmos,* Pittsburgh: University of Pittsburgh Press, 1966.
Shoenfield, J. "Measurable Cardinals," in R.O. Gandy and C.E.M. Yates (eds.), *Logic Colloquium '69.* Amsterdam: North-Holland, 1971, 19-49.
Sierpinski, W. "Sur une Hypothèse de M. Lusin," *Fundamenta Mathematica,* **25** (1935):132-135.
Sklar, L. *Space, Time and Space-Time.* Berkeley, University of California Press, 1974.
Solomonoff, R.J. "A Formal Theory of Inductive Inference," *Inform. Contr.,* **7** (1964) Mar. 1-22, June 224-254.
Solovay, R.M. and Tennebaum, S. "Iterated Cohen Extensions and Souslin's Problem," *Annals of Mathematics,* **94** (1967):201-245.
Specker, E. P. "The Axiom of Choice in Quine's New Foundations for Mathematical Logic," *Proceedings of the National Academy of Sciences,* **39** (1953):972-975.
Spengler, O. *Der Untergang des Abendlandes.* Munchen: C.H. Beck, vol. 1, 1918, vol. 2, 1923.
Steiner, M. *Mathematical Knowledge.* Ithaca: Cornell University Press, 1975.
Stockmeyer, L. "The Complexity of Decision Problems in Automata Theory and Logic," Ph.D. Thesis, MIT, Cambridge, Mass., 1974.
Struik, D.J. *Concise History of Mathematics.* New York: Dover, 1967.
——— . (ed.). *A Source Book in Mathematics, 1200-1800.* Cambridge: Harvard University Press, 1967.
Suppes, P. *Introduction to Logic.* New York: Van Nostrand, 1957.

Swart, E.R. "The Philosophical Implications of the Four-Color Problem," *American Mathematical Monthly,* **87** (1980):697–707.

Tarski, A. "On Undecidable Statements in Enlarged Systems of Logic and the Concept of Truth," *Journal of Symbolic Logic,* **4** (1939):105–112.

———. "Comments on Bernays," *Revue Internationale de Philosophie,* **8** (1954):17–21.

———. "The Concept of Truth in Formalised Languages," in J.H. Woodger (ed.), *Logic, Semantics and Metamathematics*, Oxford: Clarendon press, 1956.

Taub, A.H. (ed.). *J. von Neumann—Collected Works.* New York: Macmillan, 1963.

Thom, R. "Topologie et linguistique," in A. Haefliger and R. Narasimham (eds.), *Essays on Topology and Related Topics*, New York: Springer-Verlag, 226–248.

———. "Modern Mathematics: An Educational and Philosophic Error?" *American Scientist,* **59** (1971):695–699. Reprinted in this volume.

———. "Modern Mathematics: Does it Exist?" in *Developments in Mathematical Education*, edited by Howson, A.G., Cambridge: Cambridge University Press, 1973, 194–209.

Toulmin, S. *Human Understanding*. vol. 1. Princeton: Princeton University Press, 1972.

Tymoczko, T. "The Four-Color Problem and its Philosophical Significance," *Journal of Philosophy,* **76** (1979):57–83.

———. "Computers, Proofs and Mathematicians," *Mathematics Magazine,* **53** (1980):131–138.

———. "Computer Use to Computer Proof," *Two year College Mathematics Journal,* **12** (1981):120–125.

———. "Making Room for Mathematicians in the Philosophy of Mathematics," *Mathematical Intelligencer* (1986).

———. "Gödel, Wittgenstein and the Nature of Mathematical Knowledge," in P. Asquith (ed.), *PSA 84* (1986).

Ulam, S.M. *Adventures of a Mathematician*. New York: Scribner's, 1976.

Vuillemin, J. *De la logique à la theólogie*. Paris: Flammarion, 1967.

Wang, H. *From Mathematics to Philosophy*. New York: Humanities Press, 1974.

———. "Theory and Practice in Mathematics," in Wang and this volume.

———. "The Concept of Set," in Wang, 1974.

Webb, J.C. *Mechanism, Mentalism and Metamathematics*. Dordrecht: D. Reidel, 1980.

Weyl, H. "Diskussionsbemerkungen zu dem Zweiten Hilbertschen Vortag über die Grundlagen der Mathematik," *Abhandlungen aus dem Mathematischen Seminar der Hamburgischen Universitat,* **6** (1928):86–88.

———. "Mathematics and Logic," *American Mathematical Monthly,* **53** (1946):1–13.

———. *Philosophy of Mathematics and Natural Science*. Princeton: Princeton University Press, 1949.

Whewell, W. *On the Philosophy of Discovery*. London: Parker, 1860.

White, L.A. "The Locus of Mathematical Reality," *Philosophy of Science,* **14** (1947):289–303.

———. *The Science of Culture*. New York: Farrar, Straus, 1949.

Whitehead, A.N. *Science and the Modern World*. New York: New American Library, 1948.

Whitehead, A.N. and B. Russell. *Principia Mathematica*. 3 vols. Cambridge: Cambridge University Press, 1910–1913.

Whiteside, D.T. (ed.). *The Mathematical Works of Isaac Newton*. London and New York, Johnson, vol. 1, 1964, vol. 2, 1970.

Whitney, H. and W.T. Tutte. "Kempe Chains and the Four Colour Problem," in *Studies in Graph Theory, Part II*, Mathematical Association of America, 1975.

Wilder, R. "The Cultural Basis of Mathematics," *Proceedings of the International Congress of Mathematicians, 1950*. vol. 1, 258–271. Reprinted in this volume.

——— . "The Role of Intuition," *Science* **156** (1967):605–610.
——— . *The Evolution of Mathematical Concepts.* New York: Wiley, 1968.
——— . *Mathematics as a Cultural System.* Oxford: Pergamon Press, 1981.
Wilf, H.S. "The Disk with a College Education," *American Mathematical Monthly*, **89** (1982):4–8.
Williams, M. *Groundless Belief.* New Haven: Yale University Press, 1977.
Wittgenstein, L. *Tractatus Logico Philosophicus.* London: Routledge and Kegan Paul, 1922.
——— . *Philosophical Investigations.* Oxford: Blackwell, 1951.
——— . *Remarks on the Foundations of Mathematics.* Oxford: Blackwell, 1956.
——— . *The Blue and Brown Books.* Oxford: Blackwell, 1960.
Yessenin-Volpin, A.S. "The Ultra-Intuitionistic Criticism and the Antitraditional Program for Foundations of Mathematic," in A. Kino, J. Myhill and R.E. Vesley (eds.), *Intuitionism and Proof Theory*, Amsterdam: North-Holland, 1980, 3–45.
Zadeh, L.A. "Fuzzy Algorithms," *Information and Control,* **12** (1963):94–102.